What Is Life? A Guide to BIOLOGY with Physiology

What Is Life?

A Guide to BIOLOGY with Physiology

Jay Phelan

University of California, Los Angeles

Complete text available January 2010

W. H. FREEMAN AND COMPANY
NEW YORK

ISBN 13: 978-1-4292-4309-4
ISBN 10: 1-4292-4309-0

Printed in the United States of America

W. H. Freeman and Company
41 Madison Avenue, New York, NY 10010
Houndsmills, Basingstoke RG21 6XS, England

www.whfreeman.com

BRIEF CONTENTS

CONTENTS

PART 6 Health and Physiology

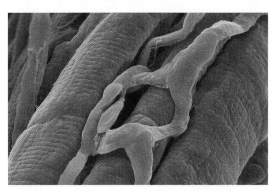

20 • Introduction to Animal Physiology

PRINCIPLES OF ANIMAL ORGANIZATION AND FUNCTION

21 • Circulation and Respiration

TRANSPORTING FUEL, RAW MATERIALS, AND GASES INTO, OUT OF, AND AROUND THE BODY

22 • Nutrition and Digestion

AT REST AND AT PLAY: OPTIMIZING HUMAN PHYSIOLOGICAL FUNCTIONING

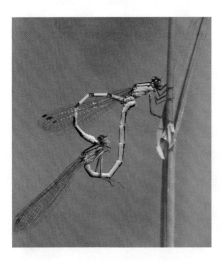

25 • Reproduction and Development

FROM TWO PARENTS TO ONE EMBRYO TO ONE BABY 25-1

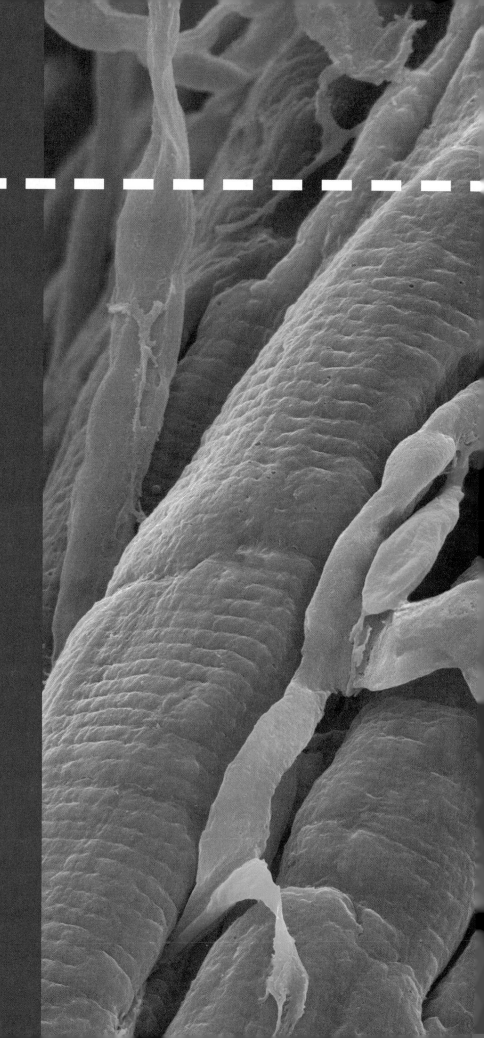

20

Introduction to Animal Physiology

Principles of animal organization and function

① Animals have an internal environment.

Heat radiates from warm bodies in cold weather.

20•1 --

Our bodies function best within a narrow range of internal conditions.

Following an extremely rigorous practice in the summer of 2001, 27-year-old Minnesota Vikings football player Korey Stringer walked into an air-conditioned tent to recover. Almost immediately, however, the 6 foot 4 inch, 335-pound all-pro player began to feel weak and dizzy; his breathing became rapid and his blood pressure dropped. He was rushed to the hospital, but as a consequence of his body temperature allegedly reaching 108.8° F (42.7° C), many of his organs failed, and he died that night.

Normal body temperature is approximately 98.6° F (37° C). **Hyperthermia** occurs when too much heat is produced or when high environmental temperature and humidity overwhelm the body's ability to dissipate heat. (It is unlike a fever, in which the body sets its core temperature slightly higher in response to an infection by pathogens.) Korey Stringer's death is an example of the disastrous consequences that can result from extreme cases of hyperthermia, called

Q What is heat stroke? Why is it dangerous?

heat stroke, and illustrates the danger when organisms fail to maintain an internal environment within a safe range.

Although the environmental temperature range you experience every day may involve a 20°, 30°, or even 40° F difference between high and low, humans cannot tolerate such large internal temperature swings. Even deviations of less than 10° F can lead to a cascade of biochemical problems with serious health implications. For mammals, the risks of getting too hot include reduced enzyme activity and, at extreme temperatures, the complete breakdown of enzymes. Excessive water loss, too, can occur, leading to numerous problems—including organ failure. For these reasons, heat stroke can be life-threatening (**FIGURE 20-1**).

At the other extreme, **hypothermia,** or extremely low body temperature, can cause difficulties in coordination and movement, along with disorientation and confusion, irregular heartbeat, and, ultimately, death. Similarly disastrous

▼
The Internal Environment   How Does Homeostasis Work?   Form Reflects Function

consequences can occur as a result of the failure to maintain a consistent internal environment in other ways, including in blood sugar levels, blood pH, and tissue concentrations of oxygen and carbon dioxide.

In this chapter, we explore a fundamental characteristic of organism function, **homeostasis,** the body's use of physical and chemical processes to maintain a consistent internal environment, even in the face of changing external and internal environmental forces. We also examine the forms behind those functions—cells, tissues, organs, and organ systems.

Failure to maintain homeostasis—a consistent internal environment—can lead to multiple problems in the normal functioning of cells, tissues, and organs, and can result in death.

TAKE-HOME MESSAGE 20·1

Failure to maintain a consistent internal physical and chemical environment can lead to multiple problems in the normal functioning of cells, tissues, and organs, and can result in death.

20·2

Animals regulate their internal environment through homeostasis.

When it comes to **physiology**—the functions and activities of an organism—taking care of business is straightforward in single-celled organisms. Food and other necessary materials for life do not have far to go to get into the cell—all they have to do is cross a plasma membrane. Moving waste products out of the cell is similarly simple. Such are the advantages to living close to the external environment. But direct contact with the external environment has its costs, too. Perhaps most important among these costs is that the cell is, to a large extent, at the mercy of its external environment. Changes in the environment—such as in temperature or pH—can have a great impact on the cell itself.

Like single-celled organisms, multicellular animals also must acquire food and other materials, as well as get rid of waste. These tasks become increasingly complex as organisms become more complex and more of their cells are not in direct contact with the external environment. On the other hand, when it's not in direct contact with the external

environment, a cell can be protected from harsh or changing environmental conditions. To most cells in a multicellular organism, the more important environment is the "internal environment."

With multicellularity and increasing size, then, an animal's internal environment takes on greater importance than the external environment in influencing cell functioning. In vertebrates, this internal environment consists of the **extracellular fluid** that fills the space between cells (also called the **interstitial fluid**), bathing the cells. This fluid is primarily water, but also contains nutrients and raw materials for growth and development, as well as waste products that have diffused out of or been removed from cells. The volume of interstitial fluid is not insignificant. In fact, one-third of the water in the human body is outside the body's cells, with more than two and a half gallons (10 liters)—picture five 2-liter soda bottles!—surrounding and bathing the cells.

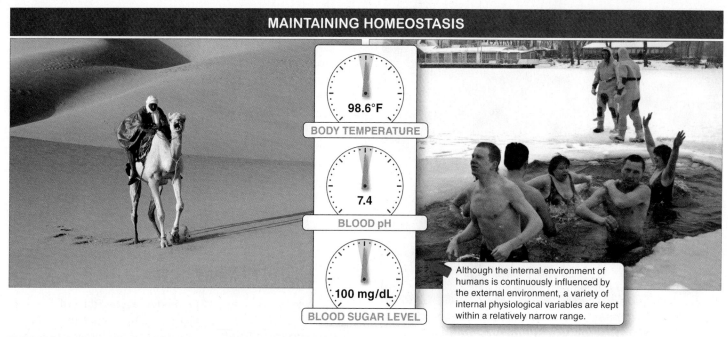

Although the internal environment of humans is continuously influenced by the external environment, a variety of internal physiological variables are kept within a relatively narrow range.

FIGURE 20-2 Homeostasis: maintaining a stable internal environment.

The internal environment of multicellular animals is continuously influenced by their external environment as well as by the cellular activities that add and remove materials. One of the hallmarks of animal physiology, however, is that organisms generally maintain homeostasis, or the ability to return to a narrow range of physical and chemical conditions, even in the face of changing external environmental forces. In this relatively constant, steady internal environment, variables such as temperature, water-solute balances, pH, blood sugar levels, and O_2 and CO_2 concentrations in blood and other tissues are maintained within narrow ranges by the activities of cells within the organism's tissues, organs, and systems (**FIGURE 20-2**).

Homeostasis is of huge value to the organism. Cellular functioning (from DNA replication to protein production to intercellular communication) depends, in large part, on the activities of enzymes. In turn, an enzyme's activity depends critically on the temperature and other characteristics of its immediate environment. Even slight changes in these variables can disrupt, reduce, or even stop enzyme functioning. And this can have catastrophic consequences, such as in the case of heat stroke described above.

Enzyme activity is just one of many facets of cell function influenced by temperature and other physical features of the cell's internal environment: membrane permeability and the rates at which materials diffuse across membranes also respond to changes in the environment. Through homeostasis, organisms maintain optimum metabolic functioning—the processes by which organisms take up nutrients from their environment and use them for growth, movement, reproduction, and all the other actions necessary for life. In the next section, we explore how homeostasis is maintained.

TAKE-HOME MESSAGE 20·2

Although the internal environment of multicellular animals is continuously influenced by their external environment, animals maintain homeostasis: they keep a variety of internal physiological variables—including temperature, water-solute balances, pH, blood sugar levels, and blood gas concentrations—within a relatively constant range.

The Internal Environment   How Does Homeostasis Work?   Form Reflects Function

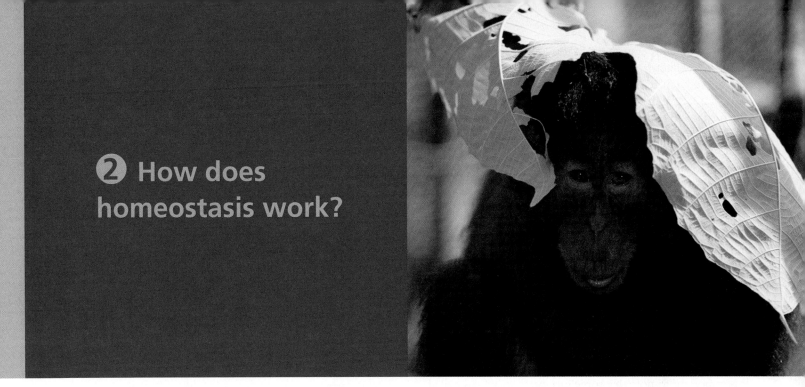

❷ How does homeostasis work?

Relief from heat: A young orangutan seeks shelter under a leaf.

20•3

Negative and positive feedback systems influence homeostasis.

For animals to maintain homeostasis with regard to a particular physiological variable, that variable must have a **set point,** a target value or range to which the organism can return. Most vertebrates have set points for a variety of physiological variables, including body temperature, water-solute balances, blood sugar levels, blood pH, and tissue O_2 and CO_2 concentrations.

In the face of changes in its external environment, how does an organism maintain its homeostasis, its constant internal environment? The most common method involves the phenomenon of **negative feedback,** in which sensors detect a change in the internal environment and trigger structures called **effectors** to oppose or reduce the change. This cycle of detection, response, and change is called a negative feedback loop (**FIGURE 20-3**).

An example of a negative feedback loop that we encounter in everyday life is the regulation of room temperature in a house, which involves a sensor (the thermostat) and two effectors (a furnace and an air conditioner). Within the thermostat is a sensor that detects the temperature in the

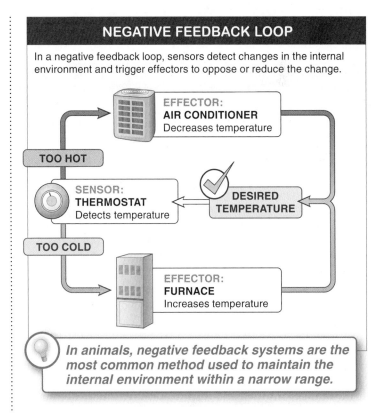

NEGATIVE FEEDBACK LOOP

In a negative feedback loop, sensors detect changes in the internal environment and trigger effectors to oppose or reduce the change.

**EFFECTOR:
AIR CONDITIONER**
Decreases temperature

TOO HOT

**SENSOR:
THERMOSTAT**
Detects temperature

DESIRED TEMPERATURE

TOO COLD

**EFFECTOR:
FURNACE**
Increases temperature

In animals, negative feedback systems are the most common method used to maintain the internal environment within a narrow range.

FIGURE 20-3 A negative feedback loop restores the internal environment to a set point.

house. If the temperature drops too low, the thermostat triggers an effector—the furnace—to turn on, bringing the room temperature back up to the desired level. Once the temperature reaches a specified level, the thermostat tells the furnace to shut off. Similarly, if the temperature gets too high, the thermostat can trigger the air conditioning to turn on, which brings the temperature back down to the desired level, after which it shuts off. In both cases, a negative feedback system senses a change in the temperature, triggers events that reverse the change, and restores the house's internal environment to its desired level.

In the human body, negative feedback systems are the most common method used to maintain the internal environment within a narrow range. These systems include those that maintain body temperature, regulate levels of sugar in the bloodstream, and control levels of salt and other solutes in body fluids. We explore these systems in detail later in this chapter.

It is important to note that some groups of organisms, called **regulators,** maintain homeostasis for a certain variable (as we've just described for temperature), while other organisms, called **conformers,** may have no set point for that variable at all and the variable may fluctuate with external changes. Animals vary in the traits for which they are regulators and conformers. Most fishes, for example, conform to the

temperature of the water but regulate closely the concentration of salt in their blood and tissues, independent of the salt concentration in the water (**FIGURE 20-4**).

In addition to negative feedback systems, organisms also have a small number of **positive feedback** systems, in which deviations from conditions normally found in the internal environment cause an increase or acceleration of the change, in the same direction. Such systems push the body away from homeostasis and often initiate cascading processes that increase the rate at which the system deviates from the normal range. For this reason, positive feedback systems, if unchecked, can become highly unstable.

An example of a positive feedback system is the blood-clotting process (**FIGURE 20-5**). Injury to a blood vessel causes platelets—cellular fragments involved in clotting—to release their Super Glue–like contents, which begin to seal any rip or tear in the blood vessel (see Section 21-6). Within the bloodstream, the contents released from a platelet have another effect as well: they cause other platelets to release their contents. This is a positive feedback system, because the release of some blood-clotting molecules into the bloodstream causes the release of more, which causes the release

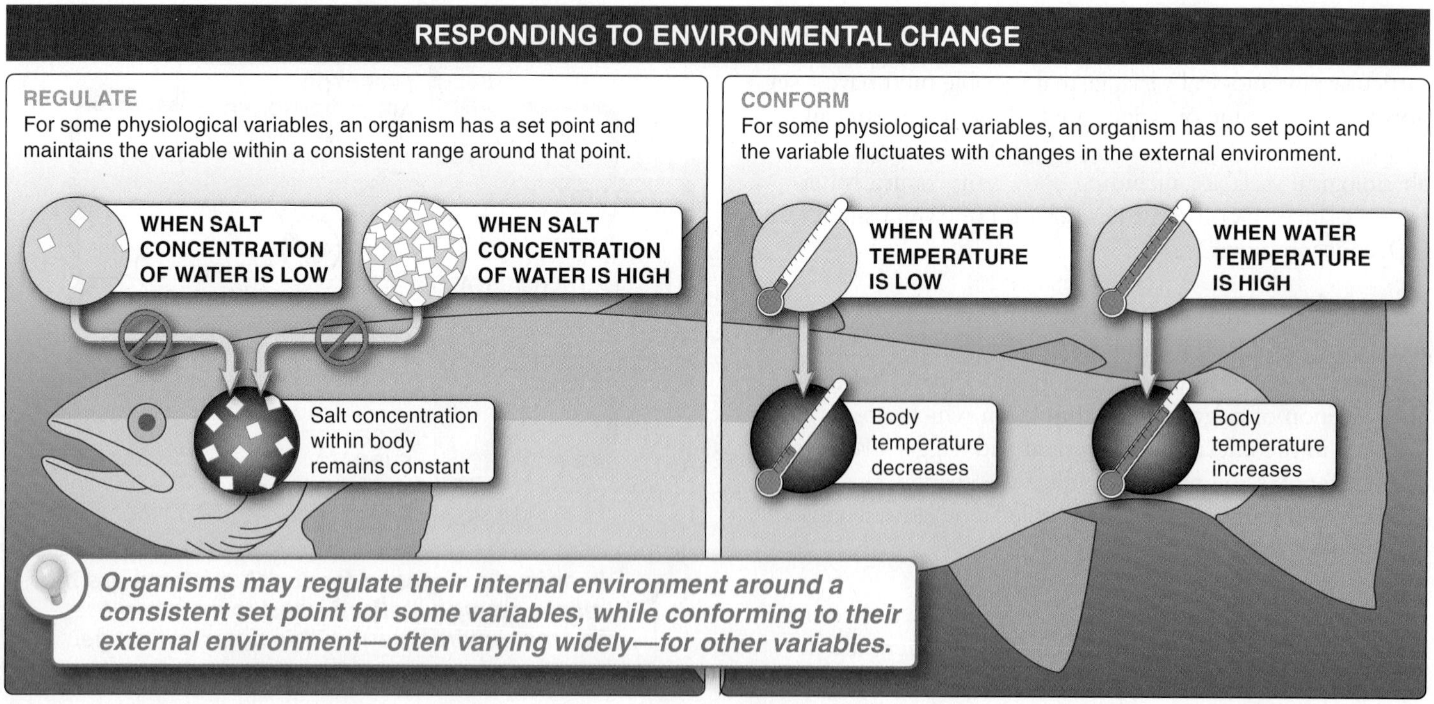

Q *Why don't we bleed to death when we get a cut?*

RESPONDING TO ENVIRONMENTAL CHANGE

REGULATE
For some physiological variables, an organism has a set point and maintains the variable within a consistent range around that point.

WHEN SALT CONCENTRATION OF WATER IS LOW

WHEN SALT CONCENTRATION OF WATER IS HIGH

Salt concentration within body remains constant

CONFORM
For some physiological variables, an organism has no set point and the variable fluctuates with changes in the external environment.

WHEN WATER TEMPERATURE IS LOW

WHEN WATER TEMPERATURE IS HIGH

Body temperature decreases

Body temperature increases

Organisms may regulate their internal environment around a consistent set point for some variables, while conforming to their external environment—often varying widely—for other variables.

FIGURE 20-4 Regulate or conform? Two strategies to cope with a changing environment.

The Internal Environment　　　How Does Homeostasis Work?　　　Form Reflects Function

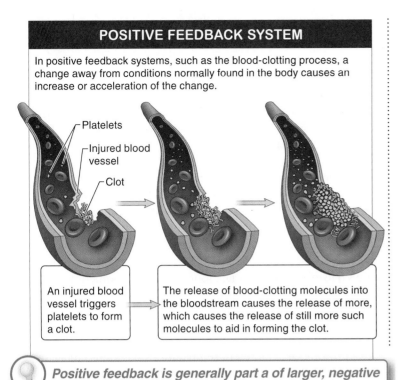

POSITIVE FEEDBACK SYSTEM

In positive feedback systems, such as the blood-clotting process, a change away from conditions normally found in the body causes an increase or acceleration of the change.

- Platelets
- Injured blood vessel
- Clot

An injured blood vessel triggers platelets to form a clot.

The release of blood-clotting molecules into the bloodstream causes the release of more, which causes the release of still more such molecules to aid in forming the clot.

💡 *Positive feedback is generally part a of larger, negative feedback system; after a period of positive feedback, the variable is brought back within its typical range.*

FIGURE 20-5 Patching a tear. The blood clot that forms after an injury is a result of a positive feedback system.

of still more. The result is that a dangerous situation, injury to a blood vessel, is quickly remedied.

Generally, positive feedback systems are part of larger, negative feedback systems, which, after a short period of positive feedback, bring the variable (and the organism) back to within its original, normal range of internal environmental conditions. After blood clotting has stopped the loss of blood from a damaged vessel, other chemical signals interrupt the positive feedback loop, stop the further release of blood-clotting molecules, and even begin to break down blood clots that no longer serve a function.

TAKE-HOME MESSAGE 20·3

For animals to maintain homeostasis with regard to a particular physiological variable, that variable must have a set point to which the organism can return. Through negative feedback, sensors detect a change in the internal environment and trigger effectors to oppose or reduce the change. Positive feedback systems, much less common, oppose homeostasis in response to a change, pushing the body away from normal conditions and increasing change in the same direction.

20·4

Temperature control is a component of homeostasis.

As we saw in the case of Korey Stringer, one of the most important environmental factors that affect animals is temperature. And for many animal species, the control of temperature, called **thermoregulation,** is an important component of homeostasis.

When it comes to thermoregulation, the biggest distinction among animal species is in how they generate their body heat. **Endotherms** (sometimes described as "warm-blooded") generate their heat internally, within their own bodies. Most mammals and birds are endotherms. **Ectotherms** (sometimes described as "cold-blooded") get their heat primarily from the environment, usually the sun. Invertebrates, fishes, amphibians, and reptiles are all ectotherms. While these groups are often distinguished as

Q *Why do some cold-blooded animals have "hot" blood and some warm-blooded animals have "cold" blood?*

"warm-blooded" and "cold-blooded" (**FIGURE 20-6**), closer investigation reveals that such terms do not always accurately describe the two groups. Some animals, including numerous mammalian species, **hibernate,** going into a state of reduced metabolic activity for days or weeks, during which their body temperature can drop considerably. The body temperature of some hibernating ground squirrels, for example, can drop below freezing for more than three weeks. Some hibernating mammals can become quite cold, while some lizards basking in the sun can get very warm.

These observations highlight another important aspect of thermoregulation. Some organisms (such as humans) are **homeotherms,** meaning that they maintain a relatively

GENERATING BODY HEAT

ENDOTHERMS
• Animals that generate body heat internally
• Sometimes described as "warm-blooded"
• Include most mammals and birds

ECTOTHERMS
• Animals that get their heat primarily from the environment
• Sometimes described as "cold-blooded"
• Include invertebrates, fishes, amphibians, and reptiles

FIGURE 20-6 Strategies to heat the body.

constant body temperature. Other organisms (such as the lizards and hibernating mammals) are **heterotherms,** and their body temperatures, at times, fluctuate as the environmental temperature changes (**FIGURE 20-7**). As a consequence, animals are most accurately categorized by describing their source of heat (internal or external) *and* the degree to which they maintain a constant temperature or have a temperature that fluctuates.

Whether or not an animal generates its own heat and maintains a constant body temperature, all animals exchange heat with the environment. Ultimately, an organism's body temperature is a function of the heat it produces in conjunction with the heat that is transferred from the environment to its body or from its body to the environment. This heat exchange can occur in four ways (**FIGURE 20-8**), and these four mechanisms sometimes make it challenging for organisms to acquire heat, and sometimes make it challenging to dissipate heat.

1. *Conduction* is the transfer of heat that occurs when two objects at different temperatures come in contact. Holding an ice cube or sitting on a hot car seat dramatically reveals conduction in action.

2. *Convection* is the transfer of heat from an object to a medium such as water or air as it passes next to the object. This is particularly noticeable to us when a cold breeze blows.

3. *Radiation* is the transfer of heat, without direct contact, from a warmer object to a colder object. You are experiencing radiant heat when you feel the warmth of the sun on your face or the heat from a fireplace on your feet.

4. *Evaporation* is the loss of heat that occurs as a liquid substance, such as liquid water, turns to a gas. When you sweat and the sweat evaporates, it cools you off.

MAINTAINING BODY TEMPERATURE

Reptiles can often be found on the edges of roads in the afternoon and early evening, using the warmth of the road to elevate their body temperature.

HOMEOTHERMS
Body temperature remains relatively constant.

HETEROTHERMS
Body temperature fluctuates as environmental temperatures change.

FIGURE 20-7 Stable body temperature versus variable body temperature.

The Internal Environment   How Does Homeostasis Work?   Form Reflects Function

EXCHANGING BODY HEAT WITH THE ENVIRONMENT

Animals exchange heat with the environment in four ways.

CONDUCTION
The transfer of heat that occurs when two objects at different temperatures come in contact.

CONVECTION
The transfer of heat to a medium such as water or air as it passes next to an object.

RADIATION
The transfer of heat, without direct contact, from a warmer object to a colder object.

EVAPORATION
The loss of heat that occurs as a substance such as liquid water turns to a gas.

An organism's temperature depends on the heat that it gains or loses to the environment, in conjunction with the heat the organism produces.

FIGURE 20-8 How organisms acquire or dissipate heat.

We'll find further examples of each of these mechanisms as we look at four of the methods—physical, behavioral, physiological, and cellular—by which animals regulate body temperature (**FIGURE 20-9**).

Numerous physical features have evolved in organisms that influence the organism's body temperature. These include the organism's body size, surface area, and levels of insulation. The thick lipid-rich coat of blubber in walruses, whales, and many other marine mammals, for example, can account for up to 50% of the body weight of some animals and provides effective insulation, helping them to maintain a constant body temperature.

An organism can also use behavioral strategies to regulate its body temperature. Most lizards, for example, bask in the sun during the early morning hours, increasing their body temperature. Later, when the day is at its hottest, they may retreat to a burrow to reduce their body temperature. Many large mammals that cannot get to shade orient their bodies to minimize the angle at which the sun strikes them. The African ground squirrel even shades itself with its tail as it forages.

Animals also employ many physiological methods of thermoregulation. One specific example of this occurs as cells maintain concentration gradients of various ions, such as potassium (K^+) and sodium (Na^+). Many cell membranes are somewhat permeable to K^+ and Na^+ ions. The ions "leak" across the membrane, requiring active transport to restore and maintain the concentration gradients necessary for some cellular processes. Because the reactions involved in active transport are not perfectly efficient in their use of energy,

METHODS FOR REGULATING BODY TEMPERATURE

PHYSICAL METHODS
The walrus has a thick coat of blubber that provides insulation from the external environment.

BEHAVIORAL METHODS
The African ground squirrel shades itself with its tail while foraging, to minimize heat from the sun.

PHYSIOLOGICAL METHODS
By panting, dingos make use of the efficient loss of heat due to evaporation.

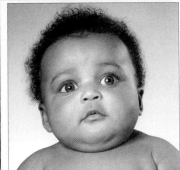

CELLULAR METHODS
Human infants have a special type of fat that produces heat, rather than ATP, when broken down.

FIGURE 20-9 Adaptations that aid in temperature regulation.

Most organisms must maintain water and solute concentrations within a narrow range. Imbalances can lead to serious health problems and even death.

FIGURE 20-10 **Heat exchange.** Sweating can help cool us off through evaporation. By leaning up against a cool rock wall, we can also lose some heat through conduction.

some energy is released as heat with each reaction. This heat can help maintain an organism's body temperature. Interestingly, as it turns out, cell membranes in endotherms, such as humans, are leakier than the cell membranes in ectotherms, such as fishes, suggesting that such "leakiness" is an adaptation that helps endotherms generate heat internally. It is also likely that it's because mitochondria are the sites of greatest heat generation that endotherms have, on average, three to four times as many mitochondria per cell as ectotherms.

Another physiological method by which animals—both ectotherms and endotherms—can regulate their body heat is by controlling the flow of blood to the skin. To lose heat, such as during periods of extreme exertion or at extremely high external temperatures, they increase blood flow to the skin, allowing greater heat loss by convection. Through panting and sweating, too, many animals make use of the efficient loss of heat due to evaporation (**FIGURE 20-10**). Alternatively, in cold environments, the loss of heat can be reduced by reducing the flow of blood to the skin and by shivering, through which animals can increase their heat production.

One cellular method of temperature regulation is particularly important to human babies. It takes place in a special type of connective tissue called "brown fat." Unlike the cells of "white fat," or adipose tissue (most of the

Q Why does "baby fat," unlike regular fat, act like a built-in heating pad?

fat in adult's bodies), in which there are few mitochondria, the cells of brown fat have a high density of mitochondria along with the stored fat. When brown fat cells oxidize their fat, however, they don't generate ATP. Instead, a special protein causes protons to leak directly across the mitochondrial membrane, rather than passing through the enzyme that synthesizes ATP (see Section 4-15), causing the production of heat rather than ATP from the fat breakdown. Human infants have significantly more brown fat than adults. This probably evolved because their small body size gives them a large surface-area-to-volume ratio, which results in a relatively large surface area over which they can lose heat and a relatively small body mass in which they can generate heat.

TAKE-HOME MESSAGE 20·4

The control of body temperature, called thermoregulation, is an important component of homeostasis. Body temperature is a function of internal heat production and heat transfer between an organism and its environment. Heat transfer to and from the environment is regulated physically, behaviorally, physiologically, and at the cellular level.

20-10 CHAPTER 20 • INTRODUCTION TO ANIMAL PHYSIOLOGY

The Internal Environment ▼ How Does Homeostasis Work? Form Reflects Function

Animals must balance their water content within a narrow range.

Organisms, whether they live in the water or on land, require water. But they can't take in too much or they will burst. And they can't lose too much or they will shrivel up and die. **Osmoregulation,** an important component of homeostasis in animals, is the regulation of water content and of the concentrations of dissolved solutes that influence osmosis. The most abundant solutes in animal fluids are sodium, chloride, potassium, magnesium, and calcium.

Although a variety of mechanisms of water regulation have evolved in animals, there are just four ways that animals get water: by drinking it, by eating foods that contain it, by absorbing it through osmosis, and as a by-product of cellular respiration. Similarly, there are four ways that animals lose water: urination, defecation, evaporation (including panting, breathing, and sweating), and osmosis.

Osmoregulation revolves around controlling and regulating these mechanisms of water loss and gain. Through osmosis, water flows from areas of low solute concentration to areas of high solute concentration. Thus organisms often control their water content indirectly by regulating their solute content. They generally balance the total amount of solutes—which influences the direction and magnitude of osmosis—and the concentration of each solute individually. Imbalances in the concentrations of certain solutes can cause serious health

problems, from muscle spasms to confusion to paralysis, and even death.

Because animals live in such a wide range of habitats, they encounter a similarly wide range of osmoregulation challenges. The challenges are very different for aquatic organisms than for terrestrial organisms, for example. And among the aquatic organisms, the challenges facing organisms living in saltwater habitats are very different from—almost the opposite of—those faced by organisms living in fresh water.

Different strategies have evolved for coping with such diverse osmoregulation challenges. Most invertebrates that live in salt water are **osmoconformers,** meaning that they let the solute concentration of their body fluids reflect that of their environment. Most vertebrates, on the other hand, are **osmoregulators,** maintaining their fluids and solute concentrations within narrow ranges that differ from those of their environment (**FIGURE 20-11**).

A variety of structures have evolved that enable animals to regulate their water balance. In insects, for example, very small tubes branch off the digestive tract, near its end at the rectum. These extensions from the gut, called Malpighian tubules, function as the animals' chief excretory organs. Using active transport (see Section 3-10), an animal moves potassium ions

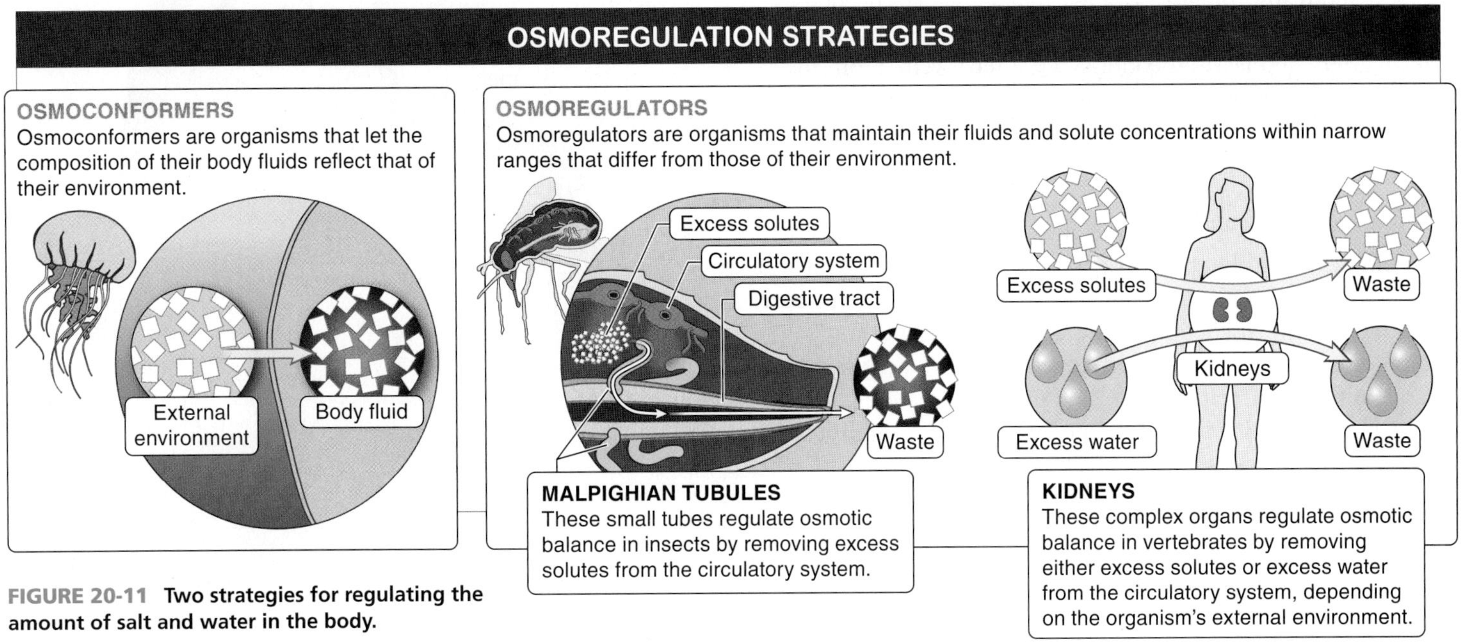

OSMOREGULATION STRATEGIES

OSMOCONFORMERS
Osmoconformers are organisms that let the composition of their body fluids reflect that of their environment.

External environment | Body fluid

OSMOREGULATORS
Osmoregulators are organisms that maintain their fluids and solute concentrations within narrow ranges that differ from those of their environment.

Excess solutes
Circulatory system
Digestive tract
Waste

Excess solutes
Excess water
Kidneys
Waste
Waste

MALPIGHIAN TUBULES
These small tubes regulate osmotic balance in insects by removing excess solutes from the circulatory system.

KIDNEYS
These complex organs regulate osmotic balance in vertebrates by removing either excess solutes or excess water from the circulatory system, depending on the organism's external environment.

FIGURE 20-11 Two strategies for regulating the amount of salt and water in the body.

(K$^+$) and cellular waste products from its body cavity—where its blood is—into the Malpighian tubules. As a consequence of the increase in solutes in the tubules, water moves into them by osmosis. The K$^+$ ions, water, and waste products move down the digestive tract until, near its end, the K$^+$ ions and water are mostly reabsorbed into the circulatory system. This is a very effective system for conserving water, leaving mostly waste products to be excreted as feces.

Q **Do fish drink water?**

Another osmoregulatory structure is the vertebrate kidney. The kidney, as we shall see, is a complex organ that filters blood, removing metabolic waste products—particularly excess nitrogen from the breakdown of proteins and nucleic acids—and other ions while regulating the organism's water balance. The specific details of kidney function vary across the different groups of vertebrates. Let's consider, for example, the challenges faced by two groups of aquatic vertebrates: freshwater and saltwater fishes. A freshwater fish faces the problems of high concentrations of water entering its body and solutes leaving its body. A saltwater fish, on the other hand, tends to lose water to its environment while taking in high concentrations of solutes from the environmental water. As a consequence, vertebrate kidneys—depending on the type of animal—may function either to conserve water or to remove it. (This explains why a freshwater fish does not drink water, but a saltwater fish drinks large amounts.)

In the next section, we examine the details of kidney functioning, focusing specifically on the human kidney and how it is able to produce urine that has a solute concentration more than four times that of blood, and how it is able to eliminate the many potentially harmful molecules contained within the food and drink consumed in the diet.

TAKE-HOME MESSAGE 20·5

Many organisms maintain their water content within a narrow range. To maintain osmotic balance, organisms must be able to take up water and get rid of water, and they must be able to regulate concentrations of ions in their body fluids. Various mechanisms and strategies have evolved for coping with these challenges.

20·6

In humans, the kidney is the chief excretory organ.

The kidney is an organ in vertebrates that helps maintain homeostasis by regulating water balance and solute concentration in body fluids. It accomplishes this by filtering blood and reabsorbing water and other substances needed by the body. Blood flows into capillaries within each kidney via a renal artery and leaves the kidney via a renal vein. From the kidneys, waste products and water removed from the bloodstream pass to the bladder, and from there are excreted as urine (FIGURE 20-12).

A human has two kidneys, each about the size of a fist, located on either side of the spine, just above the waist. Each kidney is made up of approximately one million nephrons. A **nephron** consists of two basic components: a nephron tubule and a mass of blood vessels that work together to accomplish the tasks of filtration, reabsorption, and excretion (FIGURE 20-13). The blood-filtering unit of the nephron is a mass of capillaries called a **glomerulus,** and the ball-like structure that surrounds it is called **Bowman's capsule.** Each Bowman's

FIGURE 20-12 **Structure of the kidney.** Human kidneys filter blood, reabsorb water and solutes, and excrete waste.

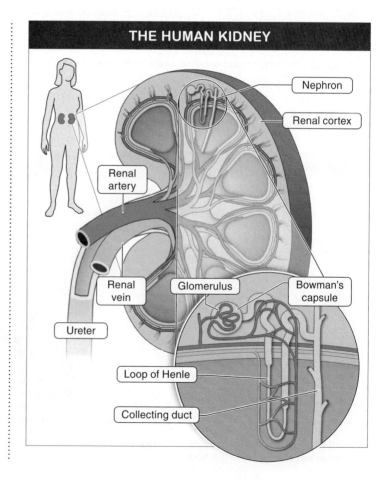

THE HUMAN KIDNEY

Nephron

Renal cortex

Renal artery

Renal vein

Glomerulus

Bowman's capsule

Ureter

Loop of Henle

Collecting duct

The Internal Environment   How Does Homeostasis Work?   Form Reflects Function

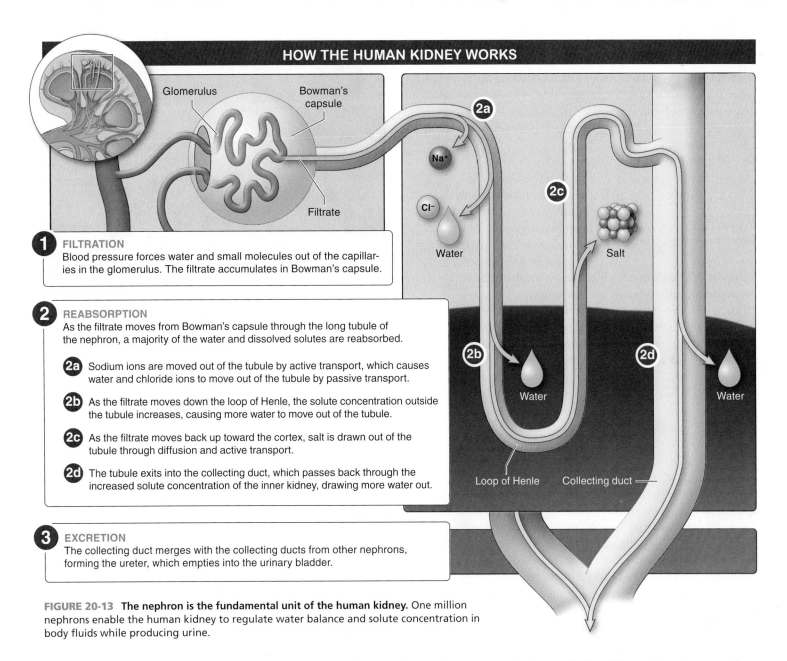

Glomerulus

Bowman's capsule

Filtrate

2a

Na⁺

Cl⁻

Water

2c

Salt

1 FILTRATION
Blood pressure forces water and small molecules out of the capillaries in the glomerulus. The filtrate accumulates in Bowman's capsule.

2 REABSORPTION
As the filtrate moves from Bowman's capsule through the long tubule of the nephron, a majority of the water and dissolved solutes are reabsorbed.

2a Sodium ions are moved out of the tubule by active transport, which causes water and chloride ions to move out of the tubule by passive transport.

2b As the filtrate moves down the loop of Henle, the solute concentration outside the tubule increases, causing more water to move out of the tubule.

2c As the filtrate moves back up toward the cortex, salt is drawn out of the tubule through diffusion and active transport.

2d The tubule exits into the collecting duct, which passes back through the increased solute concentration of the inner kidney, drawing more water out.

2b Water

2d Water

Loop of Henle   Collecting duct

3 EXCRETION
The collecting duct merges with the collecting ducts from other nephrons, forming the ureter, which empties into the urinary bladder.

FIGURE 20-13 The nephron is the fundamental unit of the human kidney. One million nephrons enable the human kidney to regulate water balance and solute concentration in body fluids while producing urine.

capsule is connected to a single, long, urine-producing tube that excretes its filtered fluid into a collecting duct.

The capillaries in the glomerulus are porous, and blood pressure forces out water and small molecules and ions (but not blood cells or most proteins) through the capillary walls. Fluid that accumulates in Bowman's capsule, called **filtrate,** contains salts, sugars, amino acids, vitamins, and many other molecules, all at the same concentration as in the blood.

As the filtrate moves from Bowman's capsule through the urine-collecting tubule of the nephron, the vast majority of the water and dissolved solutes must be reabsorbed. In fact, up to 2,000 liters of blood (about 275 times the total volume of blood in your body) passes through the kidneys each day, but only about 1.5 liters of urine is produced and excreted.

Reabsorption in the long tubule of the nephron is a complex process. It begins with the active transport of sodium ions out of the tubule, which causes water and chloride ions to follow, moving out of the tubule by passive transport.

The tubule (and the filtrate it contains) then loops from the outer part of the kidney, called the cortex (see Figure 20-13), down into the innermost part of the kidney and back again, in a path called the loop of Henle. As the tubule passes to the innermost part of the kidney, the solute concentration of the interstitial fluid, outside the tube, increases. This causes more and more water to move out of the tubule, from the filtrate and into the interstitial fluid. As the filtrate moves up toward the kidney cortex again, more salt is lost, through diffusion and active transport. From the cortex, the tubule passes into the collecting duct, which passes through the innermost part of the kidney again, returning additional water to the interstitial fluid and further concentrating the urine for excretion. The collecting duct eventually merges with collecting ducts from other nephrons, forming the ureter, which empties into the urinary bladder. From the bladder, urine passes through the urethra and is excreted from the body.

Q Why do some desert mammals never need to drink water?

Filtering the blood and producing urine not only follows a complicated path but is very energetically expensive. Considerable amounts of energy are expended in the active transport of solutes that leads to the recovery of water. Nonetheless, some animals, such as kangaroo rats, are so efficient at reabsorbing water that they can recover nearly all of the water filtered by their kidneys. They never have to drink water at all; the water contained in their food and the water generated as a by-product during cellular metabolism is sufficient.

Among the most important of the metabolic waste products that must be filtered and removed from the blood by the kidneys are those containing nitrogen. Produced from the breakdown of proteins and nucleic acids, this nitrogen tends to be in the form of ammonia, which is generally very toxic to organisms. Some organisms—mostly aquatic organisms—are able to rid their bodies of excess nitrogen by simply excreting the ammonia. Terrestrial animals (and many marine animals), however, cannot consume sufficient water to keep ammonia diluted enough so that it is not toxic. These organisms instead combine ammonia with carbon dioxide, producing urea, which can be stored for longer periods of time and at higher concentrations (thereby requiring much less water). There is a cost to this system, however; the production of urea from ammonia and carbon dioxide is energetically expensive. Besides ammonia and urea, there is a third form in which nitrogenous wastes can be excreted, as a paste called uric acid. This method requires even less water than urea excretion, but is even more energetically expensive. It is used by insects, terrestrial snails, birds, and many reptiles.

The kidneys are so effective at filtering blood and concentrating the many waste products of metabolism in urine that it is possible to detect the use of many drugs

FIGURE 20-14 Detectible remainders. Drugs break down into metabolites, chemicals that sometimes linger in the body and urine. Here an individual tends to marijuana plants grown for medicinal purposes.

through urinalysis. Most drug-screening urinalysis does not actually involve testing for the presence of the drugs themselves, which may remain in the body for only a short time. Instead, the tests look for the presence of chemicals, called metabolites, that result from the breakdown of the drugs (**FIGURE 20-14**). Metabolites have been identified for many drugs, including Ecstasy, cocaine, methamphetamines, and marijuana. In the case of marijuana, the metabolites are fat-soluble. This means that they are stored in fat cells indefinitely, and released only when fat from those cells is metabolized for energy. As a consequence, marijuana can be detected a month or longer after the last use.

Q How can some drugs be detected by urinalysis even months after the last intake?

TAKE-HOME MESSAGE 20·6

The kidney is the organ in vertebrates that helps maintain homeostasis by regulating water balance and solute concentrations in body fluids, filtering blood, and removing potentially harmful ions and metabolic waste products, excreting them in urine.

The Internal Environment   How Does Homeostasis Work?   Form Reflects Function

❸ Form reflects function: animal anatomy.

An elephant uses its trunk to forage for tree-top leaves.

20·7

Most animal bodies are organized into cells, tissues, organs, and organ systems.

Form follows function. This simple statement captures one of the most universal relationships in the living world. For example, fast-swimming organisms, from penguins to tuna to sharks, share a common streamlined body shape (**FIGURE 20-15**). If a structure is adaptive—the product of natural selection— then its physical features closely reflect its function. And just as form follows function for large animal structures, so, too, does the relationship hold true for molecules, organelles, and cells. In this section we examine the levels of organization in animal bodies and see how form fits function in each.

Animals are multicellular organisms. And multicellularity makes it possible for animals to attain much larger sizes and much greater physiological complexity than single-celled organisms. Increased size and complexity bring many benefits, including a reduction in the number of potential predators, an increase in the number of potential prey, and, more generally, a

FORM FOLLOWS FUNCTION

If a structure is the product of natural selection, the structure commonly reflects closely its function. For example, fast-swimming organisms have streamlined body shapes.

FIGURE 20-15 **Adapted for swimming: the streamlined body of the penguin.**

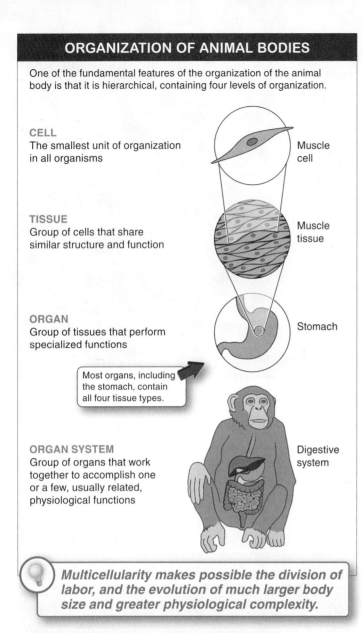

ORGANIZATION OF ANIMAL BODIES

One of the fundamental features of the organization of the animal body is that it is hierarchical, containing four levels of organization.

CELL
The smallest unit of organization in all organisms

Muscle cell

TISSUE
Group of cells that share similar structure and function

Muscle tissue

ORGAN
Group of tissues that perform specialized functions

Stomach

Most organs, including the stomach, contain all four tissue types.

ORGAN SYSTEM
Group of organs that work together to accomplish one or a few, usually related, physiological functions

Digestive system

Multicellularity makes possible the division of labor, and the evolution of much larger body size and greater physiological complexity.

FIGURE 20-16 **From cells to organ systems.**

reduction in the influence of the external environment. For these reasons, among others, the transition from a single-celled to a multicellular body is one of the most important evolutionary transitions.

Possibly the chief benefit of multicellularity is that it makes possible a division of labor and specialization at the cellular level. No longer is it necessary for each cell to carry out every single physiological process (such as generating movement, detoxifying harmful chemicals, digesting macromolecules, and sensing and responding to environmental changes). Instead, cells can be organized into groups, and groups organized into larger groups, to carry out specific life-sustaining functions such as exchanging gases between the organism and its

environment, thinking and feeling, and fighting pathogens (**FIGURE 20-16**).

One of the fundamental features of the organization of the animal body is that it is hierarchical. Cells, as you'll recall from Chapter 3, are the smallest unit of organization in all organisms. Sponges, structurally the simplest of all animals, have cells specialized to perform a few distinct tasks. For example, some cells form the covering of the sponge's body, and others obtain food to provide nutrition and energy to sustain the sponge's activities. At the other end of the spectrum are humans—with 210 different cell types.

In most animals, groups of cells with similar structure, along with some products of those cells, form **tissues,** in which the cells act together to perform specific functions in the body. Adult animals generally have four main types of tissue (**FIGURE 20-17**), which we'll discuss in more detail in Sections 20-8 through 20-11.

Connective tissue consists of cells embedded in a large amount of extracellular material, called **matrix,** which together contribute to body structure and support. Found throughout the human body, connective tissue can also serve to anchor cells, regulate communication between cells, and influence growth and wound healing. Some of the most important structures formed from connective tissue include tendons, cartilage, blood, adipose, and bone.

Epithelial tissue covers and lines most exterior and interior surfaces of the body. Skin is an epithelial tissue, as are the tissues that line the nose, throat, lungs, blood vessels, and digestive tract.

From the circulatory and respiratory systems that deliver oxygen and remove carbon dioxide, to the muscle tissue that generates the flapping of wings, to the neurons in the eyes that detect prey, to the epithelial tissue across which nutrients from food are absorbed, the working together of cells, tissues, organs, and organ systems make many complex actions of organisms possible—such as flight in these red-and-green macaws in Peru.

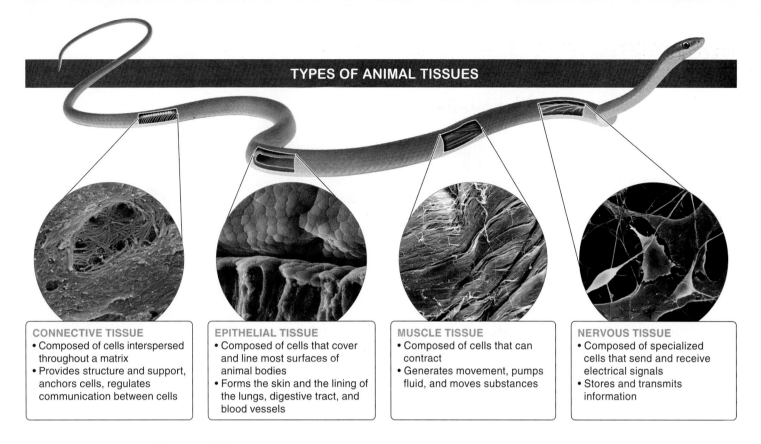

CONNECTIVE TISSUE
• Composed of cells interspersed throughout a matrix
• Provides structure and support, anchors cells, regulates communication between cells

EPITHELIAL TISSUE
• Composed of cells that cover and line most surfaces of animal bodies
• Forms the skin and the lining of the lungs, digestive tract, and blood vessels

MUSCLE TISSUE
• Composed of cells that can contract
• Generates movement, pumps fluid, and moves substances

NERVOUS TISSUE
• Composed of specialized cells that send and receive electrical signals
• Stores and transmits information

FIGURE 20-17 **Tissues perform specific functions in the body.**

Muscle tissue is made up of cells that can contract. This characteristic gives muscle tissue the ability to generate movement or pump fluids through the body.

Nervous tissue, found throughout the human body, is specialized to send and receive electrical signals and, in doing so, can store and transmit information. The brain and spinal cord are made up of large amounts of nervous tissue.

Just as cells with similar functions are grouped into tissues, so tissues are often grouped into organs or organ systems. **Organs** are structures that serve specialized functions, and they usually contain several types of tissue. The heart, liver, kidneys, and brain are examples of organs in the human body. Most organs—including the stomach and the small intestine, for example—have all four types of tissue. **Organ systems** are groups of organs that work together to accomplish one or a few, usually related, physiological functions. The circulatory system, for example, includes the heart, blood vessels, and blood.

In the remaining chapters of the book, we explore the complex functions carried out by each of the organ systems in animals. We describe the structures that are part of each system, how they function, and how they have evolved. As we do this, we see that an organism is greater than the sum of its parts. The working together of cells to form tissues, and of tissues to form organs and organ systems, gives multicellular organisms the abilities to reproduce, defend themselves, and communicate (among many other abilities), in ways that are not possible for a single cell or a single type of tissue.

TAKE-HOME MESSAGE 20•7

Animal bodies are highly organized, and at all levels of organization, the physical features are closely related to function. In most animals, cells with similar structure and function are organized into tissues. There are four types of tissue: connective tissue, epithelial tissue, muscle tissue, and nervous tissue. Tissues are often organized into organs, which serve specialized functions and can contain several types of tissue. In turn, organs can be organized into organ systems that accomplish highly complex tasks.

Connective tissue provides support.

Connective tissue is usually the most abundant type of tissue in an animal. Connective tissue is sometimes called "cellular glue," because it holds cells together and, as bone and cartilage, for example, gives shape, structure, and support to other tissues, structures, and organs throughout the body. Connective tissue, however, isn't restricted to supporting roles; it also includes tissues such as fat cells and blood.

Regardless of the function it performs or the form it takes, all connective tissue consists of cells that are embedded in matrix—a mass of non-living extracellular material (**FIGURE 20-18**). Matrix, in vertebrates, consists chiefly of polysaccharides and protein (and some minerals, in the case of bone), which are produced and secreted by various cells within the matrix. The matrix can be liquid, jelly-like, or solid. With the exception of blood, all connective tissue contains cells called *fibroblasts,* which produce and secrete the matrix proteins **collagen** and **elastin.** So common is connective tissue that collagen, which often forms a sort of net surrounding organs, is the most abundant protein in humans and other mammals.

CONNECTIVE TISSUE STRUCTURE

Connective tissue is a collection of cells arranged within an extracellular matrix that gives shape, structure, and support to other body tissues.

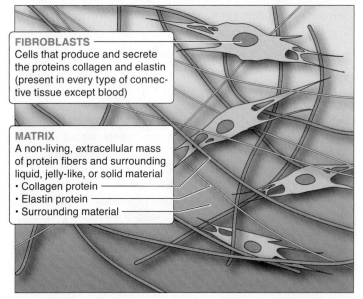

FIBROBLASTS
Cells that produce and secrete the proteins collagen and elastin (present in every type of connective tissue except blood)

MATRIX
A non-living, extracellular mass of protein fibers and surrounding liquid, jelly-like, or solid material
• Collagen protein
• Elastin protein
• Surrounding material

FIGURE 20-18 Connective tissues consist of cells embedded in an extracellular matrix.

Connective tissue proper functions much like packing material. It can be loose or dense. In loose connective tissue, the cells are in a semi-fluid, flexible matrix that generally has many fibers, usually collagen, embedded in it (**FIGURE 20-19**). Loose connective tissue includes the soft padding under your skin, the tissue surrounding most organs, and adipose (fat) tissue, which aids in cushioning, lubricating, and insulating other tissues. Dense connective tissue is stronger than loose connective tissue. It also has collagen as its chief matrix element, but it has many more, tightly packed collagen fibers than loose connective tissue. Examples of dense connective tissue include **tendons,** which connect muscle to bone, and **ligaments,** which bind bone to bone. A sprained ankle is a common injury in which a twisting of the ankle overstretches and tears part of a ligament in the foot.

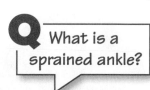

Q What is a sprained ankle?

The second type of connective tissue, called **special connective tissue,** includes bone, cartilage, and blood (see Figure 20-19). In these tissues, the matrix differs from that of connective tissue proper in that it is rigid or liquid. In **bone,** the mineral calcium is incorporated into the extracellular matrix, which then hardens into a solid material. Bones can give significant protection to organisms (the skull protects the brain, ribs protect the lungs and heart) or can provide structural support, as the backbone does. **Cartilage,** a dense connective tissue with an extracellular matrix rich in collagen, elastin, and proteins bound to long carbohydrate chains, has a hardness between that of bone and of tendons. Strong, but also flexible, cartilage is found in the ears and tip of the nose in humans, and it cushions the bones in joints throughout the body. In some organisms, including sharks, the entire skeleton is made of cartilage. **Blood** is unique among the connective tissues because it has a liquid extracellular matrix. This liquid matrix, called plasma, is made up mostly of water, but also contains dissolved proteins, sugars, and other molecules. Blood cells, including red blood cells and white blood cells, and the cellular fragments called platelets (see Chapter 21), are suspended within plasma as they transport gases and other substances throughout the body.

All connective tissues in the body, as we've seen, have essentially the same structure: cells embedded within an extracellular matrix that may be solid, soft and flexible, or

20-18   CHAPTER 20 • INTRODUCTION TO ANIMAL PHYSIOLOGY

The Internal Environment   How Does Homeostasis Work?   Form Reflects Function

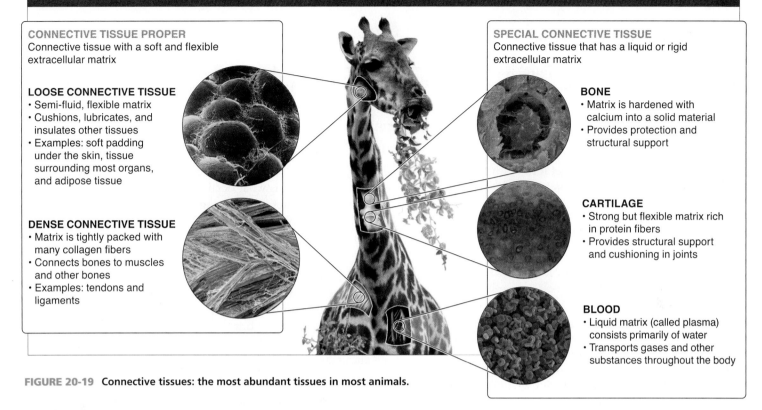

CONNECTIVE TISSUE PROPER
Connective tissue with a soft and flexible extracellular matrix

LOOSE CONNECTIVE TISSUE
- Semi-fluid, flexible matrix
- Cushions, lubricates, and insulates other tissues
- Examples: soft padding under the skin, tissue surrounding most organs, and adipose tissue

DENSE CONNECTIVE TISSUE
- Matrix is tightly packed with many collagen fibers
- Connects bones to muscles and other bones
- Examples: tendons and ligaments

SPECIAL CONNECTIVE TISSUE
Connective tissue that has a liquid or rigid extracellular matrix

BONE
- Matrix is hardened with calcium into a solid material
- Provides protection and structural support

CARTILAGE
- Strong but flexible matrix rich in protein fibers
- Provides structural support and cushioning in joints

BLOOD
- Liquid matrix (called plasma) consists primarily of water
- Transports gases and other substances throughout the body

FIGURE 20-19 Connective tissues: the most abundant tissues in most animals.

Most activities rely heavily on connective tissue, often in conjunction with muscle tissue. Playing tennis, for example, relies on blood to deliver oxygen to muscle, tendons that connect muscles to bones, and cartilage, cushioning the joints. (Collagen from the intestines of cows is even used as a material for producing the strings in some tennis rackets!)

fluid. An inflammation or weakness in any of the types of connective tissue, particularly problems with the maintenance of collagen, is the cause of many diseases with widespread effects, including scleroderma and Marfan syndrome. The most common type of arthritis, osteoarthritis, results from the breakdown of connective tissue, usually the cartilage, around joints. The reduced cushioning often leads to inflammation of tissue around the joint, with stiffness and pain, and is commonly treated with anti-inflammatory drugs including aspirin and ibuprofen.

Q The most common form of arthritis is called "wear and tear" arthritis. Why?

TAKE-HOME MESSAGE 20·8

The most abundant type of tissue in most animals is connective tissue. Connective tissue is a collection of cells arranged within an extracellular matrix, usually containing collagen, that holds the cells together and gives shape, structure, and support to other body tissues. Examples of connective tissue include tendons, ligaments, fat, blood, bone, and cartilage.

Epithelial tissue protects.

Epithelial tissue (also called **epithelium**) is a sheet-like tissue that covers the surfaces of an animal's body. It is made up of a single layer or a few layers of cells, called epithelial cells, that are tightly bound together so that fluids and gases must pass through the cells, rather than around or between the cells, to get into or out of the body (**FIGURE 20-20**). When you look at a vertebrate, most of what you see is epithelium, because skin is an epithelial tissue.

Epithelial tissue is not just found on the outer surfaces of organisms, however. It also forms **glands**—collections of cells producing secretions for use elsewhere in the body—and lines the internal tubes and cavities of the body, such as the stomach and intestine, lungs, and blood vessels. In each location, epithelium always has two distinctive sides. The "outside" can be in contact with the outside of the body or with an internal cavity such as the stomach, where it plays a protective role. The "inside" (or underside) faces away from the surface and is generally secured to underlying tissues. Epithelium plays multiple roles in organisms. Three of its most important functions are protection, transport, and secretion (**FIGURE 20-21**).

> **Q** Damage to the lining of the stomach can have painful consequences. Why?

1. *Protection.* Acting as a barrier, epithelial cells are linked closely by tight junctions and desmosomes (see Section 3-12), which keep fluids from leaking into or out of tissue. If the strong acids in the stomach, for example, were to leak out, they would seriously damage surrounding tissue. This is what occurs in individuals with stomach ulcers, open sores in the lining of the stomach. The tight fit between epithelial cells is also why the skin of terrestrial vertebrates is usually waterproof.

2. *Transport.* Epithelium forms small finger-like projections in the lining of the small intestine, where nutrients are absorbed from digested food into the bloodstream. In blood vessels, epithelium controls which molecules can enter other tissues of the body. And in the kidneys, epithelium helps to regulate which molecules from the bloodstream are eliminated with urine.

EPITHELIAL TISSUE

Epithelial tissue covers the surfaces of an animal's body. It consists of a single layer or a few layers of cells that are tightly bound together, and acts as a barrier between the inside and outside of an organism, and around body cavities and organs.

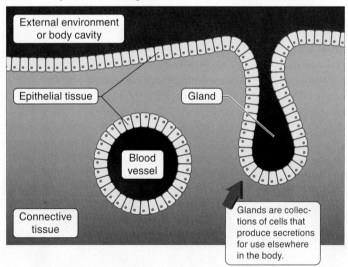

External environment or body cavity

Epithelial tissue

Gland

Blood vessel

Connective tissue

Glands are collections of cells that produce secretions for use elsewhere in the body.

FIGURE 20-20 Epithelial tissue forms with two distinct sides.

FUNCTIONS OF EPITHELIAL TISSUE

PROTECTION
Epithelial tissue acts as a barrier between the inside and outside of an organism and keeps fluids from leaking into or out of tissue.

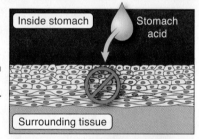

Inside stomach

Stomach acid

Surrounding tissue

TRANSPORT
Epithelial tissue regulates the movement of nutrients and other molecules into and out of body tissues.

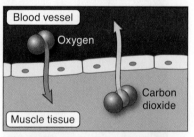

Blood vessel

Oxygen

Carbon dioxide

Muscle tissue

SECRETION
Epithelial tissue can form exocrine glands, which secrete products such as saliva, sweat, and mucus, and endocrine glands, which secrete hormones.

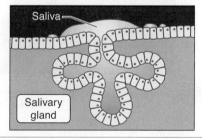

Saliva

Salivary gland

FIGURE 20-21 The multiple roles of epithelial tissue.

The Internal Environment | How Does Homeostasis Work? | Form Reflects Function

3. *Secretion.* Epithelium can also form glands. **Exocrine glands** generally secrete products—including earwax, sweat, saliva, milk, mucus, and, in the case of some frogs, toxic poisons—onto the surface of the epithelium. **Endocrine glands,** on the other hand, produce hormones, chemical messengers that affect cells elsewhere in the body, which are released into the fluid surrounding the glands and usually enter the bloodstream for distribution to other parts of the body.

Because epithelial cells are often in contact with a large variety of materials, they tend to experience more damage than other tissues. For this reason, they tend not to last long and are replaced frequently. Human skin cells, for example, are replaced approximately every two weeks. (Dandruff is mostly dead skin cells.) Cells lining the digestive tract have an even shorter life span, lasting only about five days. Liver epithelium experiences slightly less wear and tear, lasting a year or two before replacement.

TAKE-HOME MESSAGE 20·9

Epithelium is a very thin, sheet-like tissue that covers most of the exterior and interior surfaces of an animal's body. Made up of a single layer or a few layers of cells that are tightly bound together, epithelium acts as a barrier between the inside and outside of an organism. It also can be specialized to aid in the secretion and transport of molecules.

20·10

Muscle tissue enables movement.

Most animals move. And muscle tissue, made up of elongated cells capable of generating force by contracting, is responsible for much of that movement. Most muscle tissue cells are packed with protein filaments that slide together as they break down ATP, causing the entire cell to shorten and thus the muscle to contract. The action of muscle cells, which is usually stimulated by nerve cells, enables organisms to generate force and motion. There are three types of muscle tissue: skeletal, cardiac, and smooth muscles (**FIGURE 20-22**).

Skeletal muscle (sometimes called voluntary muscle) is usually attached to bones and is responsible for generating most movement we see in animals, including facial expressions and breathing. Muscles account for about 40% of human body

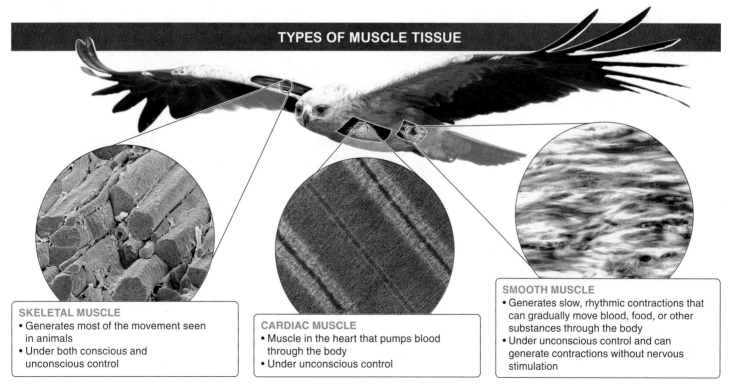

TYPES OF MUSCLE TISSUE

SKELETAL MUSCLE
• Generates most of the movement seen in animals
• Under both conscious and unconscious control

CARDIAC MUSCLE
• Muscle in the heart that pumps blood through the body
• Under unconscious control

SMOOTH MUSCLE
• Generates slow, rhythmic contractions that can gradually move blood, food, or other substances through the body
• Under unconscious control and can generate contractions without nervous stimulation

FIGURE 20-22 Muscle tissues are made up of elongated cells capable of generating force when they contract.

weight. Individual skeletal muscle cells, called **muscle fibers,** are very long and contain multiple nuclei, and the repeating units of protein filaments in the cells give the fibers a striped, or striated, appearance. Skeletal muscles are controlled by the nervous system, and the individual nerve cells (neurons) attached to each muscle fiber stimulate its contraction. Skeletal muscles can be under conscious control, such as when you choose to flex your biceps, or unconscious control, such as those that control breathing or moving your eyes around.

Cardiac muscle, as the name indicates, is located only in the heart, and it causes the heart to pump blood through the body. Take a look at the large colorized photo that opens this chapter. You will see capillaries passing among the muscle fibers of the heart. Because of the tremendous amount of energy that cardiac muscles use, contracting incessantly throughout our life, the cells contain many more mitochondria than other types of muscle cells. The cells of heart muscle are fused together and connected by gap junctions (see Section 3-12). The electrical signals that initiate each contraction of the cardiac muscle pass through these gap junctions. Cardiac muscle tissue is not under conscious control.

Smooth muscle is found in the walls surrounding blood vessels, the stomach and intestines, bladder, and many other organs and inner "tubes" within the body. Smooth muscle generates slow, rhythmic contractions that can gradually move blood, food, or other substances through the tube. Not under conscious control, smooth muscle is regulated by other physiological systems and can generate contractions without nervous stimulation.

TAKE-HOME MESSAGE 20·10

Muscle tissue consists of elongated cells capable of generating force when they contract. Skeletal muscle is responsible for generating most of the movement we see in animals. Cardiac muscle causes the heart to pump blood through the body. And smooth muscle, surrounding blood vessels and many internal organs, generates slower contractions that can gradually move blood, food, or other substances.

20·11

Nervous tissue transmits information.

The fourth type of animal tissue is nervous tissue, specialized to store and transmit information. It is responsible for much of the communication that occurs within an animal's body. Nervous tissue enables animals to sense and respond to stimuli such as the smell of food, the sight, smell, or sounds of a predator or a potential mate, or the heat of a fire.

There are two types of nervous tissue cells: neurons and glial cells (**FIGURE 20-23**). **Neurons** are the "excitable" cells that receive and transmit a signal. Neurons have three distinctive elements: dendrites, a cell body, and an axon. **Dendrites** are a bit like an antenna system, specialized for receiving signals from the external environment or from other neurons. The **cell body** contains the nucleus and other cellular machinery found in eukaryotic cells. And the **axon** is a single projection that transmits impulses away from the cell body and can extend over very long distances—sometimes 3 feet (1 m) or more!

Glial cells, also called **neuroglia,** are like the support staff to neurons. They do not carry signals but assist and nourish neurons. There are numerous types of glial cells, and they vastly outnumber neurons. Together, the various types of glial cells produce insulation for neurons, protect and regulate the chemical environment around neurons, hold

STRUCTURE OF NERVOUS TISSUE

Nerve tissue is responsible for much of the communication that occurs within an animal. There are two types of nervous tissue: neurons and glial cells.

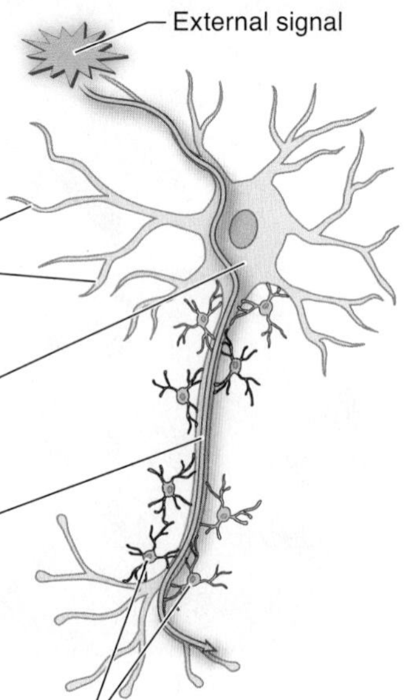

NEURONS
Cells that can receive and transmit signals. They are composed of three distinct elements:

- **DENDRITES**
  Receive signals from the external environment or from other neurons

- **CELL BODY**
  Contains the nucleus and other cellular machinery

- **AXON**
  A single projection from the cell body that transmits impulses away from the cell body

— External signal

GLIAL CELLS (NEUROGLIA)
Assist neurons by insulating, protecting, and regulating their chemical environment, holding them in place, destroying pathogens, and providing nutrients and oxygen

FIGURE 20-23 Neuron and glial cells.

The Internal Environment   How Does Homeostasis Work?   Form Reflects Function

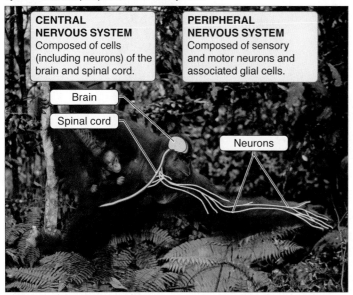

ORGANIZATION OF THE VERTEBRATE NERVOUS SYSTEM

In vertebrates, the nervous system is divided into the central nervous system and the peripheral nervous system.

CENTRAL NERVOUS SYSTEM
Composed of cells (including neurons) of the brain and spinal cord.

PERIPHERAL NERVOUS SYSTEM
Composed of sensory and motor neurons and associated glial cells.

Brain

Spinal cord

Neurons

FIGURE 20-24 **The vertebrate nervous system: brain, spinal cord, and neurons.**

the neurons in place, destroy pathogens, and provide nutrients and oxygen.

All of the nervous tissue of an organism makes up its nervous system (**FIGURE 20-24**). In vertebrates, the nervous system is divided into the **central nervous system,** which includes the brain and spinal cord, and the **peripheral nervous system,** which includes the sensory neurons that detect a stimulus and the neurons that transmit signals to the muscles and glands of an organism in response to that stimulus. (The nervous system is discussed in detail in Chapter 23.)

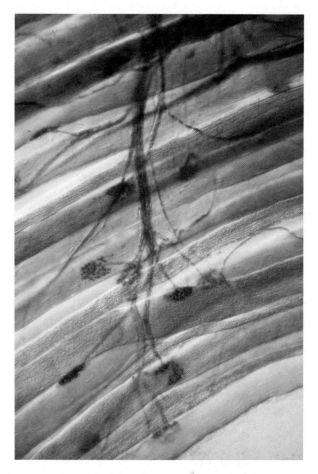

Motor neurons of the peripheral nervous system convey signals that can initiate contractions (and movement) in muscle cells.

TAKE-HOME MESSAGE 20·11

Nervous tissue is specialized to store and transmit information. There are two types of nervous tissue cells: neurons, which can receive and transmit a signal, and glial cells, which assist and provide nutrients for neurons.

20·12

Each organ system performs special tasks.

With the exception of sponges and some cnidarians, all animals have some tissues that are organized into organs—structures such as the heart, brain, lungs, and liver—that serve specialized functions and consist of multiple tissue types. And just as cells make up tissues and tissues make up organs, organs, too, are part of larger functional units, the organ systems, which carry out the various physiological

processes necessary for the growth, development, maintenance, and reproduction of organisms.

We briefly describe 11 animal organ systems in **FIGURE 20-25**, and we'll discuss them in greater detail in Chapters 21–26. It's important to keep in mind that these systems do not operate in isolation: in carrying out its tasks, each system not only

DIGESTIVE SYSTEM
Disassembles and absorbs food so the body can acquire the nutrients it needs to function

CIRCULATORY SYSTEM
Transports nutrients and respiratory gases to the tissues and eliminates wastes from the tissues

RESPIRATORY SYSTEM
Provides a site for gas exchange between the external environment and an organism's circulatory system

REPRODUCTIVE SYSTEM (MALE)
Produces sperm and delivers it to the female reproductive system, where fertilization may occur

REPRODUCTIVE SYSTEM (FEMALE)
Produces eggs and provides an environment that can nurture a developing embryo and fetus, if fertilization occurs

NERVOUS SYSTEM
Acts as the control center of the body and interprets, stores, and transmits information using electrical impulses and chemical signals

FIGURE 20-25 The major organ systems of animals.

depends on the proper functioning of one or more of the other systems, but often influences the functioning of other systems. The act of running, for example, might be initiated when the *nervous system* detects a threat and sends impulses to the *musculoskeletal system* (which causes the body to move), to the *respiratory system* (which increases the rate of oxygen consumption), and to the *circulatory system* (which increases the rate at which the heart pumps blood and thus increases the oxygen available to muscle tissue). Even though these 11 systems constantly add, modify, and remove substances in the body, the body maintains a consistent internal environment through homeostasis.

The Internal Environment   How Does Homeostasis Work?   Form Reflects Function

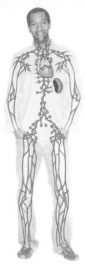

IMMUNE AND LYMPHATIC SYSTEM
Attacks pathogens that threaten the body and plays a supporting role in circulation by recycling fluid that leaks from the circulatory system

URINARY/EXCRETORY SYSTEM
Purifies the blood by filtering out wastes and transports wastes out of the body

ENDOCRINE SYSTEM
Regulates body activities by releasing hormones that travel through vessels in the circulatory system to reach target cells

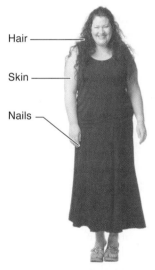

Hair

Skin

Nails

INTEGUMENTARY SYSTEM
Provides protection by forming a barrier between the inside and outside of an organism and can aid in the secretion and transport of molecules

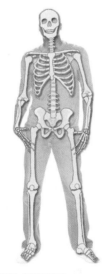

SKELETAL SYSTEM
Supports and protects the body and internal organs, manufactures blood cells, and provides a surface for muscle attachment, creating a foundation for movement

MUSCULAR SYSTEM
Generates force through contraction, which enables movement of the body and of blood, food, and other substances throughout the body

As we explore organ systems in more detail in the following chapters, we will pay particular attention to the ways in which the form and function of the systems' components are intimately related and what this relationship reveals about how these systems (and the organisms of which they are a part) evolved.

TAKE-HOME MESSAGE 20·12

In nearly all animals, some tissues are organized into organs (such as the heart, brain, lungs, and liver) that serve specialized functions and consist of multiple tissue types, and into organ systems (such as the circulatory system) that carry out the various physiological processes necessary for the growth, development, maintenance, and reproduction of the organism.

streetBio

Knowledge You Can Use

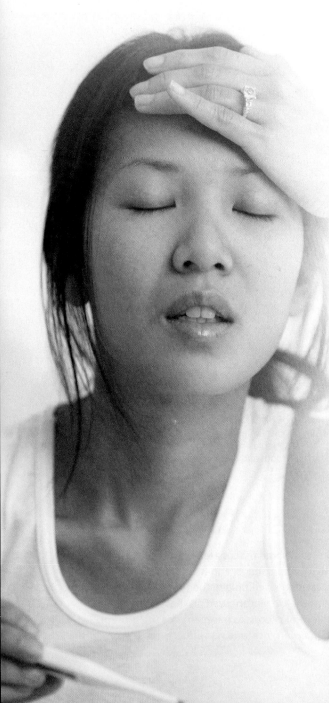

Your body sometimes deliberately upsets homeostasis. (And you might not want to fight it.)

Q: What do you usually do when you have a fever? At the first sign of fever, many people take aspirin, Tylenol, Advil, or Motrin.

Q: What is the result? Aspirin, acetaminophen (Tylenol), and ibuprofen (Advil and Motrin) quickly reduce a fever.

Q: Why did you have a fever? Generally, fever is not itself an illness. Rather, it is your body's response to cues that there is a bacterial or viral infection. In response to infection, your temperature set point is raised, because pathogens are more easily brought under control by the body's defenses at higher temperatures. (Ectotherms use a similar strategy, moving to warmer areas when they have an infection!)

Q: How does reducing a fever interfere with your body's defenses? Blocking a fever by taking aspirin or other medication may reduce your body's ability to fight infection. A recent well-controlled study demonstrated, for example, that chicken pox lasts longer, on average, when aspirin is used to treat it, compared with placebo.

Q: Is the lesson here about more than fever? Yes. There are other "symptoms" of infection that, as defenses rather than part of the illness itself, maybe shouldn't be fought. For example: (1) *Coughing:* the use of codeine to block coughing after surgery increases the risk of pneumonia; the coughing is *helpful.* (2) *Diarrhea:* anti-diarrhea medications delay recovery and slow the eradication of bacteria from the digestive tract; the diarrhea is *helpful.* (3) *Vomiting* and *inflammation,* too, appear to be important parts of our evolved defenses and, as such, blocking them can have serious health consequences.

What can you conclude? Is this the dawn of Darwinian medicine?
This new perspective on when to treat and when not to treat symptoms is called "Darwinian medicine." It represents a newfound appreciation for the fact that organisms have evolved many protective responses that may be useful. Of course, suffering is not always the solution. There can be real costs to vomiting, diarrhea, coughing, fever, and other body defenses. Opting not to treat them isn't necessarily the best solution if, for example, antibiotics can bring an infection under control easily. Either way, bringing an evolutionary perspective to medical decision making can be valuable.

1 Animals have an internal environment.

Failure to maintain a consistent internal environment can lead to multiple problems in the normal functioning of cells, tissues, and organs, and can result in death. Organisms maintain a variety of internal physiological variables, including temperature, water-solute balances, pH, blood sugar levels, and blood gas concentrations, within relatively constant ranges. The process of maintaining an organism's internal environment is called homeostasis.

2 How does homeostasis work?

Organisms generally maintain homeostasis through negative feedback, in which sensors detect a change in the internal environment and trigger structures, called effectors, to oppose or reduce the change. For animals to maintain homeostasis, the variable must have a set point, a target value or range to which the organism can return. Methods for controlling temperature, blood sugar levels, and water and solute concentrations, among many other variables, are important components of homeostasis. To maintain osmotic balance, organisms must be able to take up water and get rid of water, and must also be able to regulate concentrations of ions in their fluids. The kidney is the organ in vertebrates that helps maintain homeostasis by regulating water balance and solute concentration in body fluids, filtering blood, and enabling the removal of potentially harmful ions and metabolic waste products in urine.

3 Form reflects function: animal anatomy.

At all levels of animal organization, from molecules to whole organisms, the physical features of a structure are closely related to its function. Cells with similar structure and function are organized into groups, called tissues, that work together. There are four types of tissue: connective tissue, epithelial tissue, muscle tissue, and nervous tissue. In nearly all animals, some tissues are organized into organs that serve specialized functions and consist of multiple tissue types, and into organ systems that carry out the various physiological processes necessary for the growth, development, maintenance, and reproduction of organisms.

KEY TERMS

1. The term "homeostasis" describes:
   a) the body's use of physical and chemical processes to maintain a consistent internal environment.
   b) the biochemical processes associated with the maintenance of body temperature.
   c) the metabolic patterns of active (versus stationary) animals.
   d) the metabolic patterns of stationary (versus active) animals.
   e) the health benefits of a sedentary lifestyle.

2. Interstitial fluid:
   a) is found exclusively within the spinal cord, surrounding the nerve bundles.
   b) is found exclusively within the skull, surrounding the brain.
   c) is mostly water.
   d) is found exclusively within the skull and spinal cord, surrounding nervous tissue.
   e) occurs within the organelles of all eukaryotic cells.

3. Negative feedback loops:
   a) generally lead to highly unstable internal physiological conditions.
   b) cause internal conditions to deviate from the normal range.
   c) are part of larger, positive feedback systems.
   d) rely on sensors to trigger effectors to alter an organism's internal environment.
   e) None of the above.

4. A set point:
   a) is the target value or range for a physiological variable, to which it generally returns following perturbation.
   b) is a physiological state that occurs in animals called "conformers," but not in "regulators."
   c) can occur in fishes but not in terrestrial animals.
   d) is the target value or range for a physiological variable regulated through positive feedback, but not negative feedback.
   e) Both a) and c) are correct.

5. It is not necessarily accurate to refer to endotherms as "warm-blooded," because:
   a) some endotherms allow their body temperature to drop significantly during hibernation.
   b) on average, their body temperature is colder than that of "cold-blooded" animals.
   c) they generate their heat primarily from within their own bodies.
   d) most do not actually have blood in their bodies.
   e) some are homeotherms rather than heterotherms.

6. "Form follows function" refers to the fact that:
   a) organisms' physical structures often are adaptations, shaped by natural selection, and so reflect their physiological functions.
   b) organisms' physical structures generally come to reflect their physiological function only *after* that function has been fine-tuned by evolution.
   c) natural selection can produce adaptations in physical structures but not in physiological processes.
   d) natural selection can produce adaptations in physiological processes but not in physical structures.
   e) all structures that have the same function also have the same structure.

7. Which of the following is not a type of connective tissue?
   a) bone   d) collagen
   b) cartilage   e) ligament
   c) blood

8. Epithelium plays all of the following roles in organisms except:
   a) secretion.
   b) transport.
   c) protection.
   d) preventing fluids from leaking from an organ system into surrounding tissue.
   e) cushioning, lubricating, and insulating other tissue.

9. Smooth muscle:
   a) is usually attached to bones.
   b) generates slow, rhythmic contractions.
   c) is usually under conscious control.
   d) generally contains more mitochondria than cardiac or skeletal muscle.
   e) All of the above are correct.

10. Neurons generally have all of the following components except:
    a) dendrites.
    b) a cell body.
    c) an axon.
    d) glial processes.
    e) a nucleus.

11. With the exception of _____, all animals have some tissues organized into organs.
    a) sponges and some cnidarians
    b) insects
    c) roundworms and flatworms
    d) sponges and insects
    e) amphibians

SHORT-ANSWER QUESTIONS

1. What is homeostasis? How does hyperthermia illustrate the failure of the body to maintain homeostasis? What are the potential consequences of this failure?

2. What is the hierarchical organization of cells in a multicellular organism? Name the four types of tissue they form and note their general functions.

3. What are the two kinds of connective tissue? What are their general characteristics?

4. What are the three types of muscle tissue? What are their general characteristics?

See Appendix for answers. For additional study questions, go to www.prep-u.com.

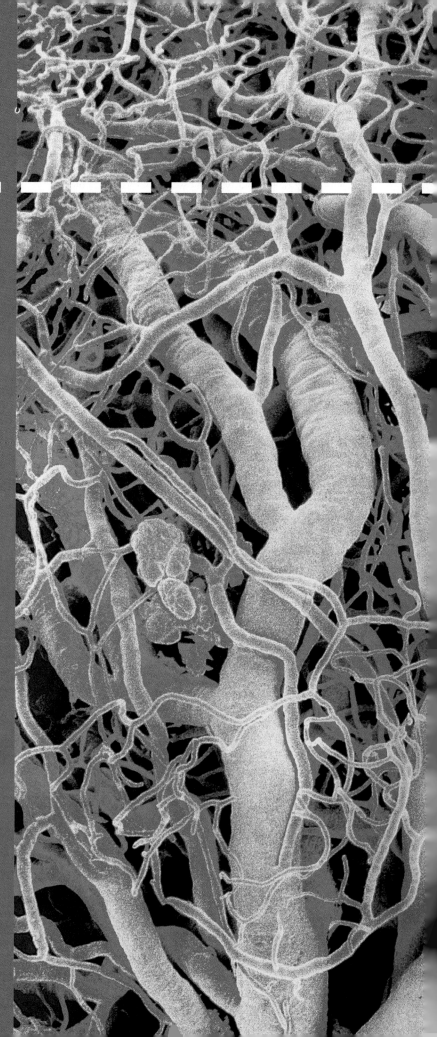

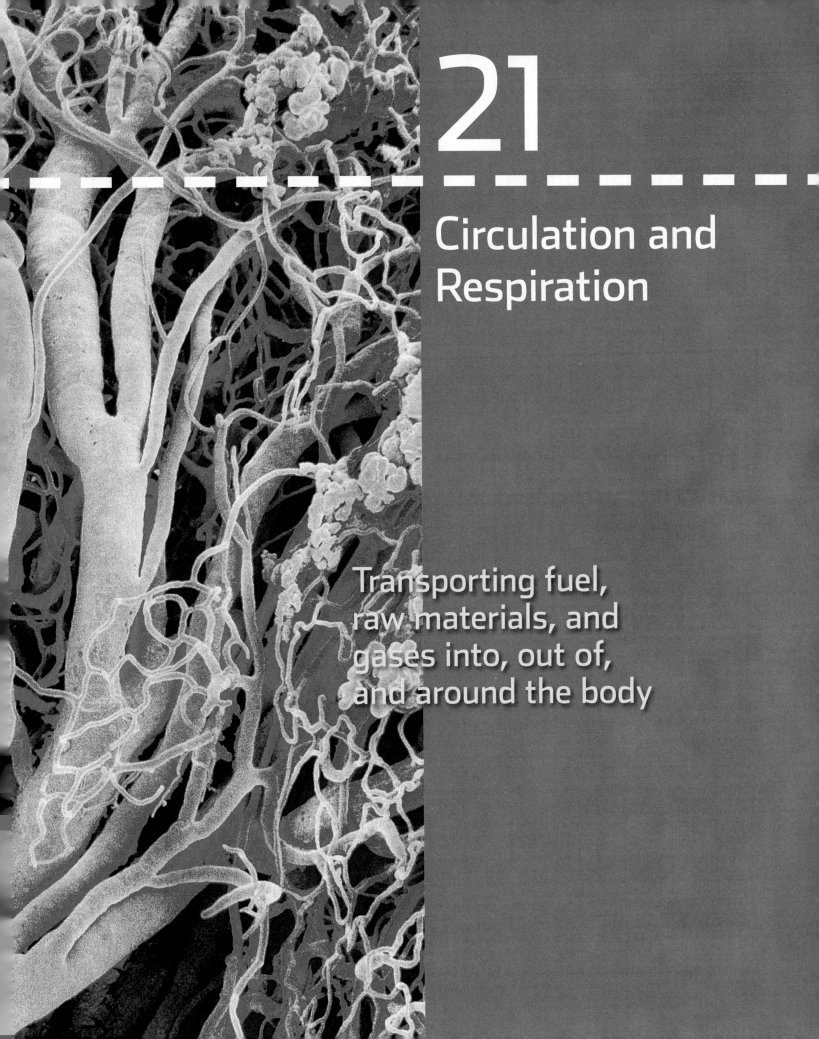

21

Circulation and Respiration

Transporting fuel,
raw materials, and
gases into, out of,
and around the body

① The circulatory system is the chief route of distribution in animals.

The swiftness of the hare and greyhound depend on efficient circulatory systems.

21·1

What is a circulatory system and why is one needed?

Size matters. When life first arose on earth, the tiny, single-celled organisms were small enough to acquire the fuel and raw materials they needed in a straightforward way: those materials could simply diffuse across the cell membrane and be used as needed. Similarly, metabolic waste products could diffuse out of the cell. Today, single-celled organisms and small multicellular organisms in which all cells are in contact with (or just a few cells away from) the external environment acquire raw materials and dispose of metabolic waste in this same way.

The evolution of large body sizes opened up a world of new niches in which organisms could exist. Physiologically, however, large body sizes created a host of new challenges. Many of these challenges resulted from the fact that with increasing size, most of an animal's cells are no longer in direct contact with the outside world, the environment from which the animal obtains oxygen, nutrients, water, and other substances it needs to survive. Consequently, these substances can no longer just diffuse in, and the waste an animal generates can no longer diffuse out. As body size increased, dedicated delivery and removal systems became a necessity.

In animals, the primary distribution system is the circulatory system. Like a system of highways for delivering important

goods and removing garbage, the circulatory system reaches all tissues of the body. In vertebrates, circulatory systems have three principal functions: transport, body temperature regulation, and protection (**FIGURE 21-1**).

1. Transport. The circulatory system transports oxygen, nutrients, waste products, hormones, and immune system cells in the blood throughout the body.

- In vertebrates, blood vessels take oxygen from the lungs or gills and deliver it to the tissues for energy-releasing cellular respiration. Blood that comes from the lungs or gills is loaded with oxygen and is said to be oxygenated or oxygen-rich.

- Simultaneously, blood vessels whisk away carbon dioxide and other metabolic wastes that are produced in cellular respiration and other cell processes and must be removed from the body. Blood that carries a lot of carbon dioxide is said to be deoxygenated or oxygen-poor.

- Once food particles are digested, the nutrients must be absorbed and delivered to all the tissues of the body, for activity, growth, and reproduction.

FUNCTIONS OF THE CIRCULATORY SYSTEM

Among vertebrates, circulatory systems have three principal functions.

TRANSPORT
The circulatory system transports oxygen, nutrients, waste products, immune system cells, and hormones in the blood throughout the body.

TEMPERATURE REGULATION
The circulatory system helps to maintain body temperature within the optimum range for metabolic functioning.

PROTECTION
The circulatory system contains a variety of cells and chemicals that contribute to the individual's defenses against infection by pathogens.

FIGURE 21-1 Like a set of highways for the body. Circulatory system functions: transport, temperature regulation and protection.

- The circulatory system delivers hormones (chemicals produced throughout the body by glands and other tissues) to target tissues to regulate growth, development, and reproduction.

2. Body temperature regulation. By expanding or contracting the blood vessels closest to the exterior of the body, animals can absorb or release heat, a process that helps them maintain their body temperature within the optimum range for metabolism.

3. Protection. A variety of cells and chemicals contribute to the individual's defenses against infection by pathogens. White blood cells, or leukocytes, have the ability to engulf and destroy many disease-causing microorganisms. Platelets and certain chemicals in the blood also provide protection by limiting blood loss and infection when the skin or other tissues are damaged.

TAKE-HOME MESSAGE 21·1

In animals, the circulatory system is the chief distribution system. It transports gases, nutrients, waste products, hormones, and immune system cells throughout the body. The circulatory system also helps animals regulate their body temperature and plays a protective role against infection.

21·2

Circulatory systems can be open or closed.

There's more than one way to build a circulatory system. And, in fact, not all multicellular organisms even need a circulatory system. In spite of their relatively large size and multicellularity, for example, flatworms, as well as jellyfish and other cnidarians, have a body plan that gives every cell easy access to oxygen and nutrients through simple diffusion (**FIGURE 21-2**). This access is possible because every cell is close to the external surface of the cnidarian's body or to its internal gastrovascular cavity. Although the gastrovascular cavity is not a true circulatory system, it serves many digestive ("gastro") and circulatory ("vascular") functions by directing water into the central mouth and through an elaborate system of channels. Cells lining the mouth and the channels can absorb nutrients and exchange gases by diffusion. The nutrients then diffuse to other cells, none of which are very far away. Once nutrients have been extracted (and waste

products picked up), fluid in the gastrovascular cavity is flushed back out of the mouth, and the process is repeated.

Among other multicellular animals, there are two distinct types of circulatory systems: open and closed (**FIGURE 21-3**). Open circulatory systems are found in insects and most molluscs, while closed circulatory systems are found in all vertebrates. The defining feature of an **open circulatory system** is that it has one fluid, called **hemolymph,** that both circulates to transport nutrients, gases, and waste products and also surrounds each cell in the body. In other words, there is no clear distinction between the circulating fluid and the interstitial fluid, the fluid that is outside the cells and bathes all the tissue of the body. There is a heart (or sometimes many hearts!) that pumps the hemolymph, but it essentially squirts the fluid throughout the extracellular spaces. Large collecting

Respiratory Adaptations

> *Some animals, like jellyfish and other cnidarians, do not have circulatory systems. Instead, they obtain oxygen and nutrients, and eliminate waste, through diffusion.*

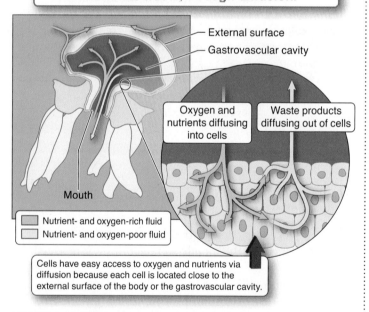

External surface
Gastrovascular cavity

Oxygen and nutrients diffusing into cells

Waste products diffusing out of cells

Mouth

☐ Nutrient- and oxygen-rich fluid
☐ Nutrient- and oxygen-poor fluid

Cells have easy access to oxygen and nutrients via diffusion because each cell is located close to the external surface of the body or the gastrovascular cavity.

FIGURE 21-2 No circulatory system required. The cells of jellyfish and other cnidarians can acquire nutrients and oxygen from the environment through direct diffusion.

vessels then channel the hemolymph back to the heart, where it can be pumped throughout the body again. These collecting vessels have little valves that close when the heart pumps to prevent the hemolymph from being pumped back through the same vessel from which it was collected. This one-way collection system gives some order to the circulation of the hemolymph fluid throughout the organism's body.

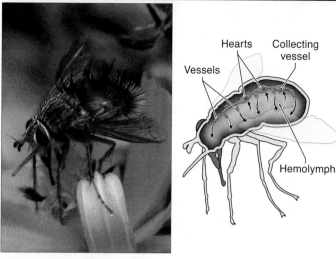

Hearts   Collecting vessel

Vessels

Hemolymph

OPEN CIRCULATORY SYSTEM
• No clear distinction between the circulating fluid and interstitial fluid
• Heart(s) pump the fluid mixture—called hemolymph—throughout the extracellular spaces inside the body
• Occurs in insects and most molluscs

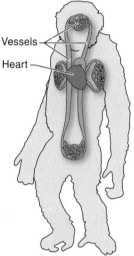

Vessels

Heart

CLOSED CIRCULATORY SYSTEM
• Blood is contained within vessels that separate it from interstitial fluid
• Muscular heart propels blood through vessels to tissues throughout the body
• Occurs in all vertebrates

FIGURE 21-3 There are open and closed circulatory systems.

In **closed circulatory systems,** the circulating fluid—called **blood**—is always contained in a vessel as it is pumped throughout the animal's body, and it is physically and chemically separated from the interstitial fluid that bathes each cell. A muscular **heart** serves as a pump, and with each contraction it propels blood at high pressure through vessels called **arteries.** Like a highway system with numerous exits

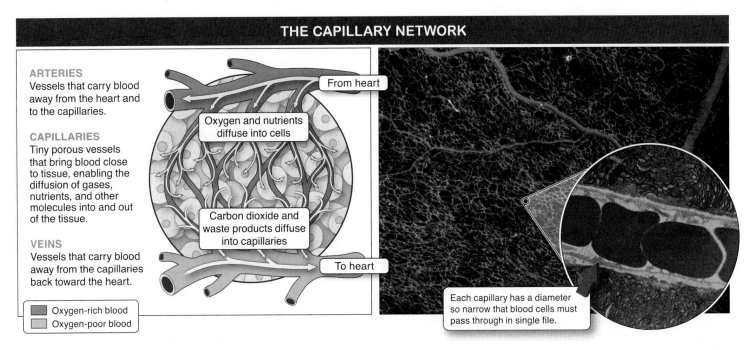

ARTERIES
Vessels that carry blood away from the heart and to the capillaries.

CAPILLARIES
Tiny porous vessels that bring blood close to tissue, enabling the diffusion of gases, nutrients, and other molecules into and out of the tissue.

VEINS
Vessels that carry blood away from the capillaries back toward the heart.

From heart

Oxygen and nutrients diffuse into cells

Carbon dioxide and waste products diffuse into capillaries

To heart

Oxygen-rich blood
Oxygen-poor blood

Each capillary has a diameter so narrow that blood cells must pass through in single file.

FIGURE 21-4 Arteries, capillaries, and veins: the three types of blood vessels in a closed circulatory system.

and connecting roads, the arteries branch extensively so that blood can be delivered to all the tissues of the body.

At the organs and tissues, arteries branch into thousands upon thousands of ever-smaller vessels, first the arterioles and then, as they become much narrower and thinner-walled, the **capillaries.** Each capillary has an inner diameter so narrow that blood cells must pass through in single file. The capillary wall is thin—just one layer of wall cells—and somewhat porous, so the diffusion of gases, nutrients, and other molecules into and out of the tissue, down their concentration gradients, readily occurs (**FIGURE 21-4**).

The network of capillaries in an organism is staggeringly large—more than 50,000 miles in an adult human! And this number is constantly in flux: gaining a single pound of fat, for example, is accompanied by the addition of more than a mile of new capillaries.

Capillaries are the last branch of the circulatory system to carry nutrients and oxygen-rich blood to cells of the body, but they are also the first branch to carry nutrient-poor, carbon-dioxide-rich, and waste-product-rich blood back from cells of the body toward the heart. After passing through the capillaries, blood returns to the heart in vessels called **veins.**

The pressure of blood in the veins is significantly less than that in the arteries. This reduced pressure occurs because, in the

Q Is it more dangerous to cut the carotid artery or the jugular vein? Why?

capillaries, an increasing proportion of the blood is in direct contact with the inside surface of the capillary wall. This contact increases the friction and slows the blood flow. As the capillaries merge to form veins, the pressure as blood moves through these larger vessels is further reduced. In fact, in most animals, blood will spurt and gush when an artery is cut, but will only trickle out of cut veins. It is not surprising, then, that most arteries are not as close to the skin as are veins. It would be too risky to put them there. This is why people who cut their wrists when attempting suicide rarely die. They generally cut only the veins in their wrists, which are closer to the surface, and rarely bleed enough to cause death.

TAKE-HOME MESSAGE 21·2

Animals that can acquire all the nutrients and oxygen they need by diffusion (such as flatworms and cnidarians) do not have circulatory systems. Among animals that do have circulatory systems, the system can be open, with no clear distinction between circulating fluid and the interstitial fluid that bathes tissues, or closed, with a clear distinction. In closed circulatory systems, tiny blood vessels called capillaries bring blood close enough to tissues that diffusion can move the necessary molecules from the blood into the cells and from the cells into the blood.

Respiratory Adaptations

21·3

Vertebrates have several different types of closed circulatory systems.

Among the vertebrates, there are several variations of the closed circulatory system. These variations evolved in concert with numerous dramatic adaptations that accompanied and made possible the transition from life in the seas to life on land. As some vertebrates developed lungs and the ability to extract oxygen from the air rather than water, their circulatory systems increased in complexity.

In fishes, the flow of blood follows a circular path (**FIGURE 21-5 FISH**). In tracing its flow, we can begin with the two-chambered heart. Blood first passes into the **atrium,** the collecting chamber, and from there is pumped into the **ventricle,** the chamber from which blood is pumped to the gills. Blood flows through the capillary beds of the gills, where it picks up oxygen. From there, the blood travels to the tissues of the body, delivering the oxygen. After passing through the capillary beds of the body tissues, the oxygen-poor blood flows back to the heart, and the cycle begins again as that blood is pumped to the gills.

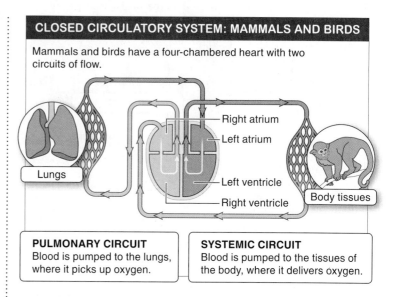

CLOSED CIRCULATORY SYSTEM: MAMMALS AND BIRDS

Mammals and birds have a four-chambered heart with two circuits of flow.

Right atrium
Left atrium
Lungs
Left ventricle
Right ventricle
Body tissues

PULMONARY CIRCUIT
Blood is pumped to the lungs, where it picks up oxygen.

SYSTEMIC CIRCUIT
Blood is pumped to the tissues of the body, where it delivers oxygen.

FIGURE 21-5 MAMMALS AND BIRDS **Blood flow in mammals and birds.** Note that the right side of the animal's heart is on the left side in the diagram, and the left side is on the right. This is because drawings of the heart are made as if the animal is facing you.

In contrast to the two-chambered heart of fishes, birds and mammals have a four-chambered heart: two atria and two ventricles (**FIGURE 21-5 MAMMALS AND BIRDS**). Twice as many chambers are required because, rather than having a single circuit of flow, birds and mammals have two circuits of flow. The two circuits can be visualized as a figure 8: blood flows into the right atrium and through to the right ventricle (see Figure 21-5). From there it is pumped out to the capillaries of the lungs, and then it returns to the heart. This first circuit of flow is called the **pulmonary circuit.** The blood returning to the heart from the lungs collects in the left atrium. It immediately passes into the left ventricle and from there is pumped to the rest of the body. After passing through the body capillaries, it completes its second circuit, called the **systemic circuit,** and collects in the right atrium, where the cycle begins again.

Mammals and birds vary widely in the size of their hearts—from tiny hummingbird hearts no bigger than a pencil eraser all the way up to the heart of a blue whale, bigger than a small car, that pumps 25 gallons with every beat—but they all share the same basic layout. And almost

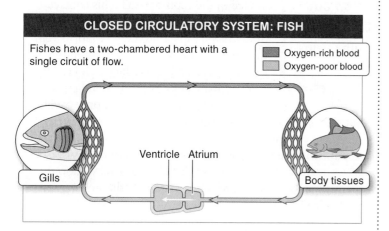

CLOSED CIRCULATORY SYSTEM: FISH

Fishes have a two-chambered heart with a single circuit of flow.

- Oxygen-rich blood
- Oxygen-poor blood

Ventricle Atrium
Gills
Body tissues

FIGURE 21-5 FISH **Blood flow in fish.**

This single-circuit flow of blood in fishes has a limitation. By passing through the numerous tiny blood vessels that make up the gill capillaries, the newly oxygenated blood slows its flow greatly, losing most of the pressure it gained following the contraction of the heart. It flows—or, more accurately, trickles—at a relatively low velocity to the oxygen-depleted parts of the body, limiting the rate at which oxygen can be delivered to the tissues. The blood is helped along through the arteries by contractions of muscles around the blood vessels as the fish swims, but the blood flow never reaches the velocity it had just after being pumped out of the ventricle.

Q The left side of mammalian and bird hearts is always bigger than the right. Why?

always, because the left ventricle has to pump blood to the entire body rather than just to the lungs, the left ventricle becomes much larger and more muscular than the right ventricle.

With two circuits of flow, mammalian and bird hearts are better than fish hearts at delivering oxygen to body tissues. In fishes, as we've seen, all the oxygenated blood flowing to the body has low pressure and velocity because it passes first through the gill capillaries. With two circuits of flow in birds and mammals, all the oxygenated blood flowing to body tissues is at higher pressure because it is pumped straight from the left ventricle and does not first pass through the pressure-robbing capillaries of the lungs. This makes it possible for bird and mammal hearts to sustain greater levels of activity with greater amounts of oxygen delivered to the muscles and organs. The single-circuit system of fishes is like trying to put out a big fire with a low-pressure garden hose, while the two-circuit system of birds and mammals is more akin to using a high-pressure fire hose. Nonetheless, the large number and diversity of fishes on earth suggests that they are able to thrive with their single-circuit system.

Amphibians have circulatory systems that appear similar, but not identical, to the mammalian and bird plan (**FIGURE 21-5 AMPHIBIANS**). They have two circuits of flow, but have hearts with only three chambers rather than four. Blood is collected from the lungs and from the rest of the body in the left and right atria, respectively, but it then flows into a single ventricle. Surprisingly, though, little mixing of the oxygenated blood from the lungs and deoxygenated blood from the rest of the body occurs in the ventricle. Rather, the two types of blood flow side by side and are pumped into vessels that direct the oxygenated blood to the body capillaries and the deoxygenated blood to the lungs.

With the exception of birds, most reptiles also have three-chambered hearts, although the ventricle is partially divided in two. In one group of reptiles (the crocodilians), however, the division is complete; they also have an extra little artery that

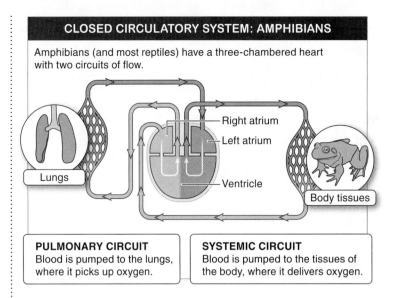

CLOSED CIRCULATORY SYSTEM: AMPHIBIANS

Amphibians (and most reptiles) have a three-chambered heart with two circuits of flow.

Right atrium
Left atrium
Ventricle
Lungs
Body tissues

PULMONARY CIRCUIT
Blood is pumped to the lungs, where it picks up oxygen.

SYSTEMIC CIRCUIT
Blood is pumped to the tissues of the body, where it delivers oxygen.

FIGURE 21-5 AMPHIBIANS Blood flow in amphibians.

allows blood to be pumped from the right ventricle to the rest of the body rather than to the lungs. This extra artery is an adaptation allowing the crocodile to bypass sending blood to the lungs when the animal is underwater. There is no sense in pumping blood to the lungs if there is no oxygen to be picked up there. Instead, the blood is sent back to the body, where the remaining oxygen in the blood can be utilized.

TAKE-HOME MESSAGE 21·3

Vertebrates' circulatory systems vary in structure. Fishes have two-chambered hearts, with one circuit of flow: from the heart through the gills through the body and back to the heart. Birds and mammals have four-chambered hearts and two circuits of flow: from the heart to the lungs and back to the heart, then from the heart to the body and back to the heart. This enables blood to be pumped to the body at higher pressure. Amphibians and most reptiles have a three-chambered heart and two circuits of blood flow.

Respiratory Adaptations

❷ The heart is at the center of the human circulatory system.

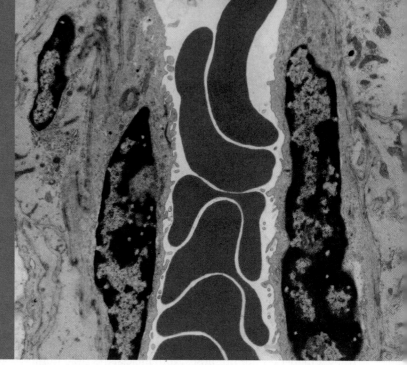

Red blood cells flow in a single file through capillaries.

21•4

Blood flows through the four chambers of the human heart.

Clench your fist. That is the size of your heart. Now clench it and relax it a hundred thousand times. That is what you require your heart to do, every day, for 70 or more years. The human heart, at the center of our circulatory system, is one of the most durable and reliable pumps ever produced (**FIGURE 21-6**).

As we saw above, the four-chambered heart sends blood on a figure 8, two-cycle path through the body, sending all blood first to the lungs for loading up on oxygen and, on its second circuit, to the tissues and organs. Let's explore the workings of this heart, tracing the flow of blood as it cycles through the heart, lungs, and tissues of the body (**FIGURE 21-7**). We'll start with the arrival of oxygen-depleted blood from the organs and tissues.

1. Deoxygenated blood from the organs and tissues enters the right atrium. The blood arriving from the lower half of the body enters through the inferior vena cava, and blood arriving from the head and arms enters through the superior vena cava.

2. Most of the blood passes directly through the right atrium into the right ventricle. A contraction pushes the

FIGURE 21-6 Heart and blood vessels. An overview of the human circulatory system.

THE HUMAN CIRCULATORY SYSTEM

The human circulatory system is composed of a fist-sized heart and an intricate system of blood vessels that transport respiratory gases, nutrients, and waste products throughout the body.

Heart

Vein

Artery

THE HUMAN HEART

Superior vena cava

Aorta

Right atrium

Left atrium

Right ventricle

Left ventricle

Inferior vena cava

Circulatory Systems   Human Circulation   Gas Exchange   Hemoglobin and Myoglobin

FLOW OF BLOOD THROUGH THE HUMAN CIRCULATORY SYSTEM

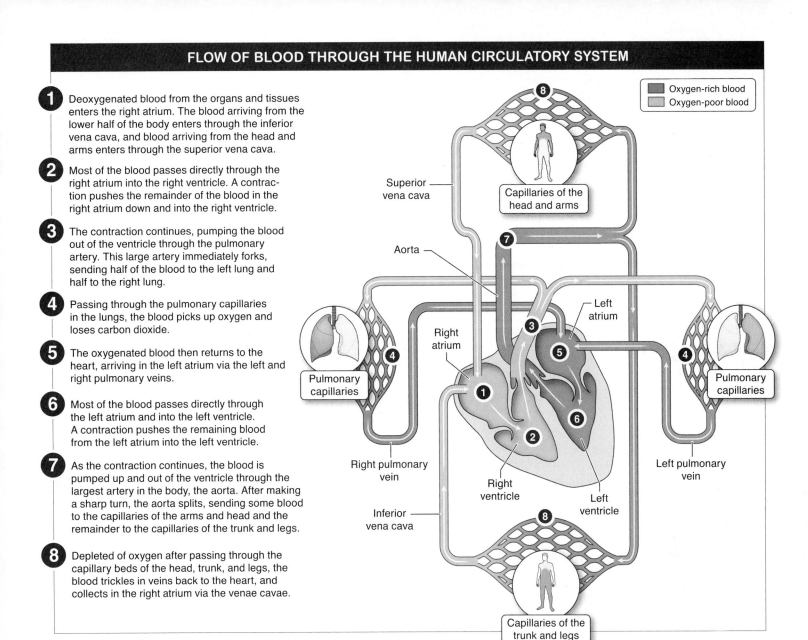

1 Deoxygenated blood from the organs and tissues enters the right atrium. The blood arriving from the lower half of the body enters through the inferior vena cava, and blood arriving from the head and arms enters through the superior vena cava.

2 Most of the blood passes directly through the right atrium into the right ventricle. A contraction pushes the remainder of the blood in the right atrium down and into the right ventricle.

3 The contraction continues, pumping the blood out of the ventricle through the pulmonary artery. This large artery immediately forks, sending half of the blood to the left lung and half to the right lung.

4 Passing through the pulmonary capillaries in the lungs, the blood picks up oxygen and loses carbon dioxide.

5 The oxygenated blood then returns to the heart, arriving in the left atrium via the left and right pulmonary veins.

6 Most of the blood passes directly through the left atrium and into the left ventricle. A contraction pushes the remaining blood from the left atrium into the left ventricle.

7 As the contraction continues, the blood is pumped up and out of the ventricle through the largest artery in the body, the aorta. After making a sharp turn, the aorta splits, sending some blood to the capillaries of the arms and head and the remainder to the capillaries of the trunk and legs.

8 Depleted of oxygen after passing through the capillary beds of the head, trunk, and legs, the blood trickles in veins back to the heart, and collects in the right atrium via the venae cavae.

Oxygen-rich blood
Oxygen-poor blood

Capillaries of the head and arms

Superior vena cava

Aorta

Left atrium

Right atrium

Pulmonary capillaries

Pulmonary capillaries

Right pulmonary vein

Left pulmonary vein

Right ventricle

Left ventricle

Inferior vena cava

Capillaries of the trunk and legs

FIGURE 21-7 **The path of blood flow in the human body.**

remainder of the blood in the right atrium down and into the right ventricle.

3. The contraction continues, pumping the blood out of the ventricle through the pulmonary artery. This large artery immediately forks, sending half of the blood to the left lung and half to the right lung.

4. Passing through the pulmonary capillaries in the lungs, the blood picks up oxygen and loses carbon dioxide.

5. The oxygenated blood then returns to the heart, arriving in the left atrium via the left and right pulmonary veins.

6. Most of the blood passes directly through the left atrium and into the left ventricle. A contraction pushes the remaining blood from the left atrium into the left ventricle.

7. As the contraction continues, the blood is pumped up and out of the ventricle through the largest artery in the body, the aorta. After making a sharp turn, the aorta splits, sending some blood to the capillaries of the arms and head and the remainder to the capillaries of the trunk and legs.

8. Depleted of oxygen after passing through the capillary beds of the head, trunk, and legs, the blood trickles in veins back to the heart, and collects in the right atrium via the venae cavae.

If you place your ear on the center of another person's chest in a quiet room, you can hear the heart working. "Lub dup, lub dup, lub dup." Over and over, the same two sounds. These are the sounds that a doctor hears when using a stethoscope. What is the source? It's not the contraction of the heart. Surprisingly, the muscular contractions don't make much noise. Rather, the sounds come from two sets of valves that help keep blood flowing in the proper direction (**FIGURE 21-8**).

The first set of valves is the atrioventricular (or AV) valves. Located between the atrium and ventricle on each side of the heart, these two valves allow blood to flow from the atrium to the ventricle. But when the ventricle contracts, these flaps of tissue slam shut, preventing blood from being pushed back into the atria: "lub." With no other escape, the blood flows out through the pulmonary arteries on the right side and the aorta on the left. At these two primary exits from the heart are two more valves. These semilunar valves, so called because of their half-moon shape, close and prevent blood from flowing back into the ventricles. Like doors slamming shut, the valves make a noise that you can hear with your ear pressed to someone's chest: "dup."

> **Q** Sometimes a doctor will hear additional sounds besides the "lub" and "dup" of normal heart valve functioning. What is the source of such heart murmurs?

When the atrioventricular or semilunar valves do not completely close, some blood can squirt back through them, flowing in the wrong direction. The blood moving backward through the valve can be heard, with a stethoscope, making a buzzing or swishing noise.

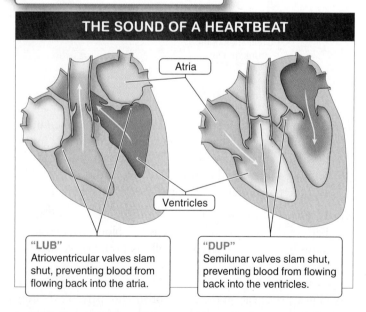

? Why does the heart make a "lub dup, lub dup" sound?

THE SOUND OF A HEARTBEAT

Atria

Ventricles

"LUB"
Atrioventricular valves slam shut, preventing blood from flowing back into the atria.

"DUP"
Semilunar valves slam shut, preventing blood from flowing back into the ventricles.

FIGURE 21-8 Audible heartbeats. Like doors slamming shut, the heart valves make noises that you can hear with your ear pressed to someone's chest.

Most heart murmurs are not life-threatening, and the individual suffers no ill effects.

The heart is not the only component of the circulatory system directing the flow of blood. Consider this: when you go out in very cold weather, your face or hands may get very cold and may even turn bluish in color. Why does this happen? Flow of blood in the capillaries is controlled by smooth muscle around the arterioles, the smaller vessels that branch off arteries and lead to capillaries. When the muscles, called precapillary sphincters, contract, blood flow can be cut off to capillaries and shunted elsewhere in the body (**FIGURE 21-9**). As a consequence of these muscles, bodies can reduce blood flow (and the heat it brings) to parts such as the face or hands in situations where such blood flow could lead to excessive and energetically wasteful heat loss. Blushing is the opposite situation: precapillary sphincters relax and blood flow to the face and neck increases.

"Food coma," that feeling of lethargy following a large meal, results from a similar shunting of blood. In this case, more blood is allowed to flow through the capillaries surrounding the digestive tract while less flows to other parts of the body. Alternatively, during strenuous exercise, more blood is directed toward the skeletal muscles in use. This accounts for the feeling of being "pumped up" during and shortly after a weightlifting session. Surprisingly, the vast majority of the capillaries have little or no blood flowing through them at any given time, and the body is constantly directing blood flow to the tissues where it is most needed.

> **Q** What is "food coma"?

Veins, too, aid in the control of blood flow. After sitting for a very long time, such as on a long plane or car ride, you may notice that your feet become swollen and it is difficult to put your shoes back on. What is the cause of this? The answer has to do with the way that blood flows back to the heart after passing through capillary beds. Remember that capillaries, with their small diameter and thin, leaky walls, reduce the pressure and speed of flowing blood. By the time it begins collecting in veins, blood has very little pressure. It is able to "limp" back to the heart only with the assistance of two important features. First, as muscles surrounding veins contract and relax during normal movement, they squeeze the veins, pushing the blood through. And second, within veins, at regular intervals, are one-way valves. Similar in function to the atrioventricular and semilunar valves of the heart, these valves allow blood to flow in one direction—toward the heart—but not in the reverse direction (see Figure 21-9).

Regulating blood flow by means of valves in the veins and the contractions of muscles surrounding the veins usually works fine. As we've noted, though, you can encounter a problem if you sit on a plane for several hours. Blood pumped to your feet must somehow climb up your legs, yet in the absence of contractions of your calf and thigh muscles, this doesn't occur so well. Instead,

Circulatory Systems   Human Circulation   Gas Exchange   Hemoglobin and Myoglobin

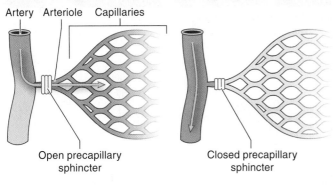

PRECAPILLARY SPHINCTERS
In the arterioles, precapillary sphincters can contract and cut off blood flow to the capillaries in order to shunt it elsewhere in the body.

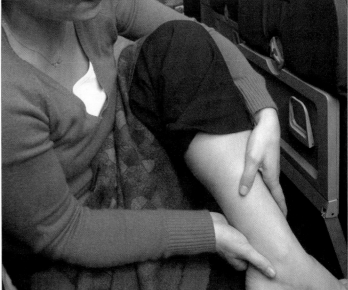

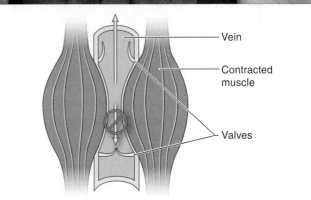

MUSCLE CONTRACTIONS AND VALVES
Contractions of muscles surrounding the veins push blood toward the heart. Valves within the veins keep the blood on course by preventing it from moving backward.

FIGURE 21-9 Controlling blood flow. Precapillary sphincters can reduce blood flow to hands or feet in cold weather, saving the blood's warmth for vital organs. When traveling on a long flight, it is helpful to move your feet and legs to help push blood back toward your heart.

Q Some individuals develop enlarged, twisted, and visible veins, a painful condition called varicose veins. Why might this occur?

the blood pools in your feet, causing them to get more swollen increasing the risk of blood clots. This is why it is good to get up and move around occasionally, or to exercise your leg muscles as you sit.

One serious circulatory problem is called varicose veins, a painful condition that occurs when the valves preventing backflow of blood malfunction and blood pools in the veins, stretching them. This can be caused or exacerbated by standing for long periods of time. Several methods are effective

for treating varicose veins, including laser surgery or injections that cause the veins to slowly fade and disappear, with deeper veins taking over the circulation in that region.

TAKE-HOME MESSAGE 21•4

The human heart, at the center of our circulatory system, is an extremely durable pump. It sends blood on a figure 8, two-circuit path through the body, first to the lungs for loading up with oxygen and, on its second circuit, to the tissues and organs of the body. Valves in the heart and veins keep blood flowing in one direction.

Respiratory Adaptations

Electrical activity in the heart generates the heartbeat.

Vertebrate hearts have a small piece of modified muscle tissue, the sinoatrial (SA) node, that initiates the regular, rhythmic contractions of the heart. Unlike most muscular tissue, which must be stimulated by a nerve before it contracts, the sinoatrial node spontaneously fires an electrical impulse that initiates contractions in the heart muscle. It begins this spontaneous firing early in fetal development and continues to give rise to every heartbeat for your entire life. As the pacemaker of the heart, the SA node initiates a carefully choreographed contraction that results in an efficient blood pump.

Beginning just above the right atrium, the electrical impulse in the SA node quickly spreads to the left atrium as well. As the atria contract, blood is pushed into the ventricles. The atria then enter a "relaxation" phase, and the wave of contraction continues, passing down the center of the heart and pausing briefly as it passes between the two ventricles. On reaching the bottom of the heart, the contraction appears to almost "bounce" back upward, causing a deep contraction that pushes the blood up from the bottom of both ventricles and into the pulmonary arteries and aorta, much like squeezing a tube of toothpaste from the bottom up. The ventricles then enter a relaxation phase, and the SA node starts the contraction anew (**FIGURE 21-10**).

Because the contraction of muscle tissue is a powerful electrical event, it can be recorded by electrodes placed on the skin that detect the changing electrical charges as the heart beats. Called an electrocardiogram, or EKG (from the German *Elektrokardiogramm*), these readings allow quick and easy display and analysis of the cardiac cycle.

Q **What is an artificial pacemaker?**

In some individuals, the sinoatrial node does not function properly or may be damaged by infection. This malfunctioning can lead to a heartbeat that is too slow or erratic and can cause reduced blood flow, leading to problems such as fainting. An artificial pacemaker is a battery-operated electronic device that generates stimulation to the heart, causing a more regular heartbeat.

TAKE-HOME MESSAGE 21•5

The sinoatrial node, modified muscle tissue in the vertebrate heart, initiates regular, rhythmic contractions. A heart contraction begins with an electrical impulse in the SA node in the right atrium. The contraction quickly spreads to the left atrium, and passes down the center to the bottom of the heart, then moves upward, pushing blood from both ventricles out through the pulmonary arteries and aorta.

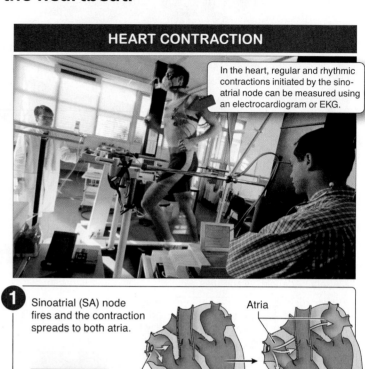

HEART CONTRACTION

In the heart, regular and rhythmic contractions initiated by the sino-atrial node can be measured using an electrocardiogram or EKG.

1 Sinoatrial (SA) node fires and the contraction spreads to both atria.

Atria

SA node

EKG reading

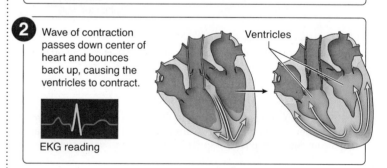

2 Wave of contraction passes down center of heart and bounces back up, causing the ventricles to contract.

Ventricles

EKG reading

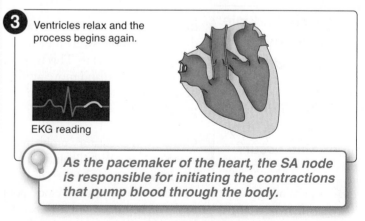

3 Ventricles relax and the process begins again.

EKG reading

As the pacemaker of the heart, the SA node is responsible for initiating the contractions that pump blood through the body.

FIGURE 21-10 **Rhythmic contractions of the heart.**

Circulatory Systems   Human Circulation   Gas Exchange   Hemoglobin and Myoglobin

Blood is a mixture of cells and fluid.

If circulatory systems are like highways throughout our bodies, transporting goods and garbage, then blood is the traffic. Endlessly circulating, this viscous fluid—its consistency is closer to that of motor oil than water—is a salty, protein-rich mixture of cells and fluid. The average human body has 4–5 quarts of blood, and the blood makes up just under 10% of our total body weight. Blood's functions revolve primarily around its transport and delivery capabilities, including the transport of (1) respiratory gases such as oxygen and carbon dioxide, (2) vitamins and minerals, (3) nutrients, (4) hormones, (5) cells of the immune system, and (6) metabolic wastes. Blood also helps to maintain body temperature and homeostasis (see Chapter 20).

Blood has several distinct components. Putting a small sample of blood in a test tube and spinning it rapidly in a centrifuge makes it possible to identify them (**FIGURE 21-11**). The lighter-weight part of the blood, the creamy yellow layer in the test tube, is the **plasma,** the liquid part of the blood. Plasma is 90% salty water. Dissolved within this water is a huge variety of molecules: metabolites and wastes, salts and ions, and hundreds of plasma proteins that serve to transport lipids, vitamins, and a host of other chemicals that need molecular escorts to the tissues where they are required. Most of the carbon dioxide produced in tissues as a by-product of cellular respiration is carried to the lungs dissolved in the plasma.

The heaviest components of blood get forced to the bottom of the test tube when spun in a centrifuge. This is a layer of packed cells, containing various types of blood cells, and is usually dark red in color. The proportion of the blood that consists of cells is called the **hematocrit.** In humans, a hematocrit of about 45% is normal. Individuals living at high altitudes for a few weeks or longer, however, have hematocrits of around 48% or 49%. Why? The increased hematocrit is a response to the reduced oxygen concentrations in the air at high altitudes. To continue to deliver enough oxygen to the body's tissues, there must be more blood cells to carry it.

Where do these blood cells come from? They are made in the bone marrow (the material that fills the interior of our bones) by specialized cells, called **stem cells,** that are able to develop into a diverse range of cell types. Stem cells throughout the bones in our body produce blood cells at a rate of about two million cells per second. There are two types of blood cells suspended in the plasma: red blood cells and white blood cells, as well as platelets, which are cellular fragments (**FIGURE 21-12**).

1. Red blood cells (also called **erythrocytes**). These workhorses of the circulatory system are the most common

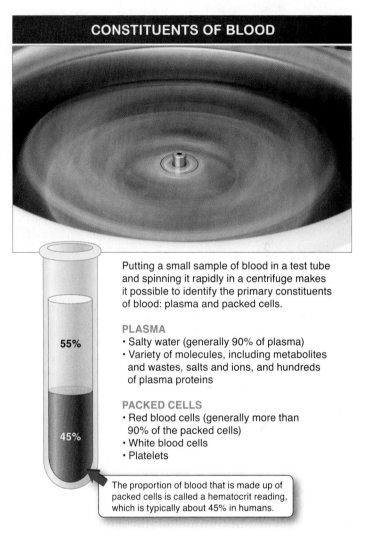

CONSTITUENTS OF BLOOD

Putting a small sample of blood in a test tube and spinning it rapidly in a centrifuge makes it possible to identify the primary constituents of blood: plasma and packed cells.

PLASMA
- Salty water (generally 90% of plasma)
- Variety of molecules, including metabolites and wastes, salts and ions, and hundreds of plasma proteins

PACKED CELLS
- Red blood cells (generally more than 90% of the packed cells)
- White blood cells
- Platelets

55%

45%

The proportion of blood that is made up of packed cells is called a hematocrit reading, which is typically about 45% in humans.

FIGURE 21-11 What makes up blood?

blood cells. In a human being, about 95% of the blood cells circulating at any given time are red blood cells. They are oxygen-transporting specialists, and their structure maximizes their effectiveness. Externally, they are shaped like flexible disks, so they can squeeze through capillaries in single file. Internally, they have hardly any organelles; they have no nucleus, mitochondria, or protein-making machinery. What are they filled with? Each red blood cell contains about 250 million molecules of **hemoglobin,** an oxygen-carrying protein molecule. Because they lack almost all internal cellular machinery for repair and upkeep, red blood cells don't last long, remaining in circulation for about four months. During its short life, though, a red blood cell will travel about 900 miles, endlessly picking up oxygen in the lungs and releasing it to body cells that need it.

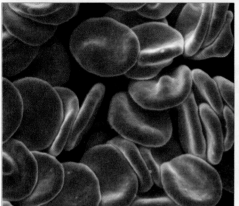
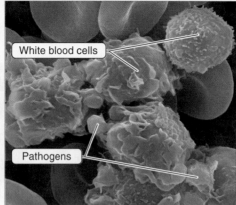
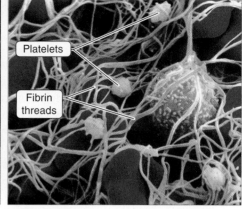

RED BLOOD CELLS (ERYTHROCYTES)
- Transport oxygen from the lungs to the rest of the body
- Flexible disks containing few organelles
- Packed full of hemoglobin

WHITE BLOOD CELLS (LEUKOCYTES)
- Destroy pathogens and foreign organisms in the bloodstream and interstitial fluid
- There are several types of white blood cells that differ in their methods of fighting disease and responding to foreign materials

PLATELETS
- Slow blood loss by initiating the constriction of blood vessels and the formation of a clot
- Composed of small pieces of cytoplasm
- Contain no organelles

FIGURE 21-12 **Erythrocytes, leukocytes, and platelets.**

2. White blood cells (also called **leukocytes**). White blood cells are the defenders of the body and are the primary components of the body's immune response system. Five different types of white blood cells can be found circulating: neutrophils, lymphocytes, monocytes, eosinophils, and basophils (see Chapter 26 for more on the roles of these white blood cells). Like red blood cells, white blood cells arise from stem cells in bone marrow. Once in the bloodstream, they patrol for **pathogens,** disease-causing foreign organisms circulating in the bloodstream. White blood cells also spend much of their time outside the circulatory system, diffusing out of the capillaries and moving about in the interstitial fluid between cells where many pathogens such as viruses and bacteria may be, and where they also can destroy cancerous body cells or body cells that have been infected by pathogens. The number of leukocytes circulating in an individual can vary greatly, depending on his or her health status. Under normal conditions, there is approximately one leukocyte for every thousand red blood cells, but the number of leukocytes increases as much as two- to threefold during an infection.

3. Platelets. With more than 50,000 miles of blood vessels in our bodies, it is inevitable that there will be occasional cuts or punctures (**FIGURE 21-13**). Fortunately, the platelets are ready to swing into action when this happens. **Platelets** are considered cellular fragments rather than full-fledged cells. In the bone marrow, large cells called megakaryocytes repeatedly pinch off little bits of cytoplasm that have no nuclei or other organelles. These cell fragments, the platelets,

are filled with critical enzymes and chemicals for patching damaged blood vessels. Hundreds of thousands of platelets circulate at any given time, with each platelet generally lasting about a week. You can envision platelets as fragile glass jars full of Super Glue. When they bump into the edge of a cut in a blood vessel, they shatter and release their cargo,

If platelets lack properly functioning clotting factors, cuts and scrapes can lead to uncontrolled bleeding.

FIGURE 21-13 **Fighting blood loss.** Platelets patch damaged blood vessels.

Circulatory Systems   Human Circulation   Gas Exchange   Hemoglobin and Myoglobin

Cooking in a cast iron skillet can increase significantly the iron content of foods!

initiating constriction of the blood vessel and the production of fibrin threads that form a blood clot to reduce blood loss.

Some individuals lack platelets with properly functioning clotting factors, and they experience uncontrolled bleeding from even minor cuts or scrapes. These problems can be due to an inherited malfunctioning gene (as in the condition of hemophilia). They can also be acquired, or environmental: if the liver—where many of the clotting enzymes are produced—is damaged by disease (such as cirrhosis, which can result from alcoholism), uncontrolled bleeding can occur. Conversely, problems of blood clotting *too* readily can also lead to health problems. Thrombosis, for example, is the formation of clots of coagulated blood within a blood vessel. When such clots block circulation in these blood vessels that supply blood to the muscle tissue of the heart itself, a heart attack occurs.

Anemia occurs when an individual has too few red blood cells. Because red blood cells deliver oxygen to the body's cells, one consequence of anemia is a reduction in the oxygen available to cells, essentially suffocating them. This causes people with anemia to feel tired and run-down. A reduction in the number of red blood cells is also associated with an increased susceptibility to infection, apparently by weakening the immune system's ability to mount a response to pathogens. Iron deficiency is the most common cause of anemia. Iron is a critical element that enables oxygen to be carried by red blood cells. If iron is in short supply, red blood cells can't deliver sufficient oxygen to the tissues where it's needed. Both men and women can be anemic, but anemia affects women much more commonly, because of the blood loss during menstruation. The relationship between iron deficiency and anemia has been known for a long time. An old folk remedy for anemia—that actually worked(!)—was sipping liquid daily from a jug containing rusty iron nails and water.

> **Q** What is anemia? Why are women more susceptible than men?

TAKE-HOME MESSAGE 21·6

Blood is a salty, protein-rich mixture of cells and fluid, important in the transport of (1) respiratory gases, (2) vitamins and minerals, (3) nutrients, (4) hormones, (5) components of the immune system, and (6) metabolic wastes. Blood also helps maintain a constant internal environment, including body temperature. Blood cells are produced throughout life by stem cells in bone marrow. There are two types of cells suspended in the plasma: red cells (oxygen transport), white cells (defense from infections), as well as cellular fragments, platelets (repair).

Blood pressure is a key measure of heart health.

Feel your pulse. With no fancy equipment at all, it is possible to get very useful information about the functioning of your heart. For some arteries, such as those on the underside of your wrist or on the side of your neck, you can feel with your fingers the pressure increase as a blood surge stretches the arteries with each contraction of the heart. Taking a person's pulse provides a quick and easy determination of the rate and rhythm of the heartbeats.

Additional information about heart health can be gained with measurement of **blood pressure,** which measures the force with which blood flows through a person's arteries. This force tells us the magnitude of each heart contraction and gives important clues about an individual's cardiovascular health. There are two different parts to a blood pressure reading (**FIGURE 21-14**). The first, called **systolic pressure,** is the pressure when the heart contracts. The powerful contraction pumps blood into the arteries, momentarily causing them to stretch as they accommodate the large pulse of blood. The second blood pressure reading is called **diastolic pressure.** This is a measure of the force that blood exerts on the artery walls while the heart is between beats. Because blood isn't being actively pumped at that moment, the diastolic pressure is always lower than the systolic pressure.

Blood pressure can be measured in four easy steps, using a blood pressure cuff.

1. The cuff is fastened around the upper arm and pumped up, clamping off the arteries in the arm so that no blood gets through.

2. Gradually, pressure on the cuff is released.

3. When the pulsing of blood getting pushed through the arteries under the cuff can first be heard with a stethoscope held to the arteries just below the cuff—heard as a little squirt—the pressure reading is noted. That is the systolic pressure. Each contraction of the heart is just strong enough to push blood through the barrier of that much pressure.

4. Additional pressure in the cuff is released until the squirting sound disappears. The pressure at that point is the diastolic pressure. Blood is flowing through the arteries with this amount of pressure between heart contractions.

If your blood pressure is "120 over 80," it means that the systolic pressure is 120 and the diastolic pressure is 80. This is

BLOOD PRESSURE

Blood pressure readings consist of two measurements:

SYSTOLIC PRESSURE
• The force that blood exerts on the artery walls when the heart contracts and pumps blood into the arteries
• Normal range is between 90 and 140 mmHg

DIASTOLIC PRESSURE
• The force that blood exerts on the artery walls while the heart is between beats
• Normal range is between 60 and 90 mmHg

 With a blood pressure above 140/90, your heart must work harder at all times and your arteries can lose some of their elasticity. This increases your health risks.

FIGURE 21-14 Blood pressure readings can reveal heart health.

written as 120/80, and the units of measure are millimeters of mercury (mmHg), representing how high a column of mercury could be lifted by such pressure.

Blood pressure above 140/90 is considered high and a potential health hazard. What does this mean, and why is it cause for concern? Imagine a pair of shorts with an elastic waistband. If you were to stretch the waistband as far as possible and hold it in that position for a long time, what would happen? The waistband would lose its elasticity. This is similar to what

Circulatory Systems   Human Circulation   Gas Exchange   Hemoglobin and Myoglobin

In order to pump blood up the steep slope to their heads, giraffes have a heart that is four times the size of a human's, relative to body size, and blood pressure that is more than twice as great.

FIGURE 21-15 **Contents under pressure.** The large heart of a giraffe pumps blood through its long neck all the way to its head.

happens to your arteries if they are stretched by high pressures for long periods of time. With high blood pressure, also called hypertension, not only must your heart work harder at all times, potentially weakening it, but your arteries have a reduced ability to expand and accommodate the increasing pulses of blood during times of exertion. Moreover, more cholesterol sticks to artery walls when they are rigid than when they are elastic, and as this narrows the diameter of the blood vessel, it further

reduces the efficiency of the circulatory system and taxes the heart. These problems all increase the risk of catastrophic heart attacks and strokes, which we discuss in Section 21.8. Although both systolic pressure and diastolic pressure are important, systolic blood pressure is more important in identifying and controlling hypertension.

Low blood pressure, or hypotension, at the other extreme, is defined as a pressure of 90/60 or lower and can cause symptoms such as dizziness, particularly just after a person stands up, due to inadequate blood flow to the brain. Sometimes caused by medications, low blood pressure can also be associated with weakness or depression. Most often it is not a problem, and it rarely has long-term risks.

Relative heart size and blood pressure are consistent among the mammals, with one notable exception: giraffes. With their necks stretching 8 feet (2.5 meters) or more, giraffes must pump blood up a pretty steep slope. Not surprisingly, their hearts are much bigger—about four times bigger (relative to body size)—than a human heart, and their blood pressure is more than twice as great. Scientists have begun studying giraffe circulation in the hope of learning physiological secrets to help humans cope with high blood pressure. Why, for example, with twice the blood pressure of a human, doesn't a giraffe's head explode when it lowers to drink from a pond (**FIGURE 21-15**)?

TAKE-HOME MESSAGE 21·7

Blood pressure measurement gives important clues about an individual's cardiovascular health. A blood pressure reading consists of two measures. The first, systolic pressure, is the force that blood exerts on the artery wall when the heart contracts and pumps blood into the arteries. The second, diastolic pressure, is the force that blood exerts on the artery wall while the heart is between beats. With high blood pressure, the heart must work harder at all times, the arteries can lose some of their elasticity, and health risks are increased.

Cardiovascular disease is a leading cause of death in the United States.

The heart is among the most neglected organs. Most people take it for granted. But every year heart attacks cause 20% of the deaths in the United States, more than any other single cause and among the most avoidable. Heart attacks are brought on by an interruption in the flow of blood through one of the **coronary arteries**—the blood vessels that deliver oxygen and nutrients to the heart muscle itself. When cells in the heart muscle are deprived of oxygen, the heart may beat irregularly or cease to beat, and the heart muscle cells deprived of oxygen die. This has serious and long-term implications, because heart cells are among the rare cells of the body that do not reproduce themselves. Once they are gone, they are really gone.

> " Broken heart. A pump after all, pumping thousands of gallons of blood every day. One fine day it gets bunged up and there you are. "
>
> —James Joyce, *Ulysses*

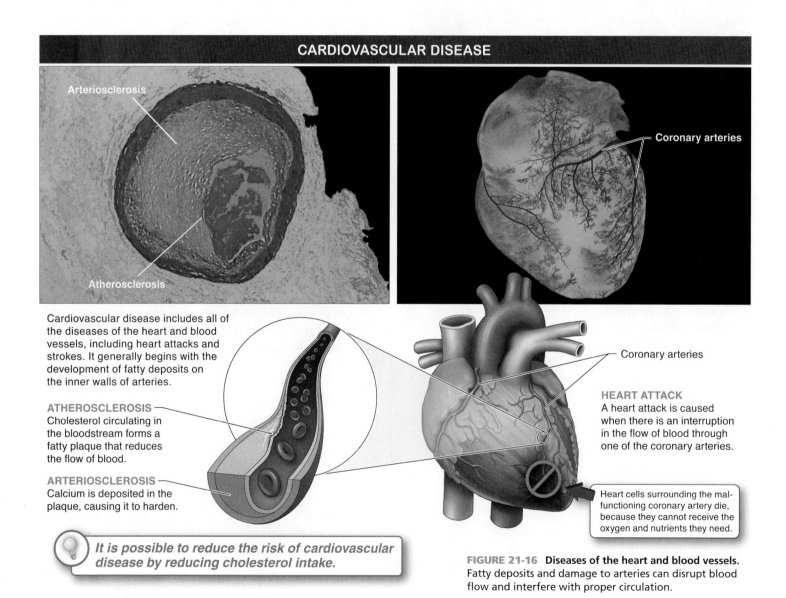

CARDIOVASCULAR DISEASE

Arteriosclerosis

Atherosclerosis

Coronary arteries

Cardiovascular disease includes all of the diseases of the heart and blood vessels, including heart attacks and strokes. It generally begins with the development of fatty deposits on the inner walls of arteries.

ATHEROSCLEROSIS Cholesterol circulating in the bloodstream forms a fatty plaque that reduces the flow of blood.

ARTERIOSCLEROSIS Calcium is deposited in the plaque, causing it to harden.

Coronary arteries

HEART ATTACK A heart attack is caused when there is an interruption in the flow of blood through one of the coronary arteries.

Heart cells surrounding the malfunctioning coronary artery die, because they cannot receive the oxygen and nutrients they need.

💡 *It is possible to reduce the risk of cardiovascular disease by reducing cholesterol intake.*

FIGURE 21-16 Diseases of the heart and blood vessels. Fatty deposits and damage to arteries can disrupt blood flow and interfere with proper circulation.

Circulatory Systems   Human Circulation   Gas Exchange   Hemoglobin and Myoglobin

Contrary to appearances—and James Joyce's belief—heart attacks rarely strike out of the blue. Although the heart attack itself is a sudden event, it usually occurs after decades of progressive deterioration of the arteries and other degradations of the circulatory system, collectively called **cardiovascular disease** (FIGURE 21-16).

Cardiovascular disease includes all diseases of the heart and blood vessels and is ultimately responsible for close to half of all deaths in the United States. In addition to heart attacks, strokes are a common outcome of advanced cardiovascular disease. Caused by blocked arteries or blood clots in the brain, strokes also lead to cell death in the brain tissues starved of oxygen. There is, however, some cause for optimism: the death rate from heart disease has been declining steadily for the past 50 years, including a 25% drop in the past 20 years. These reductions have come not from advances in heart transplants and other surgical interventions, but rather from improvements in diet and exercise as well as advances in diagnosis and preventive medicine.

Cardiovascular disease generally begins with the development of fatty deposits called plaques on the inner walls of arteries. Plaques increase the risk of formation of blood clots and, by narrowing the artery, reduce the flow of blood. Called **atherosclerosis,** this narrowing of the arteries is often followed by the depositing of calcium at the plaques, causing them to harden in a process known as **arteriosclerosis.** The initial formation of plaques usually occurs as a consequence of circulating cholesterol in the bloodstream. Because most of this circulating cholesterol comes from cholesterol in our diet, we can reduce our risk of atherosclerosis by reducing our cholesterol intake.

Cholesterol is all the same, but you may hear references to "good" cholesterol and "bad" cholesterol. Why is this? As we discussed in Chapter 3, most cholesterol circulating in the bloodstream is packaged as LDL, or low-density lipoproteins. These molecules consist of thousands of molecules of cholesterol surrounded by a phospholipid coat. Because the LDL particles are sticky, they adhere to artery walls and can initiate the buildup of dangerous plaques. Other circulating particles, high-density lipoproteins (HDL), are considered "good" cholesterol. Less well-understood than LDL, these particles seem to remove cholesterol from arteries and deliver it to liver cells where it can be broken down. This process can actually reduce the progression of cardiovascular disease. By including in your diet fish and other foods that contain a specific type of fatty acids, called omega-3 fatty acids, you can increase your HDL levels.

Both nature and nurture play a role in cardiovascular disease. As we saw in Chapter 3, the tendency to develop cardiovascular disease is inherited. Individuals vary in the number of LDL receptors they produce on their liver cells, and the more receptors an individual has, the better that individual is able to remove atherosclerosis-causing cholesterol from circulation. You cannot alter the genes you inherit for LDL receptor production. But you *can* alter the amount of cholesterol or type of cholesterol (that is, LDL vs. HDL) that is circulating in the first place. Several different behavioral changes can reduce the level of circulating cholesterol and the risk of cardiovascular disease: in the first place by increasing aerobic exercise, not smoking, and eating a low-cholesterol, low-fat diet (FIGURE 21-17).

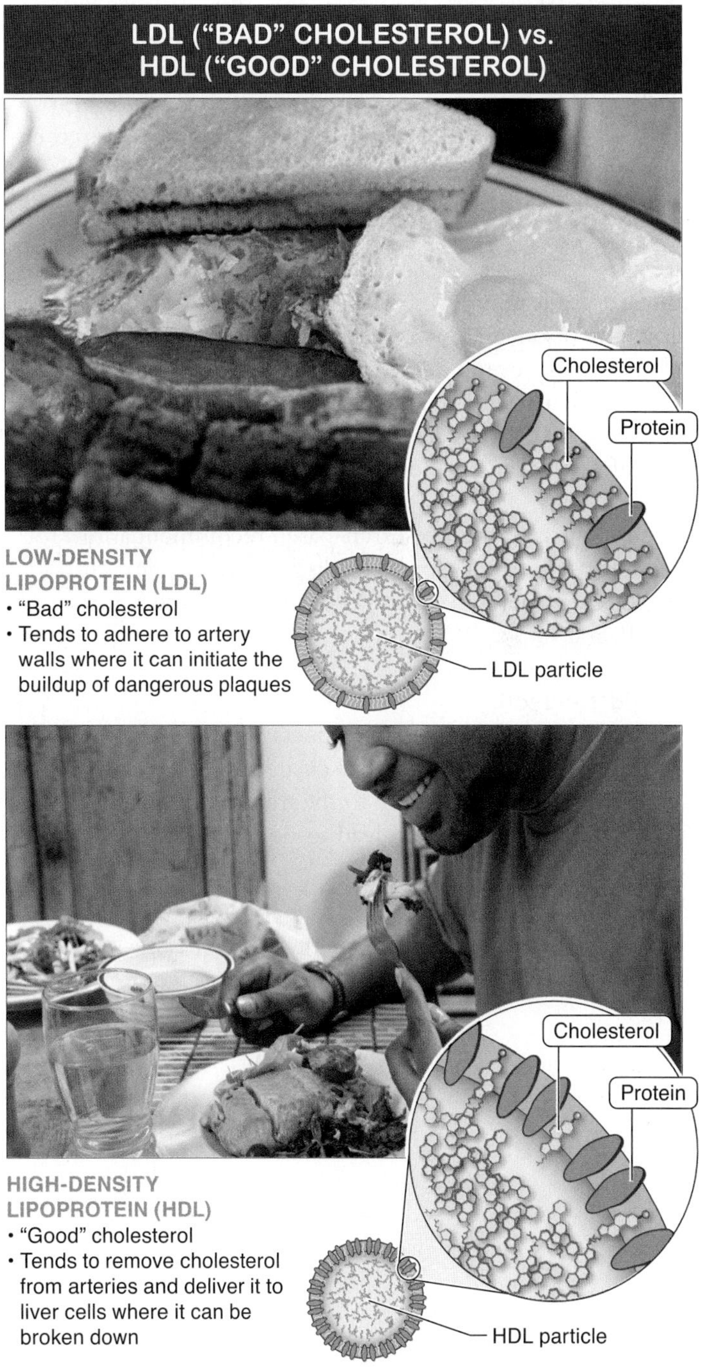

LDL ("BAD" CHOLESTEROL) vs. HDL ("GOOD" CHOLESTEROL)

Cholesterol
Protein

LOW-DENSITY LIPOPROTEIN (LDL)
- "Bad" cholesterol
- Tends to adhere to artery walls where it can initiate the buildup of dangerous plaques

LDL particle

Cholesterol
Protein

HIGH-DENSITY LIPOPROTEIN (HDL)
- "Good" cholesterol
- Tends to remove cholesterol from arteries and deliver it to liver cells where it can be broken down

HDL particle

FIGURE 21-17 Cholesterol can be helpful or harmful.

Q | If exercising makes the heart work harder and if being overweight from eating fatty foods also makes the heart work harder, why does one lead to fitness and the other to disease?

With aerobic training, such as running, the muscle fibers of the heart get bigger (in much the same way that skeletal muscle gets bigger when you lift weights), and cardiovascular health is improved. When people are sedentary, though, their hearts must work harder for reasons such as hypertension, poor diet, or increased blood pressure. The increased load on the heart causes the heart to get bigger, but in a pathological manner that increases the risk of heart failure, rather than in a manner that increases strength and efficiency.

Cardiovascular disease continues to be the most prevalent disease and leading cause of death in the United States. But, as we mentioned above, the situation has been improving over the past several decades. The onset and progression of Cardiovascular disease are strongly influenced by factors within your control, and with the proper dietary strategies and lifestyle changes most people can reduce their risk.

In summarizing their research-based recommendations for reducing risk factors for heart disease, heart attack, and stroke, the American Heart Association suggests a focus on "A, B, and C":

Avoid tobacco.
- Stop using any tobacco products and minimize exposure to tobacco smoke. Because cigarette smokers are two- to three-times more likely to die from heart disease, this behavioral change can lead to significant improvements to health and longevity.

Be more active.
- Participate in at least 30 minutes of moderate-intensity physical activity (i.e., brisk walking) on five or more days each week (or vigorous-intensity activity, such as jogging, on three or more days). Additionally, every adult should perform activities that increase or maintain muscle strength, including progressive weight training and/or stair climbing, on a minimum of two days each week.

Choose good nutrition.
- Eat a diet that balances energy intake with exercise to prevent weight gain. If you are overweight, take steps to increase physical activity and decrease energy intake to establish a healthy body weight (see Section 22-16).

- Chose a diet rich in vegetables, fruits, and whole grains, particularly those that are high in fiber.

- Limit intake of saturated fat, trans fat and cholesterol by choosing lean meats, vegetables, and low-fat dairy products. Read food labels to check for hydrogenated fats (see Section 2.13 for a refresher on hydrogenated fat and trans fats).

- Limit alcohol to one drink daily for women, and two drinks daily for men.

These behavioral changes are much easier said than done. Because they include the most effective strategies for reducing the risk of cardiovascular disease, however, the payoffs are significant.

TAKE-HOME MESSAGE 21•8

Cardiovascular disease includes all diseases of the heart and blood vessels, including heart attacks and strokes, and is the leading cause of death in the United States. It generally begins with the development of fatty deposits on the inner walls of arteries that increase the risk of blood clots and reduce the flow of blood in coronary vessels that supply oxygen to the heart (atherosclerosis). Because the hardening of arteries (arteriosclerosis) is usually initiated by circulating cholesterol, it is possible to reduce the risk of cardiovascular disease by reducing cholesterol intake.

The lymphatic system plays a supporting role in circulation.

Our bodies have another circulatory system (**FIGURE 21-18**). In addition to the cardiovascular system, and running close to it throughout the body, is the lymphatic system. Why the seeming redundancy? The lymphatic system has a supporting role in the process of circulation. It has three important functions (**FIGURE 21-19**).

1. Recycling. As diffusion occurs between the capillaries and the interstitial fluid that surrounds cells, mopeouch fluid is lost from the blood. Here's where the lymphatic system comes in. Intertwined around blood vessels, lymphatic capillaries take in, by diffusion, fluid, proteins, and other substances that have leaked into the interstitial fluid from the blood. Once recovered, this fluid, now called **lymph,**

THE HUMAN LYMPHATIC SYSTEM

The lymphatic system runs close to the circulatory system throughout the body and plays a supporting role in the process of circulation.

Lymph node

Lymphatic capillary

Lymph vessel

Valve

FIGURE 21-18 The "other" circulatory system. An overview of the human lymphatic system.

FUNCTIONS OF THE LYMPHATIC SYSTEM

RECYCLING
The lymphatic system recycles fluid and proteins that diffuse from the blood capillaries during circulation back into the bloodstream.

FIGHTING ILLNESS
As lymph circulates through the body, white-blood-cell-packed lymph nodes remove dangerous materials, including bacteria, cancer cells, and viruses, from the body.

RETRIEVING NUTRIENTS
Little projections that extend into the small intestine absorb lipids from the digestive tract and shuttle them to the bloodstream.

FIGURE 21-19 The lymphatic system supports the circulatory system while fighting illness.

travels through progressively larger lymphatic vessels that eventually join up with veins in the shoulders. At this point, the recovered proteins and fluid (which amounts to several liters each day) are returned to the blood on its way back to the heart.

2. Fighting illness. As it moves through the lymphatic system, lymph passes through patches of connective tissue called **lymph nodes.** These compartmentalized sacs are filled with pathogen-fighting white blood cells that remove dangerous materials (including bacteria, cancer cells, and viruses) from the body. This is why your lymph nodes—including your tonsils, the largest lymph nodes of all—become swollen when your body is fighting an infection.

Q It's not necessarily a good idea to have your tonsils taken out, even if they are painfully swollen. Why?

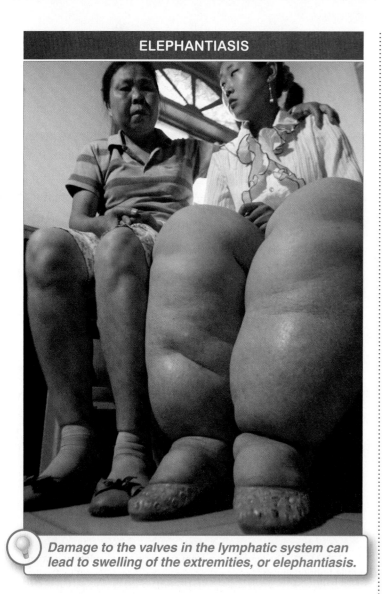

ELEPHANTIASIS

Damage to the valves in the lymphatic system can lead to swelling of the extremities, or elephantiasis.

FIGURE 21-20 **A malfunctioning lymphatic system.** When the lymphatic system is damaged, fluid builds up in the extremities.

3. Retrieving nutrients. The lymphatic system has numerous little projections that extend into the small intestine and absorb lipids from the food you have eaten and shuttle them from the digestive tract to the bloodstream.

In humans, the lymphatic system accomplishes these tasks without a pump. There is no "lymph heart." Rather, lymph is pushed through the system when muscles adjacent to lymph vessels contract and squeeze the fluid onward. Lymph vessels (like veins) have valves that keep the lymph flowing in one direction. When you sit for an extended period of time, lymph can accumulate in vessels. You can help move it along by contracting the muscles in your extremities and progressively contracting muscles closer and closer to your shoulders.

Infection by some parasitic worms can cause scarring of lymph vessels. Fluid recovered by the lymphatic system cannot be returned to the circulatory system, and elephantiasis, or a swelling of the extremities, results (**FIGURE 21-20**). Because the parasitic worms causing elephantiasis are transmitted by mosquitoes, the condition is most common in tropical regions. The condition can be treated with antibiotics that kill the symbiotic bacteria necessary for the parasitic worm to live.

TAKE-HOME MESSAGE 21·9

The lymphatic system runs close to the circulatory system throughout the body and plays a supporting role in the process of circulation, by performing three main functions: recycling fluid that leaks out of the capillaries of the circulatory system, marshaling white blood cells to help fight dangerous cells and pathogens, and absorbing nutrients from the digestive system.

21·10

The polygraph relies on cues from the cardiovascular system.

"Is your name John Doe? Do you have a driver's license? Did you stab Nick Eliot in the back?" Amazingly, measures of a person's respiratory and circulatory system functioning may help determine whether that person's answers to such radically unrelated questions are true. The **polygraph**—initially called the "lie detector" test—is a practical application of some of the physiological measures discussed above. Many law enforcement

agencies and other governmental bureaus, as well as numerous private organizations, use the polygraph to help them evaluate whether or not an individual is telling the truth.

Polygraph examiners make readings of three types of measures during an examination: (1) chest and abdominal movement during respiration, indicating breathing rate; (2) changes in

Circulatory Systems   Human Circulation   Gas Exchange   Hemoglobin and Myoglobin

skin conductance, indicating activity of sweat glands; and (3) heart rate and amplitude, and blood pressure (**FIGURE 21-21**). During the exam, the polygrapher asks a series of questions. Some of the questions are control questions for which the examiner knows the answer, such as: "Do you have a driver's license?" The questions of interest (such as the question about stabbing Nick Eliot), called relevant questions, are interspersed among the control questions.

In analyzing an individual's physiological responses to the interview questions, polygraphers are looking for evidence of the fight-or-flight response, an automatic set of responses to stress in an organism's environment. These take the form of increases in all three measurements during a relevant question—that is, in breathing rate, skin conductance, and heart rate—all of which are greater than when the respondent answers the control questions.

Interestingly, while the results of polygraph tests are not admissible in federal courts, law enforcement agencies such as the Federal Bureau of Investigation still find them to be of great value. Based on their assessments of a suspect's guilt or innocence after a polygraph test, investigators may then search for additional evidence to corroborate their belief in someone's guilt or to find another suspect when they believe, based on a polygraph, someone is innocent.

Some people have tried to develop techniques for "beating" the polygraph. These include behaviors such as putting a thumbtack in their shoe and leaning forward into it during the control questions, or biting the inside of their mouth so as to increase the magnitude of their respiration and sweating. Generally, these techniques increase the magnitude of some of the measures, but not all of them. And examiners are on the

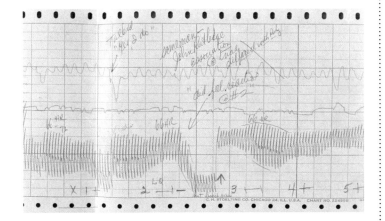

This polygraph tracing recorded Jack Ruby's physiological responses to questions about the murder of Lee Harvey Oswald.

THE POLYGRAPH TEST

The polygraph can be an effective tool for evaluating whether or not an individual is telling the truth by looking for manifestations of the fight-or-flight response.

THREE TYPES OF POLYGRAPH MEASUREMENTS

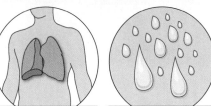
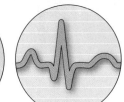

| Chest and abdominal movement during respiration, indicating breathing rate | Changes in skin conduction, indicating activity of the sweat glands | Heart rate and amplitude, and blood pressure |

FIGURE 21-21 Telling the truth?

lookout for individuals' use of such attempts at deception and interpret them as signs of guilt. Does the machine enable polygraphers to detect lies? Analyses of in-the-field examinations and laboratory simulations of examinations indicate average accuracies of between 80% and 98%, but it depends greatly on the skills of the person administering the test and remains a controversial technique.

TAKE-HOME MESSAGE 21·10

The polygraph can be an effective tool for evaluating whether or not an individual is telling the truth. A polygraph measures manifestations of the fight-or-flight response: (1) chest and abdominal movement during respiration, indicating breathing rate; (2) changes in skin conductance, indicating activity of sweat glands; and (3) heart rate and amplitude and blood pressure.

Respiratory Adaptations

❸ The respiratory system enables gas exchange in animals.

Humpback whales spouting (exhaling) while feeding in Alaska.

21•11

Oxygen and carbon dioxide must get into and out of the circulatory system.

As we've seen, circulatory systems are like trucking systems and the highways on which they move. Of the substances they transport, among the most important are the respiratory gases. After all, aerobic respiration requires cells to take up oxygen and release carbon dioxide. But how do these gases get into and out of the circulatory system? Where and how does gas exchange take place? In the remainder of this chapter, we investigate the structures where gas exchange occurs and the transport molecules that make it possible.

In single-celled and very small multicellular organisms, gas exchange can occur by direct diffusion. In larger multicellular organisms, however, gas exchange becomes a two-stage process (**FIGURE 21-22**). First comes the exchange between the external environment and the organism's circulatory system. Later comes the exchange between the circulatory system and the cells involved in cellular respiration.

The first of these two stages can occur in several different types of organs specialized for respiration, such as lungs or

---

GAS EXCHANGE IN ANIMALS

In large, multicellular organisms, gas exchange is a two-stage process.

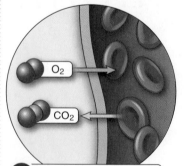

1 Respiratory gases are exchanged between the external environment and the organism's circulatory system.

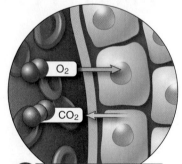

2 Respiratory gases are exchanged between the circulatory system and the cells involved in cellular respiration.

FIGURE 21-22 Overview of respiratory gas exchange in animals.

Circulatory Systems   Human Circulation   Gas Exchange   Hemoglobin and Myoglobin

DIVERSITY IN GAS EXCHANGE SYSTEMS

DIRECT DIFFUSION
- Gas exchange occurs directly between cells and the environment
- Occurs in single-celled organisms and small organisms with low metabolic demands

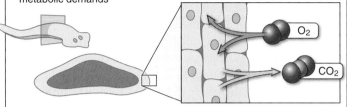

PROTRUDING RESPIRATORY SACS
- Balloon-like sacs that increase surface area for gas exchange
- Occur in sea stars and other echinoderms with low metabolic demands

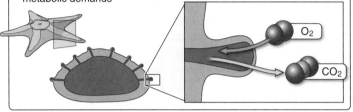

GILLS
- Elaborate extensions of the body that exchange significant amounts of gases dissolved in water
- Occur in fishes and many marine invertebrates such as lobsters and clams

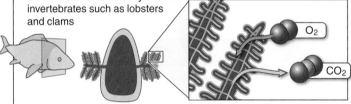

TRACHEAE
- Network of branching tubes connected to tiny openings on the body called spiracles
- Occur in most terrestrial insects

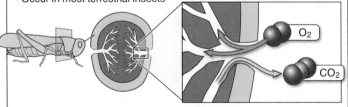

LUNGS
- Internal organs with highly branched, moist surfaces
- Occur in most land vertebrates

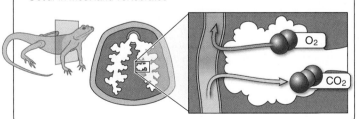

FIGURE 21-23 Gas exchange systems and the body structures that support them.

gills. In all cases, however, it requires a respiratory medium—air or water—that serves as a reservoir for the gases, and a moist respiratory surface on which the gas exchange can occur. The many different solutions for gas exchange that have evolved fall into five categories (**FIGURE 21-23**).

1. *Direct diffusion.* Single-celled organisms and many small multicellular organisms with low metabolic demands, such as marine flatworms, can accomplish respiration by direct diffusion between the cells and the environment.

2. *Protruding respiratory sacs.* Many slightly larger organisms also have low metabolic needs. Sea stars and other echinoderms have little balloon-like sacs that protrude from the skin—greatly increasing the surface area—and exchange gases between the body cavity and the environment.

3. *Gills.* Fishes and many aquatic invertebrates, such as lobsters and clams, have **gills.** These extensions of the body are tremendously elaborated structures in which the large surface area allows extensive exchange of gases between the water and the blood vessels of the circulatory system.

4. *Tracheae.* Although insect bodies look rather solid, they have a huge number of tiny openings—spiracles—that lead to tubes that branch extensively throughout the body. These inner tubes make it possible for gases in the air to come in direct contact with most of the organism's cells.

5. *Lungs.* Most land vertebrates have **lungs.** These are internal organs, characterized by highly branched, moist respiratory surfaces, across which gases in the air that is breathed in are exchanged with gases dissolved in the blood circulating through the lung tissue. Birds, reptiles, and mammals do virtually all of their respiration through their lungs, but amphibians (such as frogs) also exchange gases through their skin, which serves as a supplemental respiratory system. Their skin stays moist because of their largely aquatic lifestyle.

TAKE-HOME MESSAGE 21·11

In single-celled and very small multicellular organisms, gas exchange can occur by direct diffusion. In larger multicellular organisms, gas exchange is a two-stage process: (1) exchange between the external environment and the organism's circulatory system, which usually takes place in lungs, tracheae, or gills, and (2) exchange between the circulatory system and the cells involved in cellular respiration.

Gas exchange takes place in the gills of aquatic vertebrates.

Fishes have noses, but they don't use them for breathing. Respiration begins, instead, with a gulp. The fish opens its mouth and sucks in a mouthful of water. It then closes its mouth, opens small holes on either side of its head, and releases, or "exhales," the water. Unlike the air that humans and other mammals breathe in and out, water follows a one-way path into and out of the fish, never changing direction.

Gas exchange takes place as the water passes through the gills, complex structures adapted to extract as much O_2 as possible from water (**FIGURE 21-24**). This extraction is a difficult task, because water has only 5% of the oxygen concentration found in air. The gills generally consist of four bony or cartilaginous gill arches on either side of the head. Similar in appearance to the teeth of a comb, these arches give support to the gill. Long filaments of tissue extend like an accordion from each gill arch, spreading out and creating as much surface area as possible. The filaments are stacks of hundreds of disk-like structures, called **lamellae,** on which the gas

exchange takes place. Each membranous lamella is a semicircular disk of elaborately branched capillaries. As water rushes across the gills, it passes between the lamellae, coming in almost direct contact with the capillaries. Because the blood cells are so close to the water, dissolved O_2 can pass from the inhaled water to the blood by direct diffusion, and dissolved CO_2 can pass by direct diffusion from the blood to the exhaled water.

Blood circulation in gills is set up in a simple pattern that is highly efficient at extracting oxygen from the water. In each filament, the blood vessels are arranged so that the blood is moving in the opposite direction from the water flowing past the gills. Called a "countercurrent exchange system," this layout is dramatically more efficient than if the blood flowed in the same direction as the water. If the blood flowed in the same direction, the gills would extract a maximum of about 50% of the oxygen in the water; with the countercurrent system, the gills extract as much as 85% of the oxygen in the water.

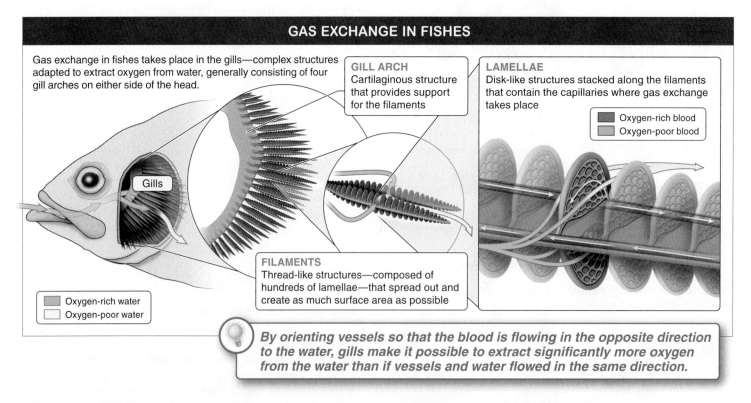

GAS EXCHANGE IN FISHES

Gas exchange in fishes takes place in the gills—complex structures adapted to extract oxygen from water, generally consisting of four gill arches on either side of the head.

Gills

GILL ARCH
Cartilaginous structure that provides support for the filaments

LAMELLAE
Disk-like structures stacked along the filaments that contain the capillaries where gas exchange takes place

Oxygen-rich blood
Oxygen-poor blood

FILAMENTS
Thread-like structures—composed of hundreds of lamellae—that spread out and create as much surface area as possible

Oxygen-rich water
Oxygen-poor water

By orienting vessels so that the blood is flowing in the opposite direction to the water, gills make it possible to extract significantly more oxygen from the water than if vessels and water flowed in the same direction.

FIGURE 21-24 Gills. The remarkable structure of gills makes gas exchange possible in fishes.

Circulatory Systems   Human Circulation   Gas Exchange   Hemoglobin and Myoglobin

COUNTERCURRENT EXCHANGE

**COUNTERCURRENT EXCHANGE:
BLOOD AND WATER FLOW IN OPPOSITE DIRECTIONS**
In a countercurrent system, water always has slightly more oxygen than blood, so a continuous concentration gradient is maintained, extracting as much oxygen as possible.

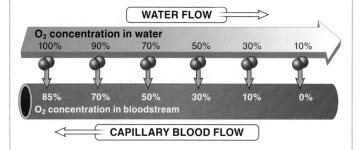

BLOOD AND WATER FLOW IN THE SAME DIRECTION
If blood were to flow in the same direction as the water, it could only become 50% saturated with oxygen, because there is no longer a concentration gradient to enable more diffusion of oxygen.

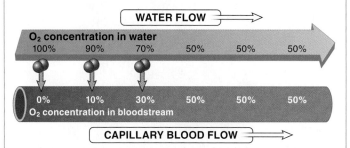

The countercurrent exchange system is dramatically more efficient at extracting oxygen than if the blood flowed in the same direction as the water.

FIGURE 21-25 Improving gas exchange. In countercurrent exchange, the direction of blood flowing through the gills maximizes the uptake of oxygen.

The countercurrent system is so efficient because it maintains a concentration gradient (that is, a difference in concentration) between the water and the bloodstream for the entire time that the water and blood vessel are in close contact (and because the gas exchange is accomplished through diffusion, which is passive, no ATP is required) (**FIGURE 21-25**). Depleted of O_2 in the tissues of the body, blood moving into the lamella encounters water that has been next to capillaries for a considerable distance and has already lost most of its oxygen.

The water may only have, for example, 10% of the O_2 it contained when first taken into the fish's mouth. Still, because the blood next to the water has been almost totally depleted of oxygen, the water still has a greater concentration of oxygen and therefore O_2 will diffuse from the water to the blood. Further along through the lamella, the blood has slightly more oxygen. The water, however, also has slightly more oxygen. Consequently, O_2 continues to diffuse from the water to the blood. By the time the blood has traveled almost completely through the lamella, it is holding about 70% or 80% of the maximum amount of oxygen that it can hold. At this point, however, the blood is encountering water that has entered the lamella straight from the fish's mouth, and this water is as saturated with O_2 as it can be. And so, even at this point, there is a concentration gradient and the blood can pick up just a bit more oxygen before returning to the tissues in the fish where it is needed. Carbon dioxide is removed from the fish's circulatory system in the same, countercurrent exchange way.

> " Relationships are like sharks; they have to keep moving or they die.
> —Woody Allen, *Annie Hall* "

Fishes are not the only aquatic animals with gills. Many other groups of vertebrates and invertebrates have gills, including molluscs, such as clams, and arthropods, such as lobsters. Gills range from simple to complex, and there is a great deal of variation in the associated structures. Most sharks, for example, move water past the gills not in the manner described above, used by most fishes, but just by swimming forward all the time. If they stop moving forward, the oxygen in the water surrounding the gills is quickly depleted and the shark will suffocate. Consequently, they spend their whole lives moving forward.

TAKE-HOME MESSAGE 21·12

In aquatic vertebrates, respiration begins when an organism opens its mouth, takes in water, and moves the water out through its gills. Gas exchange takes place in the gills, which extract as much oxygen as possible from the water by maintaining an O_2 concentration gradient between the water and the blood flowing through the gills.

Respiratory Adaptations

Respiratory systems of terrestrial vertebrates move oxygen-rich air into the lungs and carbon-dioxide-rich air out of the lungs.

Life on land is very different from life underwater, but the fundamental energetic needs remain. ATP is still the chemical that provides the energy for all the reactions necessary for life, and cells still need oxygen to produce ATP. And consequently, an organism must put air in contact with the cells that need it. Ultimately, oxygen must get into the cells and carbon dioxide must get out. These are universal challenges facing all terrestrial animals.

Terrestrial vertebrates have a general solution to these challenges. First, they suck in air through their mouth or nose. The air moves down a trachea, or windpipe, into lungs. In the lungs, O_2 diffuses from air to blood, while CO_2 diffuses from blood to air. Finally, the oxygen-depleted air is exhaled and the process begins again. The specific design of the lungs and respiratory system varies a bit from one taxon to another—we review the most notable distinctions below—but the general process is the same.

Mammalian respiration begins with a deep breath. Let's trace the air through the respiratory process (**FIGURE 21-26**). Air enters through the nose, filling the nasal cavity, where it becomes warm and moist. Additional air can be taken in through the mouth. In either case, these two entry points for air join together at the throat (also called the pharynx), in the back of the mouth. The air passes through the throat and moves through the voice box, or vocal cords—also called the larynx. The voice box can be seen as the bump on the front of your neck, called the "Adam's apple." From the larynx, the air moves into the trachea. The trachea is a long windpipe that takes the air into the chest cavity. Once there, the trachea splits, with a fork going to the left lung and a fork going to the right lung.

Lungs are like stretchy, elastic bags. Where the trachea splits, the two smaller tubes are called bronchi. These enter the lungs and branch again. And again. And again. With each successive branching, the bronchi get smaller. Under a certain size they are called bronchioles. And they all just keep branching and spreading out. Eventually, the bronchioles reach a dead end. These dead ends are tiny elastic sacs, the alveoli. Here is where the air meets the blood vessels (**FIGURE 21-27**).

There are about 300 million alveoli in each human lung, with a total surface area roughly the size of a movie screen. Alveoli are made up from the most delicate cells in our bodies and have ultra-thin walls. Completely surrounding the alveoli, the way

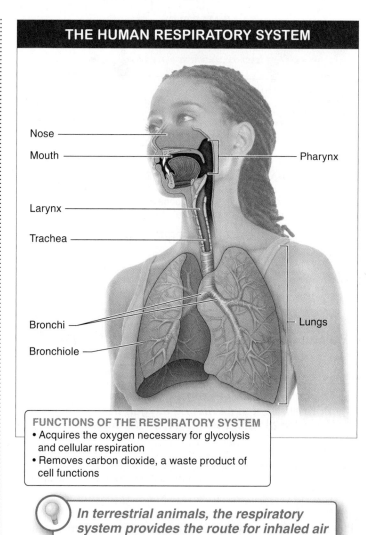

THE HUMAN RESPIRATORY SYSTEM

Nose — Pharynx
Mouth —
Larynx —
Trachea —
Bronchi —
Bronchiole —
— Lungs

FUNCTIONS OF THE RESPIRATORY SYSTEM
• Acquires the oxygen necessary for glycolysis and cellular respiration
• Removes carbon dioxide, a waste product of cell functions

In terrestrial animals, the respiratory system provides the route for inhaled air to meet the blood vessels of the body.

FIGURE 21-26 A terrestrial mammal. Overview of the human respiratory system.

your fingers might completely surround a small ball that you are grasping, are tiny capillaries. The capillaries have extremely thin walls, too. Oxygen in the alveoli dissolves in moisture on the cells lining them. It can then pass right through the two sets of thin membranes—alveolar and capillary—and get picked up by the bloodstream. Simultaneously, carbon dioxide can diffuse from the blood into the alveoli. In the short time you hold it in your lungs, the breath you inhaled is changed. When exhaled, it is depleted of O_2 and laden with CO_2.

GAS EXCHANGE THROUGH ALVEOLI

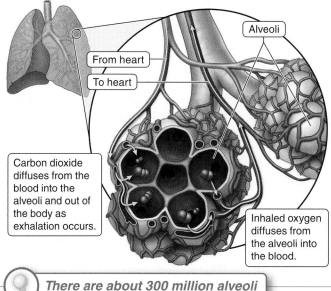

Alveoli are the delicate, thin-walled elastic sacs at the end of bronchioles where air meets the blood vessels.

Alveoli

Bronchiole

Blood vessel

From heart

To heart

Alveoli

Carbon dioxide diffuses from the blood into the alveoli and out of the body as exhalation occurs.

Inhaled oxygen diffuses from the alveoli into the blood.

There are about 300 million alveoli in each lung, with a total surface area the size of a movie screen!

FIGURE 21-27 **Alveoli in the lungs: where air meets blood vessels.**

Amphibians and reptiles are almost identical to mammals when it comes to the respiratory system. The lungs of amphibians are a bit smaller, but amphibians make up for some of this reduced lung capacity by conducting a bit of gas exchange across their skin. This is why they must keep their skin moist at all times. Reptiles are generally too thick-skinned and scaly to achieve any respiration through their skin, but they have slightly larger lungs than amphibians to pick up the slack. Birds, among the terrestrial vertebrates, are the champions of respiratory efficiency. We explore some of their unique adaptations in Section 21.14.

Smoking introduces thousands of different chemicals into the respiratory system, many of which—such as formaldehyde, ammonia, and benzene— have powerfully destructive effects on its cells. Toxic particles in tobacco smoke can damage the cilia lining the trachea. This reduces the ability to filter out dirt and microorganisms from the air we breathe. The dangerous chemicals can also kill immune system cells that help fight off infections, further reducing our immune response to pathogens. The chemicals in smoke also trigger mucous secretions that can block airways and lead to other respiratory difficulties. After chronic exposure to smoke, the walls of the alveoli become brittle, reducing respiratory capacity. And perhaps most significantly, carcinogenic chemicals in tobacco smoke can trigger unrestrained cell multiplication in lung tissues, causing cancer (**FIGURE 21-28**).

Q *How does smoking damage the lungs? Can the damage be reversed?*

TWINS: SMOKER AND NON-SMOKER

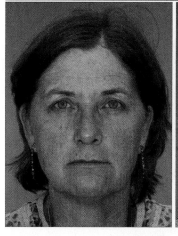
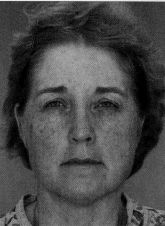

DAMAGE CAUSED BY SMOKING
- Toxic particles damage the cilia lining the trachea.
- Chemicals can kill immune cells that help fight off infections.
- Chemicals trigger mucous secretions that can block the airways.
- Walls of alveoli become brittle, reducing respiratory capacity.
- Carcinogenic chemicals can trigger cancer.

 Although smoking is destructive in numerous ways, stopping smoking at any point can begin the process of reversing some of the damage.

FIGURE 21-28 **Effects of smoking.** One of these identical twins is a smoker. Can you figure out which one?

Respiratory Adaptations

Although smoking is destructive in numerous ways, causing almost half a million deaths in the United States every year, stopping smoking at any point can begin the process of reversing some of the damage. By the end of the first year of nonsmoking, the risk of death from lung cancer and heart disease begins to decrease, and after 15 years of nonsmoking, the risk of death from these causes returns to the same levels as for individuals who have never smoked.

21·14

Birds have unusually efficient respiratory systems.

Birds take breathing to new heights. They often spend time in high-altitude, low-oxygen habitats, and they also fly for long periods of time, necessitating a great deal of oxygen (FIGURE 21-29). These extreme needs can be met by several key evolutionary adaptations that make it possible for birds to exchange gases much more efficiently than other terrestrial vertebrates.

For starters, birds' respiratory adaptations enable them to keep oxygen-rich air flowing through the lungs twice as long as in mammals. In mammals, air is inhaled and reaches a dead end at the alveoli. On the exhale, it changes direction and is breathed out. During the exhale, no new oxygen is reaching the lungs, a problematic situation during times of exertion. In birds, a more efficient system ensures that oxygen-containing air never runs into a dead end and the lungs never experience "stale" air. Here's how they do it (FIGURE 21-30).

When the bird inhales, some of the air passes through the lungs, where oxygen can diffuse into the blood. The rest of the air fills temporary holding structures called the posterior air sacs. Then, when the bird exhales, the posterior air sacs contract and push more oxygen-rich air through the lungs. With this system, even during exhales, when no "new" air is being breathed in, oxygen-rich air is passing through the lungs.

When a bird is inhaling, air moving through the lungs passes into other temporary holding structures, called anterior air sacs. Then, as the bird exhales, oxygen-poor air passing through the lungs *and* oxygen-poor air from the anterior air sacs together move into the trachea, and this mix is expelled from the bird's body.

With their circular system made possible by the air sacs and by the lungs' unique pass-through channels (called parabronchi), birds maintain a continuous and unidirectional flow of oxygen-rich air through the lungs. To increase the efficiency of the

Respiratory adaptations have evolved that enable birds to exchange gases with great efficiency—even at high altitudes where oxygen availability is low.

FIGURE 21-29 **High-altitude respiration.** Adaptations enable birds to function even when oxygen is in short supply.

Q How is bird breathing less like mammal breathing and more like fish "breathing"?

Circulatory Systems   Human Circulation   Gas Exchange   Hemoglobin and Myoglobin

CIRCULAR RESPIRATORY SYSTEMS IN BIRDS

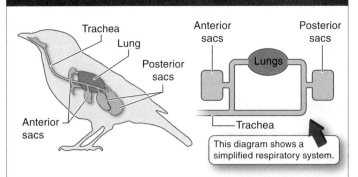

This diagram shows a simplified respiratory system.

INHALATION
- Fresh, oxygen-rich air moves down the trachea, inflating the posterior "waiting room" sacs, as well as the lungs.
- At the same time, oxygen-poor air is expelled from the lungs, inflating the anterior sacs.

EXHALATION
- The posterior sacs deflate, pushing oxygen-rich air into the lungs.
- The anterior sacs deflate, pushing oxygen-poor air out of the trachea.

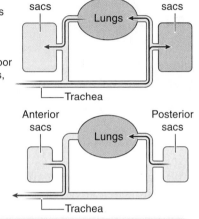

In birds, unlike in humans, air moves in one direction through the lungs. And during both inhalation and exhalation, fresh air continues flowing through the lungs.

FIGURE 21-30 Meeting extreme needs. The highly efficient gas-exchange system of birds supports the oxygen demands of flight.

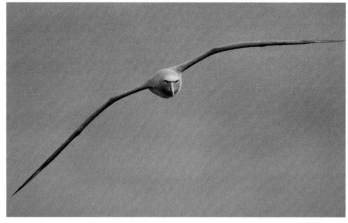

Adaptations in the bird respiratory system make prolonged flight, even at low-oxygen altitudes, possible.

system even more, all the blood vessels in the lungs are oriented so that the blood is flowing at a 90° angle relative to the direction of the air flow. This use of "cross-current flow" further increases the diffusion of gases between the air and blood. In practical terms, these adaptations make it possible for geese to fly over Mount Everest, nearly six miles above sea level, while a mammal deposited at that height would pass out almost instantly from insufficient oxygen.

TAKE-HOME MESSAGE 21·14

Birds often spend time in high-altitude, low-oxygen habitats and may fly for long periods of time, both of which require a great deal of oxygen. These extreme needs are met by a circular system of air flow and cross-current blood flow in the lungs, which make it possible for birds to exchange gases more efficiently than other terrestrial vertebrates.

Muscles control the flow of air into and out of the lungs.

Breathe in. Breathe out. It all seems simple enough. You don't even have to think about it. But over the course of your life, this simple process will happen 500 million times without fail. How does it work?

In reptiles, birds, and mammals, breathing occurs in two steps: inhalation and exhalation (**FIGURE 21-31**). The chest cavity is bordered on the bottom by a large sheet of muscle called the

The added buoyancy of lungs full of air makes it challenging to stay submerged under water.

diaphragm, which separates the chest cavity from the abdominal cavity. The rest of the chest cavity is surrounded by the rib cage and the intercostal muscles between the ribs. During inhalation, these two sets of muscles contract, pulling the diaphragm down and expanding the rib cage. This causes a rapid increase in the volume of the chest cavity and lungs, which causes air to be sucked into the lungs. When the diaphragm and intercostal muscles relax, the chest cavity returns to its original size. This reduction in the volume compresses the lungs and forces air back out of the trachea.

"I'm going to hold my breath until I die." As a child, you may have threatened your parents this way. It's actually not possible to do this, however. Although we can consciously control our breathing to some extent, chemical sensors in the body detect when carbon dioxide levels rise dangerously high, and our brain responds by sending signals to the muscles that control our breathing, spurring them to override our efforts to stop breathing.

THE MECHANICS OF BREATHING

Breathing is made possible by the following structures in the chest cavity:

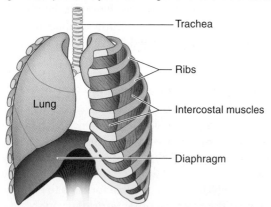

- Trachea
- Ribs
- Intercostal muscles
- Lung
- Diaphragm

In reptiles, birds, and mammals, breathing occurs in two steps.

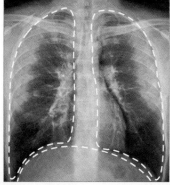 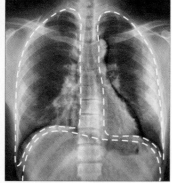

 INHALATION
- Diaphragm and intercostal muscles contract
- Diaphragm is pulled lower and rib cage expands
- Air is sucked into the lungs

 EXHALATION
- Diaphragm and intercostal muscles relax
- Chest cavity returns to its original size
- Air is forced back out to the trachea

FIGURE 21-31 Body structures that make breathing possible.

TAKE-HOME MESSAGE 21·15

In reptiles, birds, and mammals, breathing occurs in two steps: inhalation and exhalation. During inhalation, muscles contract, pulling the diaphragm down, expanding the rib cage, and increasing the volume of the chest cavity and lungs, which causes air to be sucked into the lungs. When the muscles relax, the chest cavity returns to its original size and air is forced out of the lungs.

Circulatory Systems   Human Circulation   Gas Exchange   Hemoglobin and Myoglobin

Some environments are more conducive to gas exchange than others.

Breathing is more difficult in some places than others. Because the diffusion of gases between the outside and inside of an animal depends on several physical factors, animals vary widely in their respiratory efficiency (**FIGURE 21-32**). The most important constraints on oxygen diffusion rates are temperature, viscosity, and pressure.

1. Temperature: cold versus hot. Keep some cans of beer or soda in a warm car all day and then open them. Why does the fluid fizz more than usual? As the temperature of water

CONSTRAINTS ON OXYGEN DIFFUSION RATES

Oxygen diffusion—and, hence, oxygen availability to body tissues—is influenced by features such as temperature, viscosity, and (shown here) pressure.

FIGURE 21-32 Gas exchange is more difficult in some environments than others.

(or air) goes up, its ability to hold gases goes down. Whether the respiratory medium is air or water, it doesn't hold as much oxygen when it gets warmer. This means that a fish must work harder to get enough oxygen in warmer water.

2. Viscosity (thickness): air versus water. From a breathing organism's perspective, air is much better than water. Air has much higher dissolved oxygen content than water, and oxygen diffuses from air into blood 8,000 times faster than from water into blood. It also takes less energy to move air than water.

3. Pressure: low versus high altitude. At high altitudes, much less oxygen is available. You don't even need to climb the Himalayas to experience this. A relatively short walk up a much smaller mountain will convince you. At 15,000 feet above sea level, for example, the air pressure is half of what it is at sea level. This is because there is less atmosphere above the air, pushing down on it. With lower pressure from above, less oxygen is squeezed into a given volume. This makes it hard to push air into lungs and to drive the oxygen across the alveoli and capillary membranes and into the blood. Mountain climbers often carry canisters of pressurized oxygen. In the lungs, the high-pressure oxygen can more easily diffuse into the bloodstream.

TAKE-HOME MESSAGE 21•16

The diffusion of gases between the outside and inside of an animal depends on several physical factors, including temperature, viscosity, and pressure, leading to variations among animals in their respiratory efficiency. The rate of gas exchange is higher in cold (vs. warm) temperatures, in air (vs. water), and at low (vs. high) altitudes.

④ Oxygen is transported and stored while bound to hemoglobin and myoglobin.

Rowers strain to take in enough oxygen to fuel their high-intensity racing effort.

21•17

Hemoglobin is the molecule that transports oxygen.

Red blood cells are filled with hemoglobin. Hemoglobin is like an oxygen "shuttle bus," transporting oxygen around the body. In the lungs, it picks up O_2 and hangs on to it as the blood cell returns to the heart and is pumped to the body. Only when it reaches tissues, such as organs or muscles, that are in need of oxygen but are far from sources of the vital gas does the hemoglobin bus release its O_2 "passengers." The empty hemoglobin then returns to the lungs, where it can load up on oxygen again. It is the oxygen-carrying hemoglobin that gives our blood its red color. When it gives up its O_2, hemoglobin turns more of a purplish-maroonish color. That's why books often show oxygenated blood in arteries as red and deoxygenated blood in veins as blue.

Hemoglobin is a tiny molecule—so tiny that there are about 250 million copies of it in every single red blood cell. Built right inside the blood cell, it remains there for the cell's entire life. Each molecule of hemoglobin is a tangled mass of four polypeptide chains. Nestled within the molecule are four cozy compartments, each of which can carry one molecule of oxygen gas on a seat of iron. This iron attaches to the O_2 that diffuses into the red blood cell, temporarily making it part of the hemoglobin molecule (**FIGURE 21-33**). As we saw above, a shortage of iron in your diet can lead to anemia. This is because when iron is in short supply, less oxygen can be bound by hemoglobin and transported by each red blood cell, causing muscles and organs to be starved of oxygen and leading to feelings of fatigue and weakness.

HEMOGLOBIN

Each molecule of hemoglobin is a tangled mass of four polypeptide chains with four molecules of iron that create four "seats" to which oxygen can attach.

Hemoglobin

Red blood cell

Iron Oxygen

Polypeptide chains

💡 *The hemoglobin molecule is like an oxygen "shuttle bus" that picks up oxygen in the lungs and transports it to tissues.*

FIGURE 21-33 Hemoglobin: the oxygen transporter.

Circulatory Systems   Human Circulation   Gas Exchange   Hemoglobin and Myoglobin

Although it is banned by the Olympics and most sports organizations, "blood doping" has been used by some athletes to improve their performance. One method involves withdrawing red blood cells during the weeks and months leading up to a big competition, storing them, and re-injecting them in the few days just before the competition. Because red blood cells are filled with hemoglobin, the oxygen-carrying pigment, blood doping can increase the athlete's capacity for delivering O_2 to his or her tissues. In addition to being against the rules in most competitions, however, blood doping also carries some health risks, because it increases the viscosity of the blood. In the 1990s, dozens of apparently healthy, elite cyclists died inexplicably from heart failure. It was suspected that their blood had become so thick with red blood cells from blood doping that the burden on the heart to pump their sludge-like blood became too great.

Hemoglobin binds to oxygen, but doesn't hold on to it so tightly that it never lets go. Like Post-it notes, which are useful because they are sticky enough to attach to surfaces but not so sticky as to become permanently affixed, hemoglobin "knows" when to bind to O_2 and when to release it. This hinges on something called the partial pressure of the oxygen (denoted as Po_2), the force of oxygen particles in the air pressing against the body (**FIGURE 21-34**).

Where in a body might hemoglobin encounter relatively high or low partial pressures of oxygen? When you breathe air that

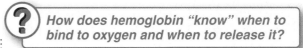

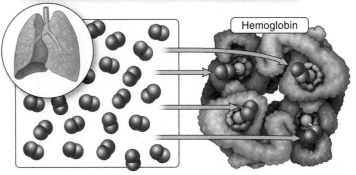

HIGH PARTIAL PRESSURE OF OXYGEN
When hemoglobin encounters a high partial pressure of oxygen, such as in inhaled air in the lungs, hemoglobin gets packed with oxygen.

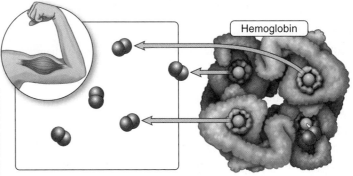

LOW PARTIAL PRESSURE OF OXYGEN
When hemoglobin encounters a low partial pressure of oxygen, such as in active muscle tissue in the body, hemoglobin releases oxygen.

FIGURE 21-35 **Hemoglobin binds and releases oxygen, depending on the partial pressure of oxygen in the vicinity.**

has a high concentration of oxygen, all four O_2 compartments in hemoglobin eagerly bind to oxygen molecules. Deep in the tissues of your body, though, oxygen is not in great supply—especially if you are exerting yourself and your muscles have been consuming oxygen as they contract. When these tissues become depleted of oxygen, any hemoglobin in the vicinity encounters a low partial pressure of oxygen (Po_2). And what does hemoglobin do when it encounters low Po_2? Because the oxygen it carries is not held too tightly, some of it is released (**FIGURE 21-35**). This oxygen is quickly soaked up by the tissue, which can then continue to generate ATP.

When you are sitting at your desk, the Po_2 in your tissues isn't very low. Your muscles aren't contracting, and your breathing rate isn't especially high. Much like a car coasting downhill, you aren't using much fuel. In these circumstances, hemoglobin only gives up about one of its four molecules of bound oxygen gas before returning to the lungs to load up again. Back and forth it cycles between getting packed with four oxygens in your lungs and being reduced to three oxygens in your tissues.

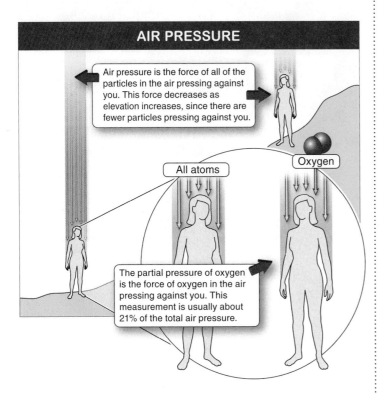

AIR PRESSURE

Air pressure is the force of all of the particles in the air pressing against you. This force decreases as elevation increases, since there are fewer particles pressing against you.

All atoms

Oxygen

The partial pressure of oxygen is the force of oxygen in the air pressing against you. This measurement is usually about 21% of the total air pressure.

FIGURE 21-34 **The force of particles on you.** Air pressure and the partial pressure of oxygen are reduced at higher altitudes.

Respiratory Adaptations

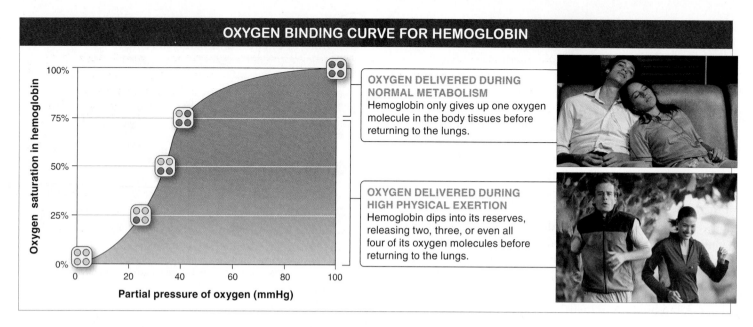

OXYGEN BINDING CURVE FOR HEMOGLOBIN

OXYGEN DELIVERED DURING NORMAL METABOLISM
Hemoglobin only gives up one oxygen molecule in the body tissues before returning to the lungs.

OXYGEN DELIVERED DURING HIGH PHYSICAL EXERTION
Hemoglobin dips into its reserves, releasing two, three, or even all four of its oxygen molecules before returning to the lungs.

FIGURE 21-36 **"Sticky, but not too sticky."** A curve showing hemoglobin's affinity for oxygen.

This seems wasteful. If your hemoglobin usually oscillates between picking up a single molecule of oxygen in the lungs and dropping off that O_2 in the organs or muscles, what is the point of its carrying around the other three oxygen molecules? These are its emergency reserves for when you need a lot more oxygen to fuel some energetic activity. If you are exercising vigorously, for instance, the Po_2 in your tissues can drop so low that hemoglobin gives up another of its oxygen molecules. In extreme cases of exertion, it might give up three or even all four of the oxygens that it carries. **FIGURE 21-36** shows an oxygen binding curve for hemoglobin, illustrating the relationship between the Po_2 and the proportion of oxygen molecules that hemoglobin holds onto.

When a woman is pregnant, the growing fetus does not breathe air. This doesn't mean that the fetus doesn't need oxygen, however. During development, oxygen needs are actually very high. How does a fetus get the O_2 it needs? It has to scavenge oxygen molecules released by the mother's hemoglobin. Fetuses do this by producing their own special type of hemoglobin that is a bit stickier than normal adult hemoglobin. At a Po_2 that is low enough that the mother releases oxygen from her hemoglobin, the fetal hemoglobin—with its greater stickiness (or oxygen affinity)—binds to the oxygen. It can then deliver that oxygen to its own, fetal tissues (**FIGURE 21-37**).

If hemoglobin isn't put together exactly right, the health consequences can be serious and painful, as is seen in sickle-cell disease. A single change in the genetic instructions for building hemoglobin causes a malfunction in the hemoglobin molecules (see Chapter 7). When they lose their oxygen molecules—such as when an individual is exercising—the hemoglobin molecules suddenly become misshapen and stick to each other, causing the entire red blood cell to collapse into a sharply pointed sickle. Once sickled, red blood cells cause a whole host of problems. Many break open, which can cause anemia if they aren't replaced promptly. Others clump together, often blocking

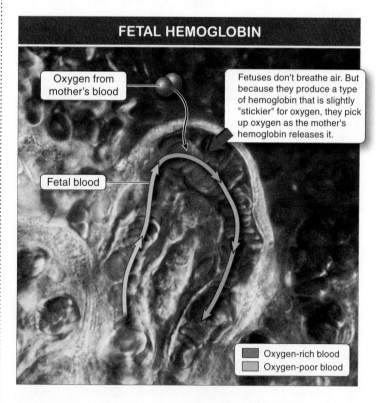

FETAL HEMOGLOBIN

Oxygen from mother's blood

Fetuses don't breathe air. But because they produce a type of hemoglobin that is slightly "stickier" for oxygen, they pick up oxygen as the mother's hemoglobin releases it.

Fetal blood

■ Oxygen-rich blood
■ Oxygen-poor blood

FIGURE 21-37 **How a fetus gets oxygen.** The fetus produces hemoglobin that binds oxygen released by the mother's hemoglobin.

Circulatory Systems   Human Circulation   Gas Exchange   Hemoglobin and Myoglobin

capillaries where, normally, they must pass through one at a time. This leads to intense pain, especially in the joints and muscles, and can cause strokes if it occurs in the brain. About 70,000 people in the United States live with sickle-cell disease. They are able to minimize the effects by avoiding strenuous activity or other situations in which the P_{O_2} in their muscles and other tissues drops too low.

Q What is carbon monoxide poisoning?

In an unfortunate coincidence, carbon monoxide (CO) also binds to hemoglobin, but with a higher affinity than oxygen does. In areas with high carbon monoxide concentrations— such as around a faulty furnace or a kerosene heater or lamp without adequate ventilation—the carbon monoxide will out-compete oxygen for hemoglobin's binding sites and it doesn't adhere like a Post-it note, rather, the binding is irreversible. Thus, when the hemoglobin travels to the body tissues, it has no oxygen to release and, in the absence of O_2, cellular respiration cannot generate the ATP the tissue needs (see Chapter 4). Consequently, the tissue is suffocated even as the person takes deeper and deeper breaths.

TAKE-HOME MESSAGE 21·17

Red blood cells are filled with hemoglobin, a molecule that picks up oxygen in the lungs and transports it around the body, releasing it in organs and tissues, such as muscles, where it is needed for cellular respiration.

21·18

Myoglobin in muscles holds a reservoir of oxygen for times of exertion.

Oxygen isn't the fuel that makes muscles contract, but it is an essential component of the process. You will quickly cramp up if your muscles try to work for long in the absence of oxygen. To increase the oxygen available beyond the amount delivered by hemoglobin, muscles have a trick for storing the valuable molecule. It's called **myoglobin,** and it is a protein embedded in the muscle cells themselves (**FIGURE 21-38**). Like hemoglobin,

Q What is the difference between white meat and dark meat?

myoglobin is an oxygen-binding molecule. It's a smaller, simpler molecule, though, and has only a single compartment for storing oxygen. And because of its structure, myoglobin has a higher affinity for O_2 than hemoglobin does. This means that at moderately low P_{O_2}, hemoglobin releases oxygen that can quickly be taken up by myoglobin. The myoglobin then just holds on tightly to the oxygen molecule, releasing it only under conditions of extremely low P_{O_2}. Think of it as a last gasp of air for an animal's muscles. As a rabbit runs full speed away from a lynx, its muscles must burn fuel at a very high rate; the value of just a tiny extra capacity can be the difference between life and death. Because myoglobin is a darkly pigmented protein, muscles with higher concentrations of myoglobin are darker. This is what distinguishes "white meat" from "dark meat," a distinction that generally reveals how metabolically active a particular muscle is. Turkeys hardly use their breast muscles, because they don't fly, but they do use their leg muscles all day. This is why breast meat is white and thigh meat is darker. We'll see later in the chapter that deep-diving marine mammals also make use of the O_2 stored in myoglobin during their long dives (as do long-distance migrating birds on their long flights).

TAKE-HOME MESSAGE 21·18

Myoglobin is an oxygen-binding protein embedded in muscle cells that can release one molecule of oxygen under conditions of extremely low P_{O_2}.

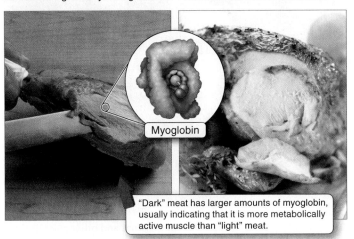

MYOGLOBIN

Myoglobin is a hemoglobin-like molecule within muscle tissue. It can hold a single oxygen molecule, which it releases only under extremely low-oxygen conditions—generally during exertion—when the muscles need it most.

Myoglobin

"Dark" meat has larger amounts of myoglobin, usually indicating that it is more metabolically active muscle than "light" meat.

FIGURE 21-38 Oxygen reserves. Myoglobin is a protein in muscles that stores oxygen for times of extreme exertion.

❺ Evolutionary adaptations maximize oxygen delivery.

Adapted to high altitudes, yaks are able to transport goods across mountain passes for farmers and Himalayan trekking expeditions.

21·19

Animals living at high altitude have special adaptations to the low-oxygen conditions.

As we saw above, because there is less atmosphere "pushing down" on air at high altitudes, the P_{O_2} is significantly reduced. It becomes hard to breathe, and activity is difficult. We struggle at high altitudes, because our hemoglobin isn't designed to pick up oxygen at such a low P_{O_2}; it isn't sticky enough. Mountain climbers can bring canisters of pressurized oxygen with them, but llamas and other animals living at high altitudes can't. How do they survive with less available oxygen? Their hemoglobin has a difficult task: it must pick up oxygen at very low pressure—precisely when hemoglobin is supposed to have a low affinity for oxygen—so that it can release it to muscles.

Living at altitudes of 5,000 meters, llamas have solved this problem by producing a slightly different form of hemoglobin, one that is adapted to low–oxygen conditions. At any given P_{O_2}, llama hemoglobin has a higher affinity for oxygen than human hemoglobin (**FIGURE 21-39**). It's stickier. This stickiness enables it to become saturated with four molecules of oxygen even when the llama breathes in

BREATHING AT HIGH ALTITUDES

Llamas can thrive in high-altitude, low-oxygen environments, because they produce a "stickier" form of hemoglobin that has a higher affinity for oxygen.

FIGURE 21-39 Built for high altitudes. Llamas and other animals that live at high altitudes have adaptations that improve respiration in low-oxygen environments.

Circulatory Systems   Human Circulation   Gas Exchange   Hemoglobin and Myoglobin

relatively "poor" air. Much like the oxygen binding curve of fetal hemoglobin, in llamas, the oxygen binding curve is shifted so that the hemoglobin is stickier for O_2, relative to adult human hemoglobin, at most P_{O_2} values. Because the P_{O_2} in llama tissues is even lower than in the air they breathe (because oxygen is being consumed by cellular respiration), the oxygen bound to the hemoglobin is still released to muscles to allow normal activity.

TAKE-HOME MESSAGE 21·19

At high altitudes, the P_{O_2} is lower, making breathing and activity difficult. Animals living at high altitudes solve this problem by producing a form of hemoglobin that has a higher affinity for oxygen, becoming saturated with four molecules of oxygen even when breathing in air with a low P_{O_2}.

21·20

Humans become acclimated to low-oxygen conditions.

Is it just a coincidence that an unusually large percentage of the world's most accomplished mountain climbers are Sherpas, who live year-round in high-altitude Nepal? No. Although llamas may be built for high altitudes from the day they are born, humans acclimate well, and Sherpas are among the most impressively acclimated high-altitude dwellers (FIGURE 21-40).

You don't need to live on Mount Everest, however, to become physiologically acclimated to the low-oxygen conditions found at high altitudes. Athletes around the world have long known that they can increase their strength, speed, and

stamina by training at high altitudes. And, as with llamas, human acclimation to low-oxygen conditions comes from modifications (though they are acquired rather than inherited) to hemoglobin.

Training for three to five weeks at high altitudes—usually 6,000–7,000 feet in elevation—triggers several physiological changes, the process of acclimation. These changes include stimulating the production of additional red blood cells, increasing blood and capillary volume, and increasing the number of mitochondria. High-altitude training also causes an

FIGURE 21-40 Humans acclimate to high-altitude living with improved respiratory efficiency.

HIGH-ALTITUDE TRAINING

BENEFITS OF HIGH-ALTITUDE TRAINING
- Additional red blood cell production
- Increased blood and capillary volume
- Increased number of mitochondria
- Increased diphosphoglyceric acid (DPG) in red blood cells, which reduces hemoglobin's stickiness and releases more of the oxygen it carries

At high altitudes, hemoglobin releases more oxygen to the tissues at any P_{O_2}.

DPG

FIGURE 21-41 Improving athletic performance by training at high altitude.

increase in a chemical called diphosphoglyceric acid (DPG) in red blood cells. This acid combines with hemoglobin in the red blood cells and alters the protein's shape ever so slightly. In doing so, it reduces hemoglobin's stickiness, giving it a lower affinity for oxygen. With this reduced oxygen affinity, at any P_{O_2}, the DPG-modified hemoglobin releases more of the O_2 that it carries (**FIGURE 21-41**). Athletes who train at high altitudes find that with the additional oxygen released to their tissues, they can improve their performance by about 3%. This difference was manifested dramatically during the 1968 Olympics in Mexico City (altitude 7,500 feet) when the top five finishers in the 10,000-meter race were all year-round high-altitude residents. The benefits of high-altitude training remain after an athlete returns to sea level—increasing performance significantly. But just as humans become acclimated to high altitudes, we also become acclimated to low altitudes, and the DPG level (and the performance enhancement it can bring) is reduced about three to five weeks after returning to sea level.

TAKE-HOME MESSAGE 21·20

Humans living at high altitudes become acclimated to low-oxygen conditions over the course of three to five weeks. This acclimation includes increasing the production of diphosphoglyceric acid (DPG) in red blood cells and thereby reducing hemoglobin's affinity for oxygen, leading to release of higher levels of oxygen to muscles during exertion.

21·21

Deep-diving mammals are masters of efficient oxygen use.

How long can you hold your breath? If you're like most people, you can last just over a minute, or maybe 2 or 3 minutes at best. The world record is an amazing, but brain-choking, 11 minutes and 35 seconds held by Stéphan Mifsud of France, set in June 2009. Even this pales, though, when compared with the abilities of the Weddell seal (**FIGURE 21-42**). Living in Antarctica, these 900-pound mammals regularly make dives 200–500 meters deep in search of fish to eat. Usually staying underwater for 20 minutes, but sometimes for more than an hour, they are able to hold their breath for so long only as a consequence of numerous evolutionary adaptations.

Four critical respiratory and circulatory features make the seals' deep diving possible.

1. They have about double the volume of blood, per kilogram of body weight, that humans have. Much of it is stored in their unusually large spleen, which contracts during a dive, putting significantly more oxygen-carrying blood into circulation.

2. The myoglobin concentration in their muscles is about twice that in other mammals, serving as an additional storehouse of oxygen that can be utilized during dives.

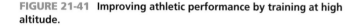

Circulatory Systems   Human Circulation   Gas Exchange   Hemoglobin and Myoglobin

ADAPTATIONS IN WEDDELL SEALS

Several circulatory adaptations enable Weddell seals to hold their breath for an hour or more as they dive for fish to eat.

FIGURE 21-42 How long can you hold your breath? The deep-diving Weddell seal can swim underwater for long periods of time without surfacing for oxygen.

3. Not only do Weddell seals store more oxygen, but during dives they also use it more sparingly, lowering their heart rate from a normal 140 beats per minute to fewer than 30 beats per minute!

4. During dives, they become more efficient with their circulation, reducing metabolism by constricting the blood vessels in most tissues and sending blood only to those parts of the body that need it most, such as the brain, eyes, and spinal cord.

Much of this "diving reflex" of Weddell seals is also seen in other mammals. We experience a slight reduction in heart rate, for example, when we begin to hold our breath. Seals are just an extreme example of how physiological traits can reveal evolutionary adaptations.

TAKE-HOME MESSAGE 21·21

Deep-diving mammals can hold their breath for an hour or more by having double the volume of blood (per kilogram of body weight) and double the muscle myoglobin concentration relative to humans, by lowering their heart rate dramatically, and by constricting the blood vessels in most tissues, sending blood only where it is needed most.

Respiratory Adaptations

Knowledge You Can Use

"Contents under pressure." Recognizing and avoiding the bends.

Q: **What do scuba divers and bottles of champagne have in common?** Under high pressure, large amounts of a gas can be dissolved in fluid. This is why champagne makers can load huge amounts of carbon dioxide into the bottle along with the champagne. It is also what happens to divers who, with tremendous water pressure on their bodies, must breathe highly pressurized air in order for oxygen to dissolve in their bloodstream.

Q: **Why are bubbles bad news for divers?** When a champagne bottle is uncorked, the pressure is suddenly released. Under low pressure, not nearly as much carbon dioxide can be held in the fluid, so it quickly bubbles out. Similarly, when a scuba diver returns too quickly to the surface, the pressure on the body is rapidly reduced, as is the capacity of the blood to hold gases. And like champagne after the cork is popped, many gases in the diver's blood—particularly nitrogen, which is the biggest component of air—quickly bubble out and can almost cause the diver to explode from within, in a condition known as "the bends." Something similar to the bends can occur if someone flies in an unpressurized plane and suddenly climbs very high, where the air pressure is lower. This was sometimes reported by pilots in World War II.

Q: **What can you conclude about avoiding the bends?** Just as the solution to opening a bottle of champagne without its bubbling over is to release the pressure very slowly by removing the cork slowly, a diver must reduce the pressure on his or her blood very slowly by rising gradually from the depths of the water. Alternatively, a diver can be placed in a chamber (called a hyperbaric chamber) to be gradually depressurized.

1 **The circulatory system is the chief route of distribution in animals.**

In animals, the circulatory system is the chief distribution system, with important functions in transport of gases, nutrients, waste products, immune system cells, and hormones, as well as maintenance of homeostasis. Circulatory systems can be open, with no clear distinction between circulating fluid and interstitial fluid, or closed, with a clear distinction. Fishes have two-chambered hearts and one circuit of blood flow; birds and mammals have four-chambered hearts and two circuits of flow, which enables them to pump blood to the body at higher pressure.

2 **The heart is at the center of the human circulatory system.**

The human heart is a muscular pump at the center of the circulatory system. It sends blood on a figure 8, two-cycle path through the body, first to the lungs and then, on its second circuit, to the tissues and organs. Blood is a salty, protein-rich mixture of cells and fluid, important in homeostasis and in the transport of respiratory gases, vitamins and minerals, nutrients, hormones, components of the immune system, and metabolic wastes. High blood pressure and cardiovascular disease impair circulatory system functioning. The lymphatic system has a supporting role in circulation: it recycles fluid from the circulatory system, moves white blood cells to help fight pathogens, and absorbs nutrients from the digestive system.

3 **The respiratory system enables gas exchange in animals.**

In very small organisms, gas exchange can occur by direct diffusion. In larger organisms, gas exchange is a two-stage process: exchange between the external environment and the organism's circulatory system, and exchange between the circulatory system and the cells involved in respiration. In aquatic vertebrates, gas exchange takes place as oxygen-carrying water passes through the gills. In terrestrial vertebrates, breathing occurs in two steps: inhalation and exhalation; O_2 diffuses across capillaries from the air to the blood, while CO_2 diffuses from blood to air.

4 **Oxygen is transported and stored while bound to hemoglobin and myoglobin.**

Red blood cells are filled with hemoglobin, which picks up oxygen in the lungs and transports it around the body, releasing it in organs and tissues for cellular respiration. Myoglobin is an oxygen-binding protein embedded in muscle cells that can release oxygen under conditions of extremely low P_{O_2}.

5 **Evolutionary adaptations maximize oxygen delivery.**

Some animals living at high altitudes cope with reduced P_{O_2} by producing hemoglobin that has a higher affinity for oxygen. Humans living at high altitudes become acclimated to the low-oxygen conditions by increasing production of diphosphoglyceric acid (DPG), thus reducing hemoglobin's affinity for oxygen. Adaptations in some deep-diving mammals include doubling of blood volume, doubling of muscle myoglobin, lowering of heart rate, and constriction of blood vessels to send blood only where it is needed most.

KEY TERMS

1. Which of the following is the name of the fluid in an insect's open circulatory system?
   a) blood
   b) hemoglobin
   c) lymph
   d) hemolymph
   e) tracheal lymph

2. How can flatworms, simple animals with a flat body shape, survive without a circulatory system?
   a) Flatworms do not have internal body fluids that need to be sectioned off and transported by vessels.
   b) Because all cells in flat-bodied animals are in direct contact with the external environment, direct diffusion is sufficient for all their respiratory needs.
   c) In flatworms, all cells are located near central body branches or near the body surface, so diffusion alone can transport important nutrients.
   d) Flatworms use the water currents in their aquatic environment to circulate the necessary nutrients throughout their body.
   e) Flatworms have multiple hearts and so can pump blood directly into tissues without needing a circulatory system.

3. Fishes have:
   a) a two-chambered heart.
   b) multiple hearts.
   c) an open circulatory system.
   d) a four-chambered heart.
   e) Both a) and c) are correct.

4. Blood pressure tends to fall with increasing distance from the heart. On the basis of this information, which of the following lists the types of blood vessel, in order, from highest blood pressure to lowest?
   a) veins, arteries, capillaries
   b) arteries, capillaries, veins
   c) veins, capillaries, arteries
   d) capillaries, veins, arteries
   e) arteries, veins, capillaries

5. The heartbeat in a vertebrate:
   a) is initiated by modified muscle tissue, the sinoatrial (SA) node, that contracts without nerve stimulation.
   b) is triggered by rhythmic stimulation from the cardiac nerve.
   c) begins at the bottom of the ventricles and moves upward through the heart.
   d) cannot be recorded by an EKG, but the neurons that control it can be.
   e) is initiated by the atrioventricular node.

6. Both red blood cells and white blood cells are derived from cells in:
   a) the heart.
   b) the liver.
   c) the spleen.
   d) the lungs.
   e) the bone marrow.

7. Which of the following components of human blood is a cell fragment?
   a) spiracle
   b) red blood cell
   c) white blood cell
   d) plasma
   e) platelet

8. How are the blood-circulation system and the lymphatic system related to each other?
   a) Blood carries nutrients to cells. The lymphatic system removes waste from the cells.
   b) Blood carries nutrients and oxygen to cells and removes their waste. The lymphatic system removes bacteria and debris from the blood.
   c) Blood carries nutrients and oxygen to cells and removes their waste. The lymphatic system takes the cellular waste to the kidneys.
   d) Blood carries oxygen to all the cells. The lymphatic system removes the carbon dioxide from the blood and carries it to the lungs.
   e) Blood carries carbon dioxide from tissues to the lungs. The lymphatic system carries oxygen from the lungs to the body tissues.

9. The polygraph, or "lie detector" test, functions by monitoring all of the following except:
   a) changes in skin conductance.
   b) changes in heart rate.
   c) changes in blood pressure.
   d) changes in chest and abdominal movement.
   e) changes in oxygen content of the blood.

10. Why do most fishes swim with their mouths open?
    a) They do this to take in any food particles suspended in the water.
    b) This is a cooling mechanism to help regulate body temperature.
    c) This allows a fish to swim faster.
    d) This helps prevent infection by mouth parasites.
    e) They do this to ventilate their gills.

11. Carbon dioxide transport differs from oxygen transport in the circulatory systems of mammals, because:
    a) CO_2 is transported mostly in the plasma, while O_2 is transported mostly in the red blood cells.
    b) CO_2 is transported mostly in the platelets, while O_2 is transported mostly in the red blood cells.
    c) CO_2 is transported mostly via the lymphatic system, while O_2 is transported mostly in the red blood cells.
    d) CO_2 is bound primarily to myoglobin, while O_2 is bound primarily to hemoglobin.
    e) CO_2 is transported mostly in the plasma, while O_2 is transported mostly in hemoglobin within the plasma.

12. Breathing in birds is more like "breathing" in fishes than in mammals, because:
    a) water and high-altitude air have similar viscosity.
    b) oxygen never runs into a dead end.
    c) both birds and fishes have gill arches.
    d) the blood vessels in bird lungs, like those in fish gills, are insulated with a fatty coating, reducing heat loss.
    e) in birds and fishes, but not mammals, the heart pumps in a two-circuit system of blood flow.

13. Which of the following are the main muscles used in breathing?
    a) back muscles and thoracic muscles
    b) intercostal muscles and pectoral muscles
    c) diaphragm and thoracic muscles
    d) diaphragm and back muscles
    e) intercostal muscles and diaphragm

14. With increasing temperatures:
    a) aquatic animals must exert more energy to obtain oxygen.
    b) aqueous environments contain more dissolved oxygen.
    c) aquatic animals require less oxygen.
    d) an aquatic animal's metabolism stabilizes.
    e) all of the above occur.

15. Under regular metabolic conditions, what percentage of oxygen is released from the blood to the tissues?
    a) 1%
    b) 75%
    c) 25%
    d) 100%
    e) 50%

16. Why is carbon monoxide (CO) so dangerous?
    a) CO prevents hemoglobin from binding to and transporting O_2 to the body tissues, resulting in oxygen starvation and death.
    b) CO prevents CO_2 from dissolving in the blood, and CO_2 builds up to toxic levels.
    c) CO modifies the structure of hemoglobin, making it more difficult for O_2 to be transported and released in the body.
    d) CO coats the inside of the alveoli, preventing diffusion of O_2 from the lungs into the blood.
    e) CO binds to myoglobin, so tissues cannot remove O_2 from the red blood cells and the tissue dies.

17. Myoglobin:
    a) is the chief O_2 carrier in mammalian circulatory systems.
    b) transports O_2 from the lungs to the body tissues.
    c) releases O_2 to the muscles when partial pressure is such that hemoglobin cannot do so.
    d) is a four-subunit protein containing iron.
    e) has a lower affinity for O_2 than hemoglobin does.

18. Which of the following has the highest binding affinity for oxygen?
    a) hemolymph
    b) human hemoglobin
    c) llama hemoglobin
    d) myoglobin
    e) All have equal binding affinity for oxygen.

19. Why does llama hemoglobin have a higher oxygen-binding affinity than human hemoglobin?
    a) Like humans, llama fetuses use a form of hemoglobin with a higher binding affinity than the mother's hemoglobin, but unlike humans, llamas continue to use this form of hemoglobin after birth.
    b) Because llamas are more active than humans, they require hemoglobin with a greater maximum oxygen saturation.
    c) Llama blood has a higher CO_2 concentration than human blood, resulting in a need for hemoglobin with a higher binding affinity.
    d) Llamas live at higher elevations than most humans and require a means to bind O_2 when oxygen is at a lower concentration in the air.
    e) Llamas lack myoglobin and need a way to ensure enough O_2 is available to their muscle tissues.

20. Diphosphoglyceric acid (DPG):
    a) causes the release of more O_2 to body tissues.
    b) makes it possible for blood to carry more CO_2.
    c) is the main reason that breathing is difficult at high altitudes.
    d) increases the binding affinity of adult hemoglobin for O_2.
    e) encourages the production of more hemoglobin.

21. Which of the following is not part of the "diving reflex" of the Weddell seal, allowing it to remain underwater for long periods of time?
    a) Weddell seals have double the muscle myoglobin concentration compared with other mammals.
    b) Weddell seals have double the blood volume (per kg of body weight) compared with other mammals.
    c) Weddell seals have an increased resting heart rate, causing more efficient oxygen usage.
    d) During dives, Weddell seals constrict blood vessels in most tissues, sending blood only to parts of the body that need it most.
    e) All of the above make deep diving possible by the Weddell seal.

SHORT-ANSWER QUESTIONS

1. Why has the evolution of multicellular organisms led to the development of circulatory systems? What characteristic distinguishes closed and open circulatory systems?

2. What is the difference between single- and double-circuit cardiovascular systems? Which would be better suited for a higher energy demand? Why?

3. Name the three main types of cells (or cell fragments) that are found in blood and describe their primary functions.

4. How is gas exchange accomplished in organisms with gills and in those with lungs?

See Appendix for answers. For additional study questions, go to www.prep-u.com.

22

Nutrition and Digestion

At rest and at play: optimizing human physiological functioning

❶ Food provides the raw materials for growth and the fuel to make it happen.

Living organisms need raw materials and fuel to function.

22•1

Why do organisms need food?

Lamb roulade with leek basil stuffing and a red wine sauce. Chili fries. Lime-marinated tofu kabobs. A big vanilla milkshake. We dress food up in an almost infinite variety of combinations. We garnish it, we heap on condiments, we daydream about it, and we even write books about it. But despite all the fuss, it really boils down to two simple biological needs: raw materials and fuel. Just as a carpenter needs wood and a car needs fuel, living organisms need raw materials and fuel to function.

Here's why: every second of every day, chemical reactions are occurring inside us. We build complex molecules. We reproduce. We respond to stimuli. And just as a car won't roll uphill without a push, most of these chemical reactions won't occur spontaneously. With a little fuel in the motor, however, the car can easily be driven up a hill. So, too, can we, and all the other animals, do things that are energetically costly. Our need for fuel is one of the two reasons why we must eat:

building a body, moving around, reproducing, and just staying alive all require energy. Food provides that energy. And the other reason is that to grow and build the myriad complex molecules required for life, we need raw materials: molecules of carbon and nitrogen and phosphorus, to name just a few. Food provides these raw materials.

What exactly happens to the food we eat? We'll examine this question in detail throughout the chapter. In **FIGURE 22-1**, though, we can see that the food we eat is physically and chemically broken down into its fundamental macromolecular components in the process of **digestion.** Regardless of the form food takes when we eat it, our body quickly breaks it down and separates it into the usable and unusable. The usable materials are carbohydrates, lipids, proteins, vitamins, minerals, and water. These six groups of **nutrients** are the substances that are used for energy, raw materials, and maintenance of the body's systems. Anything we consume that doesn't fall into

Food for Energy and Growth   Nutrients   Digestion and Absorption   Diet and Health

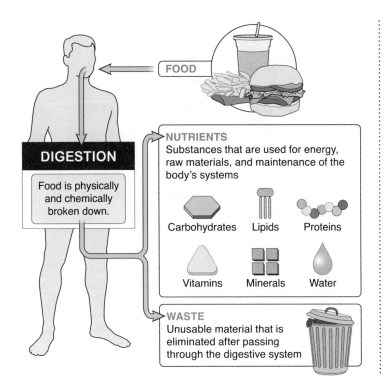

FOOD

DIGESTION
Food is physically and chemically broken down.

NUTRIENTS
Substances that are used for energy, raw materials, and maintenance of the body's systems

Carbohydrates   Lipids   Proteins

Vitamins   Minerals   Water

WASTE
Unusable material that is eliminated after passing through the digestive system

FIGURE 22-1 Made possible by food. Living organisms need raw materials and fuel to function.

one of these categories is unusable. You can't get nutrients from dirt or rocks. They just pass through the digestive system and are eliminated.

Ultimately, an organism's body weight represents the balance between the energy carried within the molecular bonds of the food it consumes and the energy that is burned in the process of living. Any surplus calories are stored, usually as fat or as glycogen (see Section 2-9), a form of carbohydrate stored primarily in muscle and liver tissue.

TAKE-HOME MESSAGE 22·1

Animals must eat for two reasons: to acquire the energy needed for all growth and activity, and to acquire the raw materials required for life.

22·2

What's on the menu? Organisms have a variety of diets.

All organisms need food. You've got two choices for how to get it. You can make it yourself, as plants and other photosynthetic organisms do through photosynthesis. Or you can eat another organism. Most animals eat the plants that make their own chemical energy, while some animals eat other animals (that eat plants). Some animals even eat animals that eat animals that eat animals (that eat plants)—but that's pretty rare (see Section 15-7). In every case, though, the choice is the same: capture solar energy to make food, or acquire that energy indirectly by consuming other organisms.

In the animal world, species fall into three groups based on their diets (**FIGURE 22-2**).

Carnivores The **carnivores** are predatory animals that consume only other animals. They include spiders and snakes; mammalian species such as wolves, seals, bats, and cats; as well as hawks, owls, and other birds of prey. Some carnivores don't actually kill their prey but instead just suck nutrient-rich fluids from them. Mosquitoes and ticks are carnivorous fluid-feeders.

Carnivory isn't just for animals. The Venus flytrap is a plant that captures and consumes insects. It does this with highly elastic, curved leaves. Water pressure inside the V-shaped leaf

Q Can plants be carnivorous?

causes it to expand into an unstable, stretched-open position that is on the verge of snapping closed. When an insect or spider lands on the leaf, it triggers an electrical signal that causes a brief, rapid change in the water pressure inside the leaf. The change in water pressure is enough to cause the leaf to snap shut, capturing the insect. The plant then releases digestive juices that break down the insect into its usable nutrients. Venus flytraps occur in places where the soil is poor and, especially, is low in nitrogen, which they are able to extract from the animal prey they capture. The green leaves and stems of Venus flytraps, however, should serve as a reminder that these plants are also photosynthetic, harnessing the energy in sunlight to build sugars.

Herbivores Food: easy to get, but hard to digest. That sums up life as a **herbivore,** an organism that consumes only plants. Because plants are plentiful in most habitats and can't run away, they are easy targets for predation. To protect themselves, however, plants tend to carry many toxic compounds that are difficult or impossible for animals to break down chemically. Nonetheless, many herbivores have developed digestive adaptations to overcome these difficulties. We'll explore a couple of them in detail in Section 22-14. Examples of herbivores include sea turtles and caterpillars. They also

CARNIVORES
Animals that consume only other animals. (Shown here: a rock python swallows a gazelle.)

HERBIVORES
Animals that consume only plants. (Shown here: a West-Indian manatee eating the plant hydrilla.)

OMNIVORES
Animals that consume both plants and animals. (Shown here: a young raccoon snacks on a plant; raccoons have a very broad diet that also includes insects, worms, fish, amphibians, and more.)

FIGURE 22-2 Animal diets: carnivores, herbivores, and omnivores.

include many species of seed–eating birds and nut–eating squirrels and a variety of large grazing mammals such as cows, horses, and deer. And just as there are fluid-feeding carnivores, there are fluid-feeding herbivores. Aphids, for example, pierce the surface of plants and suck their sugary sap.

Leaf cutter ants—which cultivate a fungus that they eat—are the only species other than humans that has been observed to have a system of agriculture.

FIGURE 22-3 **Fungus-farming ants.** Leaf cutter ants harvest leaves in order to grow fungus, which they then consume.

Omnivores Most humans, as **omnivores,** eat plants and/or animals and can digest both efficiently. We share this diet with numerous other species, including cockroaches. Omnivores come in all sizes, from bears to raccoons, from chickens to flies and wasps.

Watching farmers cultivate plants and animals for food, it might seem reasonable to assume that humans are unique in this endeavor. Agriculture is not, however, limited to humans. Leaf cutter ants chop up leaves, but rather than eating them, spit out the mulch, mold it into a honeycomb shape, and then grow fungus on the mulch (**FIGURE 22-3**). They then eat the fungus at their leisure. These ants are the only species that scientists know of other than humans with a system of agriculture (and they've been doing it for significantly longer than humans have).

Q Humans grow and tend to plants and animals with the sole purpose of eating them. Are there any other species with agriculture?

TAKE-HOME MESSAGE 22·2

All animals require food. Plants and other photosynthetic organisms produce food through photosynthesis, and animals have one of three types of diet. Carnivores consume only other animals. Herbivores consume only plants. And omnivores, including most humans, consume both plants and animals.

Food for Energy and Growth   Nutrients   Digestion and Absorption   Diet and Health

Calories count: organisms need sufficient energy.

Have you ever gone a whole day without eating? Or have you ever spent a few weeks trying to reduce your caloric intake? Living in a state of hunger can be torturous. In the early 1990s, eight human "guinea pigs" learned this the hard way. Living in the Biosphere 2 dome—a self-contained, 3.2-acre world filled with plants and animals that was designed to explore sustainable living with minimal environmental impact—they took part in an experiment on the effects of a low-calorie diet, among other things. The findings were dramatic but not surprising: all the participants lost weight, but they also became very unhappy. They argued constantly, got into ugly food spats, and frequently squabbled over dinner portions. After leaving what they dubbed "the hunger dome," one of the eight said, "If we ever all start talking to each other, that would be a major accomplishment" (FIGURE 22-4). In an earlier study, people were kept hungry for six months. Over time, study participants filled increasing hours with food fantasies. Recipes even displaced sex as the favorite topic of discussion. Put simply, humans (and all other living organisms) need a steady and sufficient flow of energy to function well.

Insufficient energy input for organisms always leads to the same outcome: death. As we saw in Section 8-1, when 27-year-old Bobby Sands went on a hunger strike in 1981, he gradually deteriorated and ultimately died after 66 days without food. In 2001, two prisoners in Turkey, Cafer Tayyar

Bektas and Huseyin Kayaci, also went on a hunger strike to protest the prison conditions. Because they started fasting at much higher initial body weights, they survived for much longer than Bobby Sands. The end result was the same, though. After 200 and 148 days respectively, both men died.

So what do we actually need to survive? And why isn't it the same for everyone? In this section, we examine the body's energy needs, and then the various nutrients necessary for growth and maintenance.

We measure the energetic value of food in very small amounts of energy called **calories,** where a single calorie is the energy required to raise the temperature of 1 gram of water by 1° C. However, the term can be a bit confusing: in discussing human consumption, the term "calorie" actually refers to a **kilocalorie (kcal)**, which is 1,000 calories. So when the label on a package of cookies says that a cookie provides "100 calories," the cookie actually provides 100 *kilocalories* or 100,000 *calories.*

As we saw from the hunger strikers, there is tremendous variation in the amount of stored energy an individual carries. Similarly, there is much variation in how many calories an individual needs each day. To determine basic energy needs, we first factor out any variation due to differences in activity levels—searching for food, finding a mate, defending a territory—and instead assess the minimal energetic needs of an individual who is doing nothing more than the equivalent of sitting on a couch all day. This is called the **basal metabolic rate,** or **BMR,** and refers to the amount of energy expended at rest, with no food in the digestive tract, in a neutral-temperature environment. For humans, the BMR can be roughly approximated as 1 calorie per hour per gram of body weight, or about 1,400 kcal/day for a woman (weighing 120 pounds) and about 1,700 kcal/day for a man (weighing 160 pounds). The difference is mostly a function of the difference in body size; the male has more cells to power. The human BMR is approximately the energy needed to keep a 75-watt light bulb burning for 24 hours or to drive a small car one mile.

Basal metabolic rate allows easy comparisons across species because it is so clearly defined. From a biological perspective, though, it is almost meaningless. To realistically evaluate organisms' energy needs, we must have a sense of how active they are. Someone moving around and involved in physical exertion will require more energy than someone sitting at a desk all day, and a very large person will require more than a small person (FIGURE 22-5). In actuality, individuals need about

"If we ever all start talking to each other, that would be a major accomplishment."

– One of the eight participants of Biosphere 2

FIGURE 22-4 Hungry Biosphere 2 crew. Living on a low-calorie diet led to weight loss and a cranky disposition for Biosphere 2 participants.

COMPONENTS OF ENERGY EXPENDITURE

Average kcal/day to cover the minimal energetic needs of an organism at rest

Female — 1,400
Male — 1,700

BASAL METABOLIC RATE (BMR)
The minimal energy expenditure of an organism at rest.

Average kcal/day to cover all of the energetic needs of an organism (including all activity)

Female — 1,400
Male — 1,700

Individuals generally need about 50% to 100% more kilocalories per day than their BMR.

ACTUAL DAILY ENERGY EXPENDITURE
The basal metabolic rate *plus* the energy required for all activity.

FIGURE 22-5 How many calories do you need? Energy expenditure varies depending on body size and activity level.

50% to 100% more kilocalories per day than their BMR. A 120-pound woman requires 1,800–2,400 kcal/day, and a 160-pound man requires about 2,400–3,200 kcal/day.

Basal metabolic rates vary tremendously among different animal species. For the tiny shrew, for instance, BMR is about 35 times higher than for a human (**FIGURE 22-6**). The shrew's heart beats more than 500 times per minute *at rest!*

With the measurement of an animal's BMR, we can begin to estimate the animal's caloric needs. Let's estimate what a shrew needs to eat each day. If it weighs 5 grams and has a BMR of 35 calories per hour per gram, we can calculate as follows:

BMR varies tremendously among different animal species. The tiny shrew has a BMR about 35 times higher than that of a human, relative to weight.

FIGURE 22-6 Live fast. This tiny shrew must meet the high calorie demands of its fast-beating heart.

body weight	×	energy needed each hour	×	hours per day	=	animal's caloric needs
5 grams	×	35 cal/gram/hr	×	24 hr/day	=	4,200 cal/day

Thus, the shrew would need 4.2 kcal/day if it were at rest. But if it needed another 4 kcal/day for its normal activities, it would have to eat about 8 kcal/day. As we will see below, a pure source of carbohydrate or protein carries about 4 kcal/gram. Thus, every day, the shrew must find and consume at least 2 grams of food. This is no small challenge when you only weigh 5 grams. The task is equivalent to a 200-pound man finding and eating 80 pounds of food every day.

The shrew is not the only species with extreme caloric needs. Animals that fast or hibernate for long periods of time must prepare for the fast by consuming many kilocalories. Male elephant seals, for example, eat little or nothing during their 100-day breeding season, instead spending their time battling with other males for dominance and mating with females. During these 100 days, a large male who begins the season at 6,600 pounds (3,000 kg) may lose one-third of his body weight. Consequently, in the months leading up to the breeding season, the male seals' caloric requirements are dramatically higher than at other times.

TAKE-HOME MESSAGE 22·3

To function well, living organisms need sufficient energy, measured in kilocalories. The minimal energy needed by an individual not engaged in any activity is called its basal metabolic rate, or BMR.

Food for Energy and Growth   Nutrients   Digestion and Absorption   Diet and Health

❷ Nutrients are grouped into six categories.

A jaguar takes a drink at a watering hole in Belize.

22•4

Water is an essential nutrient.

We saw that a human could live 60 days or more without consuming food. The prognosis is much worse in the absence of water, perhaps the single most important component of a balanced diet. In the early 1900s, an Italian man sentenced to death reportedly volunteered to determine how long he could live without food or water. The fatal "experiment" lasted only 17 days before he died.

Water, which is considered an essential nutrient, constitutes about 60-65% of the body weight in most mammals. This water plays important roles in both the intracellular fluid and the extracellular fluids, including blood, in humans and other animals (**FIGURE 22-7**). Water in body fluids serves a variety of critical purposes, all of which can be impaired when the animal becomes dehydrated.

- Water transports nutrients and waste materials throughout the body.

- It takes part in chemical reactions.

- It serves as a solvent for many vitamins and minerals, amino acids, and sugars.

- It lubricates many joints, the spinal cord, and the eyes.

- It helps regulate body temperature.

A person expending about 2,000 kcal/day needs about 2–3 liters of water each day. This can come directly from

💡 *Water is an essential nutrient and plays important roles in both the intracellular fluid and the extracellular fluids, including blood.*

FIGURE 22-7 Water is an essential component of the diet.

drinking water, but there are many other sources of water in our diet, including milk, which is about 90% water, juices, food, and water released as a by-product of many chemical reactions. It is essential that water intake offset the water lost in urine, feces, respiration, and sweating. It is important to remember, too, as we saw in the Chapter 3 StreetBio, that drinking too much water too quickly can also be dangerous. Water intoxication results from the consumption of too much water—which sometimes happens to marathon runners during a race. When coupled with the loss of salt through sweating, over-consumption of water can lead to severe sodium imbalance. This imbalance causes dizziness, nausea, confusion, and swelling of the extremities. And in serious cases, it can lead to swelling of the brain, which can cause death.

Q If water is so important, why are there some desert animals that never need to drink?

Water usage varies among some animal species. Some desert mammals, the kangaroo rat, for example, have evolved tremendous water efficiency, and some do not need to drink any water at all. Rather, they get all the water they need from their food and metabolic processes. Among the marine birds and reptiles, most are able to drink salt water. They can do this with the aid of salt glands that remove and excrete the excess salt they consume.

TAKE-HOME MESSAGE 22·4

Water is probably the single most important component of the diet. It constitutes 60-65% of the body weight of most mammals, transports nutrients and waste materials throughout the body, takes part in metabolic reactions, serves as a solvent, lubricates many body parts, and helps regulate body temperature.

22·5

Proteins in food are broken down to build proteins in the body.

When you are on the verge of starvation, any type of food can save you. So from that perspective, it's true that calories are all that matter. But for optimum health, organisms must consume many types of nutrients. In this section and the next, we investigate the chief nutritional features of the three types of calories: proteins, carbohydrates, and fats. We begin by investigating protein, a vital component of the diet and essential structural material in the body.

Protein: Raw Material for Growth

What are proteins, and what is their role in the diet? Protein in our diet is principally a building material. As described in detail in Sections 2-15 through 2-18, protein molecules are made of long chains of smaller molecules—amino acids—linked together, like beads on a string. Once eaten, protein molecules are broken down into the individual amino acids, much like removing the beads from the string one at a time. It's only in the form of individual amino acids that proteins can be absorbed by the digestive system. Our bodies can then reorder the beads, making proteins that are different from those we ate.

The process of protein digestion and protein rebuilding does seem a bit inefficient: we consume entire, intact proteins such as muscle cells or hemoglobin molecules, from chickens or fishes or other animals, which we then break down and may ultimately use to construct almost exactly the same types of protein molecules. Nonetheless, animal digestive systems are able to absorb only the simpler building blocks of proteins, not entire proteins themselves, so we must first break down all the proteins we eat and later reassemble new ones.

Besides serving as building materials, proteins function as enzymes, catalyzing reactions throughout the body (see Section 2-18). They can also be broken down to release energy or to be stored as fat. Our bodies can use protein as fuel because we have a variety of methods of converting one type of chemical to another to release or store energy (see Section 4-17). The breakdown of proteins for energy generates 4 kilocalories per gram. Protein breakdown generally happens only when we are consuming too few (or too many) calories to sustain necessary growth and activities. The reverse reaction—building proteins from fat or carbohydrates—however, cannot be done. All amino acids have elements—particularly nitrogen—that are not found in any sugars or fats that we consume. Only the proteins in our diet contain nitrogen. Thus, all of the proteins we build contain parts of proteins that we have consumed, and if a protein is broken down for energy, the nitrogen it carries is excreted in our urine.

There is a variety of sources of dietary protein, from both plants and animals (**FIGURE 22-8**). Animal sources include egg whites, shrimp, tuna, lobster, chicken, turkey, and all meat products. Plant sources of protein include grains, vegetables, nuts, seeds, and legumes, such as beans.

Try this. Put one can of Coke and one can of Diet Coke somewhere that they will get hot, and leave them for a few days. Then taste them. The Diet Coke will lose its flavor and taste

Food for Energy and Growth | Nutrients | Digestion and Absorption | Diet and Health

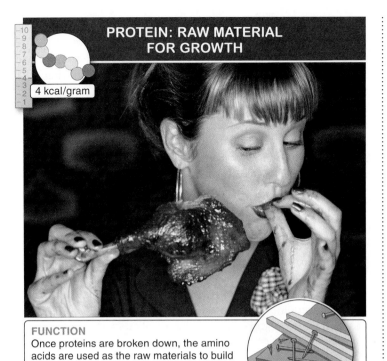

PROTEIN: RAW MATERIAL FOR GROWTH

4 kcal/gram

FUNCTION
Once proteins are broken down, the amino acids are used as the raw materials to build new complex proteins, such as hemoglobin and muscle.

SOURCE
• Animals: egg whites, shrimp, tuna, poultry, and meat
• Plants: grains and vegetables, such as beans

STORAGE
• Amino acids are usually stored for less than half a day before being reassembled into proteins throughout the body
• Can be converted to fat and stored in fat cells

FIGURE 22-8 **Versatile proteins.** Besides serving as building materials, proteins can be broken down to release energy or stored as fat.

Q Why does Diet Coke (but not regular Coke) taste bitter if you leave it in the sun for a few days?

bitter, even if you cool it down, while the Coke will taste fine. What's going on? Diet Coke, but not regular Coke, is sweetened with aspartame (NutraSweet is the brand name). Aspartame is made by linking together two amino acids, aspartic acid and phenylalanine—each of which tastes bitter by itself. When the two are joined as aspartame, however, the taste is very sweet. The reaction by which aspartic acid and phenylalanine are linked together can be reversed by heat. So if you leave a can of Diet Coke in a hot area, the aspartame decomposes to the bitter amino acids. They're not harmful, but they aren't very tasty either.

Are all proteins the same, or do they vary in important ways? All proteins are not created equal. Animals, including humans, require 20 different amino acids to make proteins. Most animals, however, can produce only about half of these amino acids

themselves. In the case of humans, we can't make 8 of the 20 amino acids. Because these 8 cannot be produced by our bodies, we must get them from the food we eat. For that reason, the amino acids we must consume in food are called the **essential amino acids,** and the remaining 12 are called **non-essential amino acids.**

Protein-containing animal products vary in their amino acid composition. All eight of the essential amino acids are found in milk, eggs, meat, poultry, cheese, and fish; these animal products have "complete" proteins (**FIGURE 22-9**). On the other hand, most proteins that we get from eating plants are not complete. Corn proteins, for example, have only six of the essential amino acids, as do beans (although they don't have the same six). In

COMPLETE PROTEINS
Proteins that contain all eight essential amino acids

INCOMPLETE PROTEINS
Proteins that do not contain all eight essential amino acids

 With the exception of soybeans, no single plant food has all eight essential amino acids.

FIGURE 22-9 **Animal versus plant proteins.** Animal proteins contain all eight of the essential amino acids. Plant foods contain varying amounts and types of essential amino acids.

fact, with the exception of soybeans, no single plant food has all eight. A healthy diet is one containing not just a sufficient *amount of protein* but a sufficient amount of each of the eight essential amino acids that we need to make proteins. Consequently, we must know more about the proteins we eat than the simple description on the food label of how many grams of protein the food contains.

Q Why is it beneficial for vegetarians to eat beans and corn over the course of the same day?

How and where do we store proteins? Proteins and the amino acid pool they generate on digestion cannot be stored very long in our bodies, usually less than a day. By that point, they are broken down and the nitrogen is excreted. Because our bodies are making proteins constantly, it is important to take in all of the essential amino acids over the course of each day.

The recommended daily intake of protein is approximately 0.8 grams per kilogram of body weight. This translates to about 45 grams of protein for a 120-pound woman (and about 25 additional grams per day for pregnant or lactating women) and 60 grams for a 160-pound man. Exercising athletes can require double or even triple this amount, but it is important to remember that it is the exercise that generates the additional need. Protein on its own does nothing to stimulate muscle growth; it simply serves as the source for the raw materials.

TAKE-HOME MESSAGE 22·5

Animals consume three different types of macromolecules for calories: proteins, carbohydrates, and fats. Proteins provide raw materials for growth and for the production of enzymes. Food sources of protein vary in amino acid composition. Humans require 20 amino acids, and 8 of these, called essential amino acids, can only be supplied by the diet.

22·6

Carbohydrates and lipids provide bodies with energy and more.

Reading these words requires carbohydrates in your body, obtained from your diet, to fuel your brain—and your muscles as well, as they help you sit up and hold your book. Food fat, too, a subset of the group of macromolecular nutrients called lipids (see Sections 2-12–2-14), provides energy for your body's functioning and gives food delicious flavor (while contributing to weight gain and heart disease if consumed in too large a quantity). In this section, we evaluate the macromolecules carbohydrates and lipids. These two crucial nutrients supply nearly all the energy that fuels your daily activities.

Carbohydrates: Fuel for Living Machines

What are carbohydrates, and what is their role in the diet? Carbohydrates are the primary fuel on which animal bodies run. In humans, nearly all of the energy used by our brain every day comes from the simple carbohydrate glucose. As we saw in Chapter 2, all carbohydrates are made primarily from carbon, hydrogen, and oxygen. When the bonds between these atoms are broken, energy is released that can be captured by the body and used to fuel movement, growth, and all the other cellular activities that require energy.

We get the majority of our dietary carbohydrates from fruits, vegetables, and grains (**FIGURE 22-10**). And, as with proteins, the breakdown of carbohydrates for energy generates 4 kilocalories per gram.

Are all carbohydrates the same, or do they vary in important ways? Although, structurally, all carbohydrates are variations on a simple theme—molecules formed from carbon, hydrogen, and oxygen in the approximate proportions of CH_2O (see Figure 2-20)—they vary dramatically in their complexity. This variation has implications for their nutritional effects (**FIGURE 22-11**). From a dietary perspective, the most important distinctions are among simple sugars (monosaccharides), digestible complex sugars, and fiber (indigestible complex sugars).

Simple sugars: These include glucose and fructose. They are linear or ring structures with three to seven carbon atoms. Animals can break them down directly through the steps of glycolysis (see Section 4-13), rapidly releasing the stored energy from the bonds of the sugar.

Digestible complex sugars: Multiple simple sugars can bond together to form complex but digestible molecules. Some complex sugars, such as sucrose (table sugar), are just two simple sugars joined together. Others, such as starch and glycogen, are large molecules that may consist of

Food for Energy and Growth | Nutrients | Digestion and Absorption | Diet and Health

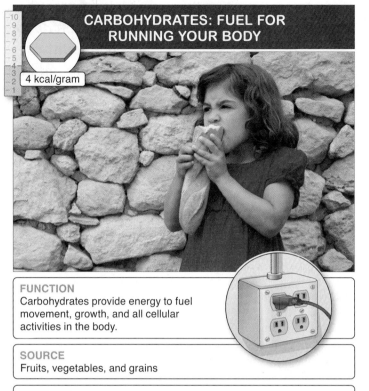

CARBOHYDRATES: FUEL FOR RUNNING YOUR BODY

10
9
8
7
6
5
4
3
2
1

4 kcal/gram

FUNCTION
Carbohydrates provide energy to fuel movement, growth, and all cellular activities in the body.

SOURCE
Fruits, vegetables, and grains

STORAGE
• Carbohydrates are stored in the liver and muscle cells as glycogen for about a day before being broken down to provide energy
• Can be converted to fat and stored in fat cells

FIGURE 22-10 Carbohydrate is the primary fuel on which animal bodies run.

hundreds or thousands of glucose molecules connected in dense branching patterns. In order for an animal to have access to the energy stored within the bonds of the individual simple sugars, it must first break the bonds that link those sugars together. As these bonds are broken, simple sugars become available for the energy–releasing reactions of glycolysis.

Fiber: This is a complex carbohydrate, such as cellulose, that forms the structural parts of plants. Fiber differs from starch and other digestible complex sugars by having a different bond connecting the simple sugars together. This bond cannot be broken by any human digestive enzyme, making fiber indigestible. As we'll see later in this chapter, although fiber isn't broken down for energy or other molecules used by the body, it still plays an important role in digestion and is necessary in the diet to maintain health.

How and where do we store carbohydrates? Carbohydrates in our body are stored mostly as glycogen in liver and muscle cells. At any given time, we can store only about one day's worth of energy. After we start exercising, or when our bodies need energy for an activity, a signal is sent causing the release of enzymes that break the bonds holding together the highly branched glycogen. This glycogen breakdown produces a flood of glucose into the bloodstream and at muscles where the energy is needed.

Large amounts of water are bound to stored glycogen: 4 pounds of water for every pound of glycogen. Consequently, as glycogen in your liver and muscles is used, the water bound to it is released from the tissue and lost as urine. This is why, as stores of glycogen are depleted in the initial stages of a diet, there is a dramatic initial weight loss from the loss of water that was bound to the glycogen. As your body starts utilizing stored fat, the rate of weight loss slows considerably.

TYPES OF CARBOHYDRATES

SIMPLE SUGARS
• Glucose, fructose
• Glycolysis reactions release energy rapidly

DIGESTIBLE COMPLEX SUGARS
• Simple sugars bonded together, such as sucrose (table sugar) or starch
• Bonds between simple sugars must be broken before the energy-releasing reactions of glycolysis occur

FIBER
• Complex carbohydrate that forms structural parts of plants
• Indigestible in humans, but has a significant role in digestion

FIGURE 22-11 Carbohydrate complexity. Some carbohydrates are readily broken down for fuel, but fiber passes through the human body undigested.

Fats: Long-Term Energy Storage Experts

What are fats, and what is their role in the diet? Dietary fats, described in detail in Chapter 2, function primarily as a dense source of energy that can be efficiently stored in the body (FIGURE 22-12). The average person has about four or five weeks' worth of stored energy in the form of fat. Compared with carbohydrates or proteins, a given amount of fat contains more than twice as much stored energy: 1 gram of fat produces 9 kilocalories. Another feature that makes fats particularly efficient as energy-storage molecules is the fact that, because they are hydrophobic, fats are stored without binding to water.

Because they also are poor conductors of heat, fats stored in a layer just beneath the skin help to keep the body warm. Penguins and walruses, for example, can maintain relatively high body temperatures despite living in very cold habitats, because of their thick layer of insulating fat.

Here's a perplexing fact: although the total amount of energy in a gram of fat is greater than that found in carbohydrates or proteins, fat isn't the optimum nutrient for most situations.

FATS: LONG-TERM ENERGY STORAGE

9 kcal/gram

FUNCTION
Fats provide a dense source of energy that can be efficiently stored in the body and aid in keeping the body warm.

SOURCE
Butter, cheese, oils, eggs, and meat

STORAGE
Fats are stored in fat cells throughout the body.

FIGURE 22-12 Energy-rich fats. At 9 kilocalories per gram, fats are rich in stored energy.

When it comes to exercise, for example, muscle cells need quick access to energy. The problem is that, in muscles, fat burns very slowly for energy. Remember from Chapter 4 that the universal source of chemical energy in the body is ATP. This means that the energy in fat or carbohydrate or protein must be captured as ATP before it is of use to muscle cells. It turns out to be much easier for the body to break down muscle glycogen and blood glucose to make ATP than to break down fat. In fact, the rate of ATP synthesis from carbohydrates is about double the rate from fats.

Q If fats contain more than double the amount of energy found in the same amount of carbohydrates or proteins, why aren't fats a better fuel to consume before exercising?

Are all fats the same nutritionally, or do they vary in important ways? With proteins, we saw that there were essential and non-essential amino acids. Similarly, with dietary fats, there are essential and non-essential fatty acids. Humans are able to produce nearly all necessary lipids. The others, the essential fatty acids—including linoleic acid, a type of fatty acids called omega-6 fatty acids—must be consumed. Linoleic acid is essential as a building block for signaling molecules, such as some hormones; a deficiency can lead to infertility and difficulty lactating. Another essential fatty acid, important in a variety of metabolic processes, is linolenic acid, a type of fatty acids called omega-3 fatty acids. Linoleic acid is essential as a building block for signaling molecules, such as some hormones; a deficiency can lead to infertility and difficulty lactating. The other essential fatty acid, important in a variety of metabolic processes, is linolenic acid. Linolenic acid is used by the body to make fatty acids that are essential for normal growth and development, especially in the eyes and brain.

Another important distinction among dietary fats is between saturated and unsaturated fats (FIGURE 22-13). In our diet, fats usually come in the form of fatty acids, long chains of carbon atoms with hydrogens attached. If each carbon within the chain is bonded to two hydrogen atoms, the molecule carries the maximum number of hydrogen atoms and is said to be saturated. (For a refresher, see Figure 2-31.) Conversely, if some of the carbons are bound to only a single hydrogen, the fatty acid is unsaturated.

When saturated, fatty acids are very straight and the fat molecules can be packed together tightly. This causes saturated fats to be solid at room temperature, like butter. When unsaturated, the fatty acids have kinks in the hydrocarbon tail and cannot be packed together as tightly. Consequently, unsaturated fats do not solidify so easily and tend to be liquid at room temperature, like vegetable oil. Because unsaturated fatty acids can accept one or more hydrogen atoms, they are a bit less stable and more reactive—that is, they will take part in a greater variety of chemical reactions—than saturated fatty acids, making them less likely to be stored as body fat.

SATURATED FATS
- Fatty acids have straight tails and can be packed together tightly
- Tend to be solid at room temperature
- More likely to be stored as fat in the body

UNSATURATED FATS
- Fatty acids have kinked tails and cannot be packed together tightly
- Tend to be liquid at room temperature
- Less likely to be stored as fat in the body

FIGURE 22-13 Saturated and unsaturated fats compared.

Trans fats have been in the news because of their tendency when consumed to raise levels of low-density lipoprotein cholesterol, increasing the risk of coronary heart disease. Trans fat is made when hydrogen is added to vegetable oil—a process called hydrogenation (see Section 2-13 for a review of trans fat chemistry.) Trans fat often can be found in some of the same foods as saturated fat, such as vegetable shortenings, crackers, candies, cookies, snack foods, fried foods, baked goods, and other foods made with partially hydrogenated vegetable oils. The American Heart Association recommends that these fats be minimized in the diet.

How and where do we store fats? If a human consumes more calories than he or she burns, most of the excess (regardless of whether these calories were consumed as carbohydrate, fat, or protein) gets converted to fat and stored in fat cells distributed throughout the body. A pound of body fat holds 3,600 kilocalories worth of energy. It is like a savings account for an uncertain future.

Given that our bodies can convert excess calories into body fat, regardless of whether the calories were initially ingested as carbohydrates or proteins, why is it still a more effective weight-management strategy to minimize dietary fat intake? The answer rests in the number of chemical conversions carbohydrates and proteins must undergo to become body fat. In the case of carbohydrates, complex sugars must first be broken down into simple sugars—a process that requires energy. Then the simple

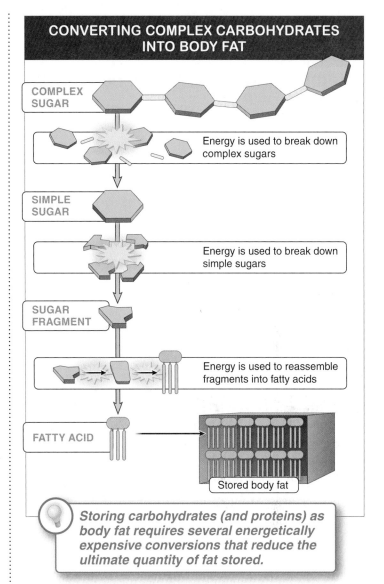

CONVERTING COMPLEX CARBOHYDRATES INTO BODY FAT

COMPLEX SUGAR

Energy is used to break down complex sugars

SIMPLE SUGAR

Energy is used to break down simple sugars

SUGAR FRAGMENT

Energy is used to reassemble fragments into fatty acids

FATTY ACID

Stored body fat

💡 *Storing carbohydrates (and proteins) as body fat requires several energetically expensive conversions that reduce the ultimate quantity of fat stored.*

FIGURE 22-14 Inefficient conversion to body fat. By the time carbohydrates can be stored as body fat, much of the original energy has been lost in fueling the conversion.

sugars must be broken down and the fragments reassembled as fatty acids—another process that requires energy. By the time those fatty acids can be stored as body fat, much of the original energy stored in the carbohydrates has been lost in fueling all the chemical conversions (**FIGURE 22-14**). And for someone trying to minimize body fat, that's good news. Storing protein as body fat also requires several energetically expensive conversions that reduce the ultimate quantity of fat stored.

TAKE-HOME MESSAGE 22·6

Carbohydrates are the primary fuel on which animal bodies run. Dietary fats function primarily as a dense source of energy that can be efficiently stored in the body.

Vitamins and minerals are necessary for good health.

> *Vitamins can double your health!*
>
> —Dr. Atkins, on *The Larry King Show* (making perhaps the most nonsensical nutritional claim ever)

It would be nice if we could take a pill that would make us more healthy or fit. Vitamins are not such a miracle pill. They're a bit like security guards at a museum: above a certain number, they don't make the museum any better, but in their absence, the museum is likely to become a whole lot worse. And while vitamin supplements are not a health panacea, vitamins and minerals do have an important role in nutrition.

Vitamins are organic compounds that are essential nutrients required by the body in small amounts for normal growth and health. **Minerals** are the chemical elements, other than those commonly found in organic molecules—carbon, hydrogen, oxygen, and nitrogen—some of which are required in the diet in small amounts. There are three features common to all vitamins and minerals.

1. They don't yield any usable energy. Rather, they serve as collaborators with enzymes to enable the processing of the proteins, carbohydrates, and fats we eat, and they catalyze a wide range of other chemical reactions around the body.

2. They need to be consumed in much smaller amounts than proteins, carbohydrates, and fats in our diet. This is because they tend to serve as reaction catalysts and so can be recycled and used again and again.

3. If we have a healthful diet, we tend to consume sufficient quantities of vitamins and minerals in our food.

Although their biological roles are frequently similar, vitamins and minerals have a fundamental chemical difference. Vitamins are organic molecules, meaning they contain carbon, whereas minerals are inorganic nutrients. Because vitamins are organic, they are more fragile, easily destroyed by heat and other chemical or physical extremes. Minerals, on the other hand, are elements, so they can't be broken down further or lose their chemical identity. They stay in your body until they are excreted. In fact, the only way they can be lost is if they are leached away—such as from food into the water as the food is cooked and the water is then thrown away. Seventeen minerals have been identified that are essential to the human diet. They are described in **FIGURE 22-15**.

Thirteen vitamins essential to humans, also described in Figure 22-15, have been discovered. They fall into two groups based on whether they are soluble in fat or water. The water-soluble vitamins include eight vitamins that are part of the vitamin B complex, plus vitamin C. There is some variation among species in the ability to manufacture (rather than needing to ingest) vitamins. Cats and dogs, for instance, do not need to consume vitamin C.

There are four fat-soluble vitamins: A, D, E, and K. Because they are stored in fatty tissue and the liver until they are needed, they don't need to be consumed as regularly as water-soluble vitamins. Also, because excess water-soluble vitamins can be removed by the kidney and excreted in urine, they tend to be less likely to reach toxic levels than fat-soluble vitamins.

Currently, more than half of the U.S. population takes regular vitamin supplements (**FIGURE 22-16**). Should so many people be taking these supplements? It is difficult to give a single answer to this question. Nonetheless, it is well established that in the United States, few adults suffer from any vitamin and mineral deficiency diseases. This is because nearly all adults get all of the nutrients they need from the food they eat. For this reason, nutritionists believe that high doses of vitamins and minerals are not therapeutic, and they suggest that most people do not need to take regular supplements.

Usually, taking vitamin supplements is a costly but harmless behavior. The consumption of increasing amounts of vitamins often just leads to a plateau of maximum benefit, after which greater consumption has no additional benefits. Occasionally, however, taking vitamin and mineral supplements is both costly and harmful: in many cases, above a certain point, additional consumption of fat-soluble vitamins can lead to toxicity and cause serious health problems. Excessive consumption of vitamin A, for example, can lead to hair loss in men, while over-consumption of vitamin D can lead to growth retardation. Liver damage, too, is a common result of excessive vitamin and mineral consumption. Moreover, research has definitively discredited claims that vitamin E supplementation slows or prevents aging or improves physical performance, and no supplement has been demonstrated to "relieve stress"—despite the extravagant claims of marketers.

ESSENTIAL VITAMINS AND MINERALS IN THE HUMAN DIET

VITAMIN	SOURCE	MAJOR FUNCTION
Water-soluble		
B_1 (thiamin)	Liver, legumes, whole grains	Coenzyme in cellular respiration
B_2 (riboflavin)	Dairy foods, meat, eggs, green leafy vegetables	Coenzyme in FAD
B_6 (pyridoxine)	Liver, whole grains, dairy foods	Coenzyme in amino acid metabolism
B_{12} (cobalamin)	Liver, meat, dairy foods, eggs	Formation of nucleic acids, proteins, and red blood cells
Biotin	Liver, yeast, bacteria in gut	Found in coenzymes
C (ascorbic acid)	Citrus fruits, tomatoes, potatoes	Formation of connective tissues; antioxidant
Folic acid	Vegetables, eggs, liver, whole grains	Coenzyme in formation of heme and nucleotides
Niacin	Meat, fowl, liver, yeast	Coenzyme in NAD and NADP
Pantothenic acid	Liver, eggs, yeast	Found in acetyl CoA
Fat-soluble		
A (retinol)	Fruits, vegetables, liver, dairy foods	Found in visual pigments
D (cholecalciferol)	Fortified milk, fish oils, sunshine	Absorption of calcium and phosphate
E (tocopherol)	Meat, dairy foods, whole grains	Muscle maintenance; antioxidant
K (menadione)	Intestinal bacteria, liver	Blood clotting

MINERAL	SOURCE	MAJOR FUNCTION
Calcium (Ca)	Dairy foods, eggs, green leafy vegetables, whole grains	Found in bones and teeth; blood clotting; muscle action
Chlorine (Cl)	Table salt (NaCl), meat, eggs, vegetables, dairy foods	Water balance; principal negative ion in extracellular fluid
Chromium (Cr)	Meat, dairy foods, whole grains, legumes, yeast	Glucose metabolism
Cobalt (Co)	Meat, tap water	Found in vitamin B_{12}; formation of red blood cells
Copper (Cu)	Liver, meat, fish, shellfish, legumes, whole grains, nuts	Found in enzymes and electron carriers; hemoglobin production
Fluorine (F)	Most water supplies	Found in teeth; helps prevent tooth decay
Iodine (I)	Fish, shellfish, iodized salt	Found in thyroid hormones
Iron (Fe)	Liver, meat, green vegetables, eggs, whole grains, legumes	Found in many enzymes, hemoglobin, and myoglobin
Magnesium (Mg)	Green vegetables, meat, whole grains, nuts, milk, legumes	Required by many enzymes; found in bones and teeth
Manganese (Mn)	Organ meats, whole grains, legumes, nuts, tea, coffee	Activates many enzymes
Molybdenum (Mo)	Organ meats, dairy foods, whole grains, green vegetables	Found in some enzymes
Phosphorus (P)	Dairy foods, eggs, meat, whole grains, legumes, nuts	Found in nucleic acids, ATP, and phospholipids
Potassium (K)	Meat, whole grains, fruits, vegetables	Nerve and muscle action; principal positive ion in cells
Selenium (Se)	Meat, seafood, whole grains, eggs, milk, garlic	Fat metabolism
Sodium (Na)	Table salt, dairy foods, meat, eggs	Nerve and muscle action; water balance
Sulfur (S)	Meat, eggs, dairy foods, nuts, legumes	Found in proteins and coenzymes; detoxification
Zinc (Zn)	Liver, fish, shellfish, and many other foods	Found in some enzymes and some transcription factors

FIGURE 22-15 Overview of essential vitamins and minerals.

? *More than half of the U.S. population takes regular vitamin supplements. Should so many people be taking these supplements?*

FIGURE 22-16 Is supplementation necessary? Shopping the vitamin aisle for health.

So, we can conclude that most people in the United States have no need to take vitamin and mineral supplements. Under special circumstances, however, supplementation is necessary.

- Women who lose unusually large amounts of blood during menstruation may need iron.

- Post-menopausal women and those allergic to milk may not get enough calcium in their diet to prevent bone degeneration.

- Pregnant and breast-feeding women may need additional vitamins and minerals to support a developing fetus or rapidly growing infant.

- Pregnant women may, in particular, need additional folate, which helps prevent neural tube defects.

Green leafy vegetables are a good source of folate.

- People on extremely low-calorie diets may need a vitamin and mineral supplement.

- People with limited consumption of milk or sun exposure may need additional vitamin D. Because of insufficient levels of ultraviolet energy from the sun at latitudes above 42 (covering a line approximately from the northern border of California across to Boston), individuals in these regions are unable to produce sufficient vitamin D from sun exposure alone.

- People with absorption problems (such as when taking antibiotics or with an infection or following surgery) may need vitamin and mineral supplementation.

Individuals who do not fall into these groups, however, generally get all of the essential vitamins and minerals simply by eating a varied diet, rich in nutritious foods.

TAKE-HOME MESSAGE 22·7

Vitamins and minerals are organic and inorganic molecules in the diet. They are used in the production and action of enzymes and other molecules involved in the processing of food and other biochemical reactions. While vitamins and minerals are essential in small amounts, most people in the United States do not benefit from taking them as supplements.

How do organisms "know" what to eat?

We take it for granted, but our bodies seem to "know" that we need food, and they seem to be able to sense whether we're consuming nutritionally valuable substances. Is this really true? To find out, researchers conducted a clever study. With some volunteer participants, they secretly gave one group of people sugar cookies while a second group got cookies that looked the same and tasted pretty good but were made with the low-calorie sugar substitute, NutraSweet. The researchers then noted how many cookies were eaten. Surprisingly, individuals in both groups ate the same number of cookies, suggesting that those eating the NutraSweet cookies might lose weight as a result of reduced caloric intake. In addition to having their cookie consumption monitored, however, study participants were also asked to keep diaries of all their eating in the days around the cookie-eating event. It turns out that those in the NutraSweet-cookie group ate more than those in the sugar-cookie group. So much more, in fact, that the total caloric intake of the two groups was identical over the period of days monitored (**FIGURE 22-17**). Similar studies have shown that individuals who switch from regular sodas to no-calorie, diet sodas increase their consumption of other foods, often unknowingly, so that their overall caloric intake is not reduced.

Why do our bodies seem to keep track of our caloric intake? It is because all animals are built to get hungry and to seek out food when in that state. Powerful, instinctual hunger kept our ancestors going in a tough, energetically demanding world. Recall from earlier in the chapter the Biosphere 2 study in which participants' diets were significantly reduced in calories. Increasingly, their thoughts and discussions were filled with food fantasies. Such hunger used to be a survival-enhancing feature in our genetic programming, but it is more of a bug in that programming now. Later in this chapter, we'll see that because most of us live in a world characterized by plentiful food, our tremendous ancestral appetites frequently lead to obesity and other health problems.

Our genes do more than instill a general hunger for calories. Humans and other animals also show a preference for fatty foods over carbohydrate- or protein-laden foods. We prefer fatty foods because our tongues have thousands of specific detectors—taste buds—that stimulate our brains when we eat foods like nuts, avocados, cheese, and red meat. With this system, a fatty meal stimulates many of the reward centers in the brain. These structures evolved because fat has the most

FIGURE 22-17 Experiment in human caloric intake.

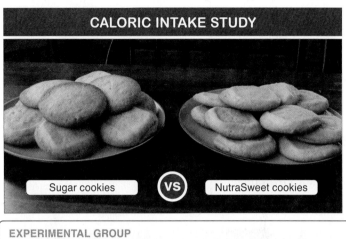

CALORIC INTAKE STUDY

Sugar cookies **VS** NutraSweet cookies

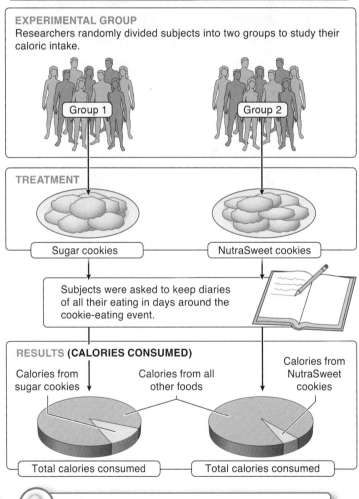

EXPERIMENTAL GROUP
Researchers randomly divided subjects into two groups to study their caloric intake.

Group 1

Group 2

TREATMENT

Sugar cookies

NutraSweet cookies

Subjects were asked to keep diaries of all their eating in days around the cookie-eating event.

RESULTS (CALORIES CONSUMED)

Calories from sugar cookies

Calories from all other foods

Calories from NutraSweet cookies

Total calories consumed

Total calories consumed

Experiments have shown that individuals eating low-calorie cookies tend to increase their consumption of other foods, so that their overall caloric intake is not reduced.

calories per serving. Our ancestral genes reward us whenever we find calories; in this quest for energy, fat deserves—and receives—the biggest reward.

To examine this in a more concrete way, let's return to the little shrew (**FIGURE 22-18**). Recall that our 5-gram shrew must consume about 8 kcal/day and that a pure source of carbohydrates or proteins carries about 4 kcal/gram, while a pure source of fat carries 9 kcal/gram. This means that a shrew can meet its energy requirements by finding and consuming 2.0 grams of a carbohydrate or protein. *Or* the shrew can find about 0.9 gram of a food that is primarily fat (such as insect larvae). Which is going to be easier? Clearly, the shrew (or any animal, for that matter) can meet its energy needs much more easily by seeking fats. Genetically based preferences for the taste of fats, then, can benefit shrews and humans, too (in their ancestral environment).

How would you describe this family's food preferences?

Animals have evolved to be sensitive to more than just total caloric intake or the fat (vs. protein or carbohydrate) content of food. It has been demonstrated in spiders, for example, that individuals will go out of their way, passing up valuable sources of food, in order to consume food items that contain certain rare but essential amino acids, so that their diet contains sufficient amounts of all of the essential amino acids. This suggests that there may actually be some underlying biological urges creating the various cravings and hunger pangs that we sometimes feel and that these feelings may not be restricted to humans. In Section 9-1, we describe how organisms have evolved to have very specific preferences when it comes to the foods they seek and prefer.

TAKE-HOME MESSAGE 22·8

Instincts cause animals to get hungry and to seek out food when in that state. Humans and other animals show a preference for fatty foods over carbohydrate- or protein-laden foods, a behavior reinforced by fat-laden meals stimulating many of the reward centers in the brain. These preferences probably evolved because fat has the most calories per serving.

Animals can meet their energy needs much more easily by seeking and consuming fats. This can significantly reduce the time spent looking for food.

FIGURE 22-18 Efficiency of a fat-rich diet.

Food for Energy and Growth   Nutrients   Digestion and Absorption   Diet and Health

❸ We extract energy and nutrients from food.

A cormorant catches a fish.

22·9

We convert food into nutrients in four steps.

The human digestive system is like an assembly line running backward. Imagine starting with an assembled car and dismantling all the parts: the tires, doors, windshield, steering wheel. The food entering the assembly line of the digestive system is like the intact car. It enters the assembly line and then passes through four distinct phases, during which the food is progressively chewed up and broken down, the nutrients absorbed by the body, and the non-usable portion of the raw materials discarded as waste products (**FIGURE 22-19**).

In the next several sections, we examine in detail the four stages in the processing of food: ingestion, digestion, absorption, and elimination. Throughout these sections, it will be useful to picture the digestive system as a long tube with an opening at each end, the mouth and the anus, and some glands along the way that produce the necessary chemicals to help the process along.

TAKE-HOME MESSAGE 22·9

The digestive process in humans includes four distinct phases during which food is progressively chewed up, broken down, and absorbed by the body, after which the non-usable portion of the raw materials is discarded as waste.

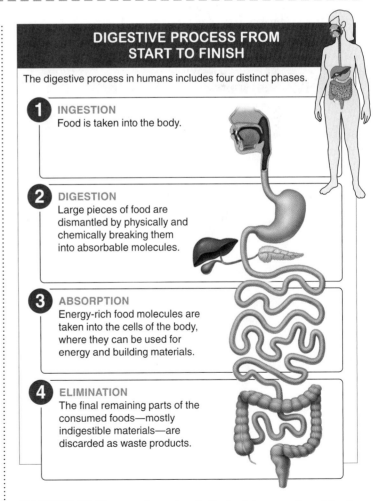

DIGESTIVE PROCESS FROM START TO FINISH

The digestive process in humans includes four distinct phases.

1 INGESTION
Food is taken into the body.

2 DIGESTION
Large pieces of food are dismantled by physically and chemically breaking them into absorbable molecules.

3 ABSORPTION
Energy-rich food molecules are taken into the cells of the body, where they can be used for energy and building materials.

4 ELIMINATION
The final remaining parts of the consumed foods—mostly indigestible materials—are discarded as waste products.

FIGURE 22-19 There are four steps in the body's processing of food.

Ingestion is the first step in the breakdown of food.

It will take you longer to read about **ingestion,** the intake of food into your body, than it would to just do it (**FIGURE 22-20**). Typically lasting less than a minute, ingestion primarily involves four parts of your anatomy: your mouth, teeth, tongue, and esophagus. We'll look at each in some detail. To start, imagine that you take a big bite of a hamburger, containing bread, lettuce, and the meat.

Putting food in your mouth stimulates your salivary glands. Via tiny ducts throughout your mouth, the salivary glands secrete mucus that lubricates the food to help it pass into your stomach. They also secrete an enzyme called alpha-amylase that initiates the process of digestion. Alpha-amylase breaks the bonds holding together the starch molecule (a highly branched carbohydrate pieced together from hundreds of linked glucose molecules) and releases a bit of glucose that can be used for energy. About 20% of the ingested starch is broken down in the mouth. Protein and fat molecules, on the other hand, are not broken down at all.

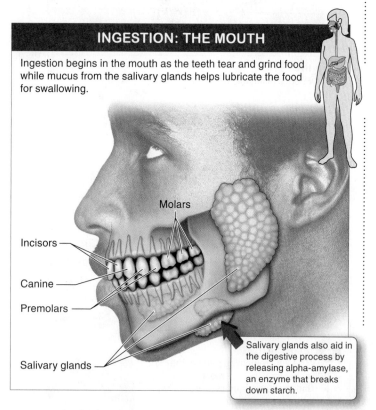

INGESTION: THE MOUTH

Ingestion begins in the mouth as the teeth tear and grind food while mucus from the salivary glands helps lubricate the food for swallowing.

Molars

Incisors

Canine

Premolars

Salivary glands

Salivary glands also aid in the digestive process by releasing alpha-amylase, an enzyme that breaks down starch.

FIGURE 22-20   Ingestion, the intake of food into the body, begins in the mouth.

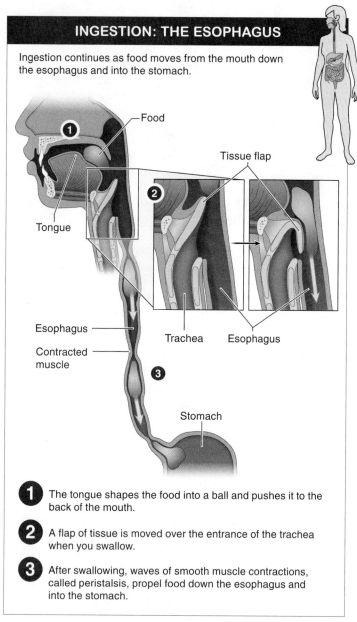

INGESTION: THE ESOPHAGUS

Ingestion continues as food moves from the mouth down the esophagus and into the stomach.

Food

Tissue flap

① ② ③

Tongue

Esophagus

Contracted muscle

Trachea

Esophagus

Stomach

① The tongue shapes the food into a ball and pushes it to the back of the mouth.

② A flap of tissue is moved over the entrance of the trachea when you swallow.

③ After swallowing, waves of smooth muscle contractions, called peristalsis, propel food down the esophagus and into the stomach.

FIGURE 22-21   Ingestion is complete when food passes from the mouth through the esophagus to the stomach.

You start chewing food in your mouth in order to tear and grind it into little bits. This is a first important step toward completely breaking down and harvesting the energy stored in the chemical bonds of the food. Several different types of teeth have evolved in mammals and other animal species that enable different types of food items to be processed. Incisor

Food for Energy and Growth   Nutrients   Digestion and Absorption   Diet and Health

and canine teeth in the front are used for biting and tearing food. Behind them are premolars and molars, used for grinding and crushing food. Just by looking at the type of teeth an animal has, we can learn a lot about its diet. Herbivores have molars primarily for grinding and crushing the tough cell walls of the plants they eat. Carnivores have sharp and lethal canines and incisors for killing and tearing apart the flesh of other animals.

Birds have no teeth. This explains why they can sometimes be seen eating gravel. Although the gravel has no nutritional value, it collects in the stomach, where it helps to grind up the food they eat. This is an important digestive step for birds because, without teeth, they must swallow their food whole. Consequently, when it gets to the stomach, it hasn't been ground up at all, which can reduce the efficiency of digestive enzymes.

Q Why do many birds eat gravel?

While you are chewing your food, your tongue assists in the process by forming the food into a ball shape that can be swallowed. The ball of partly crushed, saliva-coated food is pushed to the back of your mouth by your tongue. There, your throat opens to two passageways into your torso, the **trachea** and the **esophagus** (FIGURE 22-21). The trachea, also called the windpipe, connects to your lungs, while the esophagus connects to your stomach. Food destined for your stomach is kept from entering your trachea by a fast but critical maneuver in which your voice box moves up (due to muscle contractions), causing a flap of tissue (called the epiglottis) to be pushed over the entrance to the trachea just as you begin to swallow. If the ball of food you swallow is too big, it can get stuck at the beginning of the esophagus, wedging against the flap of tissue in front of the trachea—and this can cause you to choke by blocking all air from getting into your lungs.

Once the ball of chewed food makes it into the esophagus, waves of smooth muscle contractions, called **peristalsis,** propel the food down the esophagus and into the stomach, where digestion continues. Because of peristalsis, it's not necessary for you to be sitting upright or standing when you eat. Even if you are standing on your head, the food is pushed down the esophagus to the stomach.

TAKE-HOME MESSAGE 22·10

Ingestion is the first phase of the digestive process. Usually lasting less than a minute, ingestion involves tearing and grinding food in preparation for passing it to the stomach. Digestion also begins during this phase, with some starch being broken down by enzymes in saliva.

22·11

Digestion dismantles food into usable parts.

Food is fuel. But it is useless to an animal until it has been completely broken down into its fundamental chemical constituents. Only then can it be absorbed into the bloodstream and used constructively by a body. The process of dismantling the large pieces of food, physically and chemically breaking them down into absorbable molecules, is digestion. It occurs primarily in the stomach and small intestine.

The Stomach Let's continue tracing the bite of hamburger as it moves through the digestive system. It empties from the esophagus directly into the **stomach,** a muscular J-shaped organ with thick, elastic walls that can expand greatly in size to accommodate a large meal—as much as 4 liters of material! At the point where the esophagus connects to the stomach, there is a ring of muscle, called a **sphincter.** It seals off the stomach once the food has entered, preventing regurgitation of the stomach's acidic contents into the esophagus—even if you are eating while standing on your head. The stomach has three functions.

1. It physically breaks down and mixes food, through churning of the muscles surrounding it.

2. It secretes acid to further break down food, chemically, and to kill bacteria.

3. It begins some chemical digestion of proteins.

The presence of food in the stomach causes cells in crevices within the stomach lining, called gastric pits, to rapidly produce hydrochloric acid and a protein-dismantling enzyme known as

pepsin (FIGURE 22-22). The acid corrodes proteins in the food, breaking them into smaller pieces, which can then be broken into their constituent amino acids by the pepsin.

The burning sensation of indigestion occurs when the sphincter between the esophagus and the stomach doesn't completely prevent the acidic contents of the stomach from moving back up the esophagus. It usually occurs when a person eats too much or too quickly. Antacids can neutralize acid from the stomach. Remember, though, that the high acidity in the stomach is important for digestion, so while reducing it may alleviate heartburn, antacids can reduce the digestive efficiency of the stomach.

Q *What is indigestion? How do antacids cure it?*

The end result of all the churning and digesting is that the food you have eaten is no longer recognizable. It becomes a creamy, very acidic liquid called **chyme.** At the other end of

the stomach is another ring of muscle. About every 20 seconds, it opens just a tiny bit and squirts a few tablespoonfuls of chyme into the small intestine. While some of the hamburger's carbohydrates and proteins have been partly or completely digested in the stomach, the lettuce is undigested, as are the lipids from the meat, which are suspended as greasy droplets within the chyme.

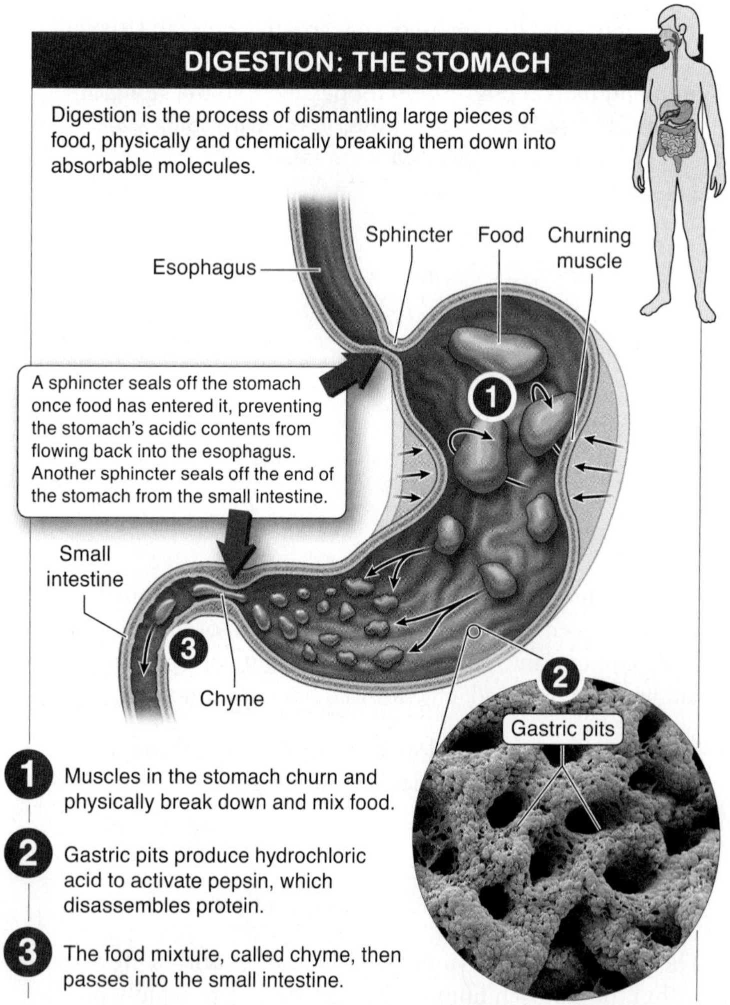

Besides helping to chemically break down food in your stomach, the strong acid also kills most of the bacteria that you might consume. Most bacteria just can't survive when the pH gets so acidic (although some microbes occasionally manage to sneak through by hiding in pockets of food with higher pH as the food passes through the stomach). In the StreetBio at the end of this chapter, we explore the ulcer-inducing effects of one species of bacteria that can live in your stomach.

Interestingly, across dozens and dozens of cultures, humans have developed common ways of preparing their food, including using heat and marinating food in acidic solutions, such as vinegar or lemon juice. Because harsh conditions such as heat

Q *Humans use heat for cooking and often marinate foods in vinegar or lemon juice. How do these processes help with digestion?*

and acid help to disrupt the tissue of food items, they increase the efficiency with which digestive enzymes can make contact with the food and break it down

The Small Intestine

Digestion only begins in the mouth and stomach. Most chemical digestion actually occurs in the **small intestine,** a long thin tube connected to the stomach in which most digestion takes place. It is about 20 feet long and winds all around your abdominal cavity (how else could 20 feet of tubing be packed into such a small area?). As we've seen, as a sphincter at the end of the stomach relaxes, creating an opening, small amounts of chyme are squirted from the stomach. The creamy substance slowly moves through the small intestine, pushed by the rhythmic contractions of peristalsis. As the chyme makes its way through the small intestine, the macromolecules are gradually digested, with help from the pancreas and the liver (FIGURE 22-23).

The **pancreas,** nestled at the point where the stomach connects to the small intestine, plays a central role in digestion by secreting pancreatic juice through a duct into the very beginning portion of the small intestine. This juice is a mixture of (1) chemicals that neutralize the acidic chyme, and

DIGESTION: THE STOMACH

Digestion is the process of dismantling large pieces of food, physically and chemically breaking them down into absorbable molecules.

Esophagus — Sphincter   Food   Churning muscle

A sphincter seals off the stomach once food has entered it, preventing the stomach's acidic contents from flowing back into the esophagus. Another sphincter seals off the end of the stomach from the small intestine.

Small intestine

Chyme

Gastric pits

1 Muscles in the stomach churn and physically break down and mix food.

2 Gastric pits produce hydrochloric acid to activate pepsin, which disassembles protein.

3 The food mixture, called chyme, then passes into the small intestine.

FIGURE 22-22 **The role of the stomach in digestion.**

Food for Energy and Growth   Nutrients   Digestion and Absorption   Diet and Health

DIGESTION: THE SMALL INTESTINE

Although digestion begins in the mouth and stomach, most of it occurs in the small intestine.

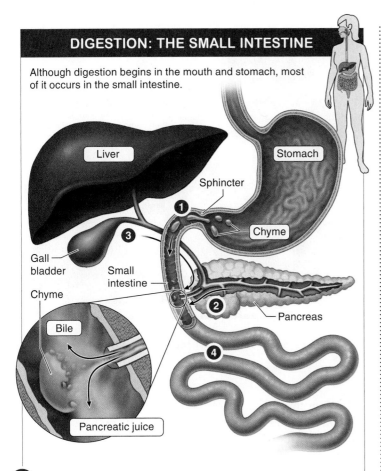

Liver

Stomach

Sphincter

1

3

Chyme

Gall bladder

Small intestine

Chyme

2

Pancreas

Bile

4

Pancreatic juice

1 As a sphincter at the end of the stomach relaxes, small amounts of chyme are squirted into the small intestine.

2 The pancreas secretes pancreatic juice, which neutralizes the chyme and aids in the digestion of carbohydrates, proteins, and fats.

3 The liver produces bile, which travels from the gall bladder, where it is stored, to the small intestine, where it acts as a detergent to break up particles of fat.

4 Cells within the walls of the small intestine produce enzymes that further digest fats, carbohydrates, and proteins.

> *Digestion is completed in the small intestine, at which point carbohydrates, proteins, and fats have been broken down into simple sugars, amino acids, and fatty acids.*

FIGURE 22-23 The role of the small intestine in digestion.

(2) enzymes that digest carbohydrates, proteins, and fats. Another organ that assists the small intestine with digestion is the **liver,** which produces **bile,** a juice that aids in the breakdown of fats. The liver sends the bile to the gall bladder, and from there it passes through a small duct into the small intestine, where the bile initiates the first step in fat digestion.

Remember, lipids are not water-soluble, so any fat from the hamburger is still suspended in the chyme, never dissolving into the watery substance of the digestive tract. Bile acts as a detergent that helps break up the suspended droplets of fat into much tinier particles. Once the lipids decrease in size, pancreatic enzymes can successfully break them down. In addition to the enzymes produced by the pancreas and the liver, the cells within the walls of the small intestine also generate enzymes that further digest fats, carbohydrates, and proteins. For a variety of reasons, people sometimes must have part of their small intestine surgically removed. Can you predict the effects this might have on digestion?

Digestion is completed in the small intestine when the consumed carbohydrates, proteins, and fats have been broken down into their component parts: simple sugars, amino acids, and fatty acids. These simple molecules can then be absorbed into the bloodstream, a process that we explore in the next section. But first let's look at a few cases in which digestion doesn't work properly or in which animals rely on some digestive assistance from bacteria, and a carnival trick that hinges on an understanding of digestion.

Intestinal Bacteria Have you noticed that certain types of food commonly give people gas? Some types of beans commonly cause such digestive distress. Enzyme deficiencies and metabolically versatile bacteria are the culprits. The beans contain the sugars raffinose and stachyose, which are indigestible by many people. And so when the sugars pass undigested through the small intestine and reach the large intestine, they are digested by bacteria. And the by-product of the bacterial feeding frenzy is gas, cramps, and flatulence. The product Beano contains enzymes that help digest the trouble-making sugars before our resident bacteria can get to them.

There is a wide variety of situations in which bacteria living inside animals similarly digest food molecules that the animals could not otherwise break down—and this has evolved as a benefit to the "host" animals as well as the bacteria. Living in termite guts, for example, are large colonies of symbiotic cellulose-digesting bacteria. The bacteria make it possible for the termite to eat wood and actually gain nutrients from it. The bacteria obtain energy by breaking down the cellulose in the wood into simple sugars that are valuable to the termite (as well as to the bacteria). If humans could figure out how to cultivate the same bacteria in our guts, perhaps we, too, could eat wood.

Leeches also have a symbiotic relationship with bacteria. As a leech sucks blood from an animal, bacteria—rather than its own enzymes—break down the blood proteins into their component amino acids, which the bacteria and the leech then share (**FIGURE 22-24**).

As a leech sucks blood from an animal, bacteria—rather than its own enzymes—break down the blood proteins into their component amino acids, which the bacteria and the leech then share.

FIGURE 22-24 Leeches and bacteria in partnership.

Because the snake venom is a mixture of proteins, they are broken down in the digestive system. Once broken down into their component amino acids, the proteins become harmless.

FIGURE 22-25 Snake venom must enter the bloodstream to cause ill effects.

Q *Snake venom is toxic, but if you drink it, in most cases it won't harm you. Why?*

Poisonous Proteins Snake venom is a mixture of toxic proteins. Yet if you "milked" a snake's venom into a glass and drank it, the toxin wouldn't necessarily harm you (**FIGURE 22-25**). At carnivals and entertainment parks, snake experts will sometimes do exactly this, with no ill effects. Because the venom is a mixture of proteins, it is broken down by the stomach acids and enzymes of the digestive system. Once broken down into their component amino acids, the poison proteins become harmless. Snake venom must enter the bloodstream to cause its ill effects. That is why snakes bite

with fangs that function as hypodermic needles, delivering the poison to the bloodstream. Of course, if you have any cuts inside your mouth or lesions elsewhere in your digestive system, some of the venom could get into your bloodstream when you drink it and poison you. For that reason, drinking venom isn't a wise stunt to attempt.

TAKE-HOME MESSAGE 22·11

Digestion—the process of dismantling large pieces of food, physically and chemically breaking them down into absorbable molecules—is the second phase of the breakdown of food in animals. It occurs primarily in the stomach and small intestine.

Food for Energy and Growth   Nutrients   Digestion and Absorption   Diet and Health

Absorption moves nutrients from your gut to your cells.

Chewing, tearing, churning, acidifying, dismantling. You put a lot of energy into reducing food to its simplest component molecules. Eventually, though, there is a payoff. That payoff is **absorption,** the process by which the energy-rich food particles are taken from the digestive tract into the bloodstream and then into the cells of the body, where they can be used for energy and building materials. Absorption occurs mainly in the small intestine; however, a few molecules are absorbed in the stomach, including aspirin and alcohol, which explains why drinking alcohol on an empty stomach can lead to unexpectedly rapid inebriation.

The secret to effective absorption is simple: surface area. For a molecule such as a sugar or an amino acid to be absorbed by the body, the molecule must be in direct contact with the cell membrane of the cell that is going to absorb it. The greater the number of cells that can come in contact with chyme passing through the small intestine, the greater the amount of nutrients that can be absorbed. For this reason,

the tremendous surface area of the small intestine allows for very efficient absorption of nutrients (**FIGURE 22-26**). How does the small intestine achieve this? There are four primary ways.

1. The small intestine is long. About 20 feet long, as we saw above.

2. Rather than being a straight, smooth tube, it has many folds.

3. The interior lining of the small intestine is made up of thousands of small finger-like projections, called villi. These create lots of nooks and crannies where chyme can come in contact with absorptive cells.

4. Each of the cells along the villi has hundreds of its own tiny thread-like projections, called microvilli. These create micro-nooks and micro-crannies that allow more of the molecules in chyme to directly touch the membranes of absorptive cells.

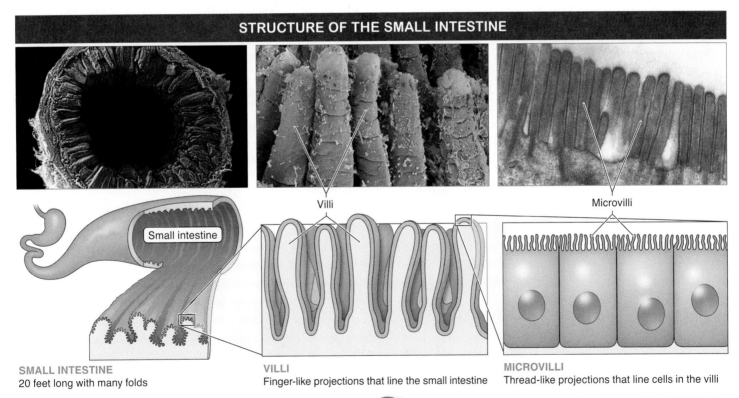

STRUCTURE OF THE SMALL INTESTINE

Villi

Microvilli

Small intestine

SMALL INTESTINE
20 feet long with many folds

VILLI
Finger-like projections that line the small intestine

MICROVILLI
Thread-like projections that line cells in the villi

FIGURE 22-26 The small intestine has a very large area for absorbing nutrients.

 The tremendous surface area of the small intestine allows for very efficient absorption of nutrients.

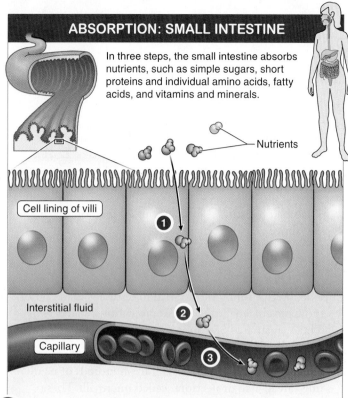

ABSORPTION: SMALL INTESTINE

In three steps, the small intestine absorbs nutrients, such as simple sugars, short proteins and individual amino acids, fatty acids, and vitamins and minerals.

Nutrients

Cell lining of villi

1

Interstitial fluid

2

Capillary

3

1 Nutrients are transported into the cells lining the villi.

2 Nutrients diffuse out of the cells and into the interstitial fluid bathing the cells.

3 Nutrients are picked up by the capillaries and move into the bloodstream, where they can be delivered to the organs and tissues that need them.

Ultimately, all of these surface-area-enhancing structural features give the small intestine a huge amount of surface area for absorption. If it were spread out as a flat surface, it would be about the size of a tennis court.

The molecules that can be absorbed in the small intestine include simple sugars, short proteins, individual amino acids,

FIGURE 22-27 Absorption moves nutrients into the bloodstream.

fatty acids, vitamins, and minerals. When a nutrient molecule is small enough to be absorbed, it gravitates toward the villi lining the interior of the small intestine. The tiny particles become trapped in the microvilli and are drawn across the cell membrane into the cells (**FIGURE 22-27**). Then the nutrient diffuses out of the cell and into the interstitial fluid bathing the cells. Finally, from here the nutrients are picked up by capillaries and thus move into the bloodstream, where they can be delivered to the organs and tissues that need them.

There is a food myth that if certain foods are combined, digestion is impaired. This is not true. The myth ignores a couple of facts: the body is able to produce its digestive enzymes for fats, proteins, and carbohydrates simultaneously, and it can absorb nutrients regardless of which other nutrients are also in the digestive tract. In fact, the contrary is often true. Many foods enhance the absorption of nutrient molecules in other foods. Vitamin C in citrus fruits, for example, increases the efficiency of iron absorption from a meal of beef or beans.

Q Is it true that certain food combinations should not be eaten together?

TAKE-HOME MESSAGE 22·12

Absorption is the process by which energy-rich food particles are taken up from the digestive tract into the cells of the body, where they can be used for energy and building materials. It takes place primarily in the small intestine.

Elimination removes unusable material from your body.

You are much better at conservation and recycling than you imagine. Especially when it comes to the fluids and solids you consume. The last phase in the breakdown of food, **elimination,** takes place as what's left of the chyme—mostly indigestible materials—leaves the small intestine and enters the **large intestine,** also called the **colon.** Much larger in diameter than the small intestine (about 3 inches, vs. 1 inch in the small intestine) but only about 3–6 feet long, the large intestine serves to absorb water, salts, and some vitamins (**FIGURE 22-28**). The last part of the large intestine is the rectum and serves as a storage compartment for the remaining parts of consumed food, the feces, which can then be defecated.

It is important to achieve just the right balance of water absorption in the large intestine. If too much is absorbed, the remaining indigestible material becomes too solid and can't move easily through the last part of the digestive system, causing constipation. Alternatively, if too little absorption occurs, the body loses more water and this causes diarrhea. Fiber—including gums and cellulose—cannot be digested or absorbed. For this reason, when fiber is consumed, it increases fecal mass and speeds the movement of chyme through the colon (**FIGURE 22-29**). With additional mass, more water is attracted, softening the feces and making it easier to eliminate (that's why too much fiber can lead to diarrhea). Fiber also binds to bile, causing some of it to be eliminated, thereby reducing the body's ability to absorb cholesterol from food.

Q Fiber is an indigestible carbohydrate. If we can't digest it, how can it be essential in our diet?

Huge colonies of bacteria live in the colon. Before we are born, our guts are sterile and free of bacteria. During birth, we acquire some of our mother's vaginal and fecal bacteria, and by the age of two we have acquired bacteria from food and the environment, so that all of the numerous species present in adults are already in residence by that age. We generally have more bacterial cells than our own body cells at any given time (see Figure 13-3). The bacteria are usually harmless and live off the undigested materials that end up in the colon. Bacteria

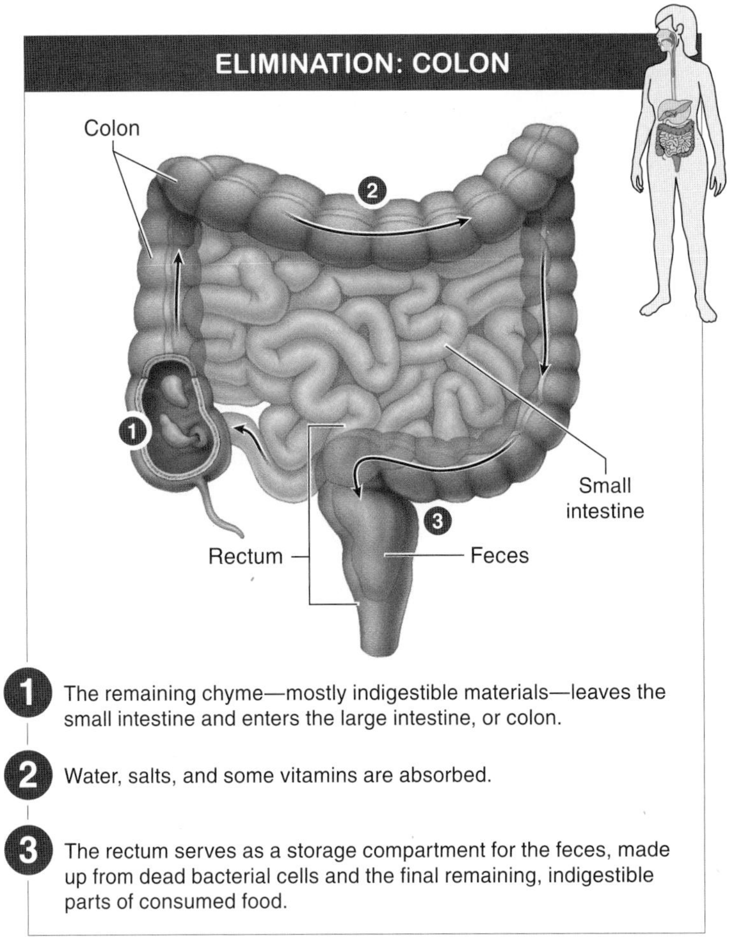

ELIMINATION: COLON

Colon

Small intestine

Rectum — — Feces

1 The remaining chyme—mostly indigestible materials—leaves the small intestine and enters the large intestine, or colon.

2 Water, salts, and some vitamins are absorbed.

3 The rectum serves as a storage compartment for the feces, made up from dead bacterial cells and the final remaining, indigestible parts of consumed food.

FIGURE 22-28 Elimination is the final step in the digestive process.

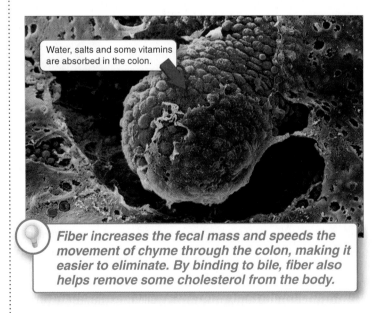

Water, salts and some vitamins are absorbed in the colon.

Fiber increases the fecal mass and speeds the movement of chyme through the colon, making it easier to eliminate. By binding to bile, fiber also helps remove some cholesterol from the body.

FIGURE 22-29 The last remnants of a meal in the colon.

also release important metabolic by-products such as vitamin K and one of the B vitamins, biotin. About half of the feces that we excrete each day is made up of dead bacterial cells, and the rest is mostly indigestible materials such as cellulose from the cell walls of plant matter and other types of fiber.

Q Why can taking antibiotics lead to vitamin deficiencies?

Antibiotics frequently (and unintentionally) kill a large proportion of the colon bacteria, in addition to whatever illness-causing microbe they were prescribed to kill. This can have multiple negative side effects. First, the transit of undigested materials through the colon may not be slowed down as much as usual, in which case less water is removed and diarrhea results. Also, a reduction in production of vitamin K and biotin can lead to deficiencies.

In the colon, water is removed from feces through osmosis. First, salts are pumped out of the colon, and then water moves out by simple diffusion (to an area where there are more ions). This process can be manipulated as a treatment for constipation. Laxatives contain magnesium salts that are so slowly absorbed that they are still largely intact when they reach the colon. Laxatives work by increasing the salt concentration in the colon, so that more water remains. This additional water makes it easier to excrete feces (but can cause diarrhea in some cases).

Q Laxatives contain salts. Why might this reduce constipation?

TAKE-HOME MESSAGE 22·13

The last phase of food breakdown takes place as the mostly indigestible materials leave the small intestine and enter the large intestine. There, water and ions are absorbed before the remaining materials are defecated.

22·14

Animals have some alternative means for processing their food.

Food, food everywhere, but not a bite to eat. Cellulose could feed the world: it's everywhere—the major carbohydrate making up the cell wall around plant cells is cellulose—and there is a tremendous amount of energy stored in its chemical bonds. But most animals don't produce enzymes that break down cellulose. If they can figure out a way to digest it—and some species have—they gain access to one of the most plentiful sources of chemical energy on the planet. Let's investigate how some animals have done it.

Ruminant animals, such as cows, bison, deer, goats, and sheep, have evolved complex four-part stomachs in which they are able to digest plant matter that humans cannot (**FIGURE 22-30**). First, the grazing animals chew on the plant material for a while, grinding the tough cell walls. Then they swallow it, and it passes into the first part of their stomach, which contains a huge pool of enzymes and cellulose-digesting bacteria. There, the plant material gets broken down, and much of the cellulose is digested. To increase their energy-extraction

Q Silverfish are insect pests in libraries rather than in kitchens. Why might this be? (Hint: they are one of only a few species of animals to produce enzymes that digest cellulose.)

efficiency, the animals then regurgitate the food back into the mouth, chew it some more, and swallow it again. Called "chewing the cud," the additional chewing further breaks up the plant cell walls so that the bacteria can have easier access to the cellulose, digesting more of it. From the first part of the stomach, the food then passes through the remaining chambers, where some additional digestion takes place, before moving into the small intestine and continuing the usual path of animal digestion. Cellulose-digesting bacteria have some of the most dangerous working conditions on earth: although cellulose is the primary component of the ruminant diet, ruminants also get a significant amount of protein every day by digesting many of the bacteria working in their gut.

Some insects, including silverfish, produce cellulose-digesting enzymes. These enzymes make it possible for them to actually eat books and paper, which are made of plant products containing cell walls made from cellulose.

FOUR-PART STOMACH

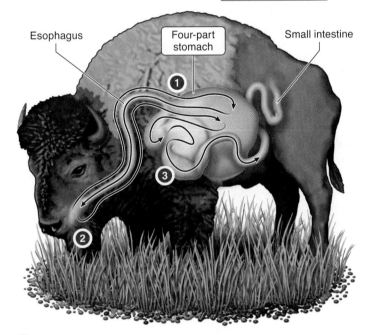

In ruminant animals, a complex four-part stomach has evolved in which they are able to digest the plant matter that humans cannot.

Cellulose-digesting bacteria

Esophagus

Four-part stomach

Small intestine

1 Plant material is swallowed and passed to the first part of the stomach, where it is broken down and digested by enzymes and cellulose-digesting bacteria.

2 Food is regurgitated, chewed more, then swallowed and passed to the first chamber again.

3 Food passes through the remaining chambers, where additional digestion takes place before it moves into the small intestine.

FIGURE 22-30 **Ruminants can digest plant material that humans cannot.**

There's more than one way to skin a plant. Other animals, without the large bacteria-filled stomach of ruminants, also employ cellulose-digesting bacteria to enable them to extract energy from cellulose. In these animals, including horses, rodents, rabbits, and koalas, the bacteria don't live in the stomach. Rather, they live farther down the digestive tract, within an outcropping of the small intestine called the cecum. This is a separate chamber where the food goes for a while and the cellulose gets digested, before the food continues down the intestine. In animals that don't break down cellulose, the cecum is much smaller. The cecum is almost non-existent in the meat-eating coyote, while the similarly-sized koala has a cecum that is 2 meters long, where bacteria can convert shredded eucalyptus leaves into usable food (**FIGURE 22-31**). In

THE CECUM

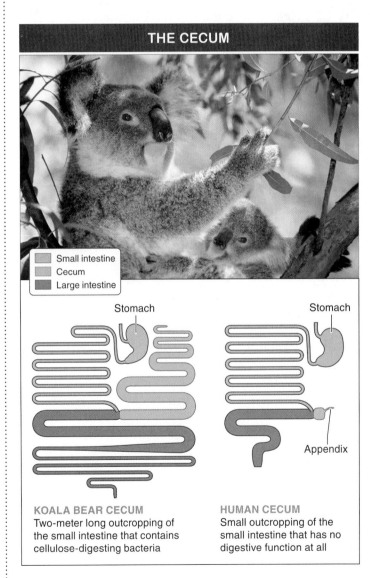

Small intestine
Cecum
Large intestine

Stomach

Stomach

Appendix

KOALA BEAR CECUM
Two-meter long outcropping of the small intestine that contains cellulose-digesting bacteria

HUMAN CECUM
Small outcropping of the small intestine that has no digestive function at all

FIGURE 22-31 **Koalas can eat foods that are indigestible for humans.** The cecum is the site of cellulose digestion in some animals.

> *Rabbits and rodents have mastered another way to increase their ability to extract energy from their food: they pass it through their digestive system twice.*

FIGURE 22-32 Coprophagy increases nutritional intake from foods high in cellulose.

There are about 150 different domestic and wild ruminant species including cows, goats, deer, buffalo, bison, giraffe, and elk.

humans, no cellulose-digesting bacteria live in the cecum (which is called the appendix in humans). Recent research suggests, however, that the appendix may play a role in immune function.

Rabbits and rodents can't increase their cellulose-digesting efficiency by regurgitating their food and chewing the cud, because the cellulose-digesting bacteria reside in the small intestine, not the stomach. But they've mastered another way to increase their ability to extract energy from their food: they pass it through their entire digestive system twice (**FIGURE 22-32**). Called **coprophagy,** eating some of their feces allows them to

significantly increase their nutritional intake from their cellulose-laden diet.

TAKE-HOME MESSAGE 22·14

Most animals don't produce enzymes that break down cellulose. In ruminant animals, complex four-part stomachs have evolved in which the animals can digest plant matter that humans cannot, in part due to the presence of symbiotic cellulose-digesting bacteria. Other animals have alternative methods of utilizing cellulose-digesting bacteria.

Food for Energy and Growth   Nutrients   Digestion and Absorption   Diet and Health

④ What we eat profoundly affects our health.

Two sweet foods with very different nutritional composition.

22 • 15

What constitutes a healthy diet?

Choosing a healthy diet can be very difficult. There are more than 50,000 different foods that a person can choose from each day. And we not only must select which foods to eat, we must also consider how much of each to consume each day. Fortunately, there is not a single "best" solution that every person must adhere to in order to ensure good health. Rather, there are many different ways, making it possible to work within any person's particular likes and dislikes.

At the most basic level, just two requirements—quality and quantity—must be satisfied in the design of a healthy diet (**FIGURE 22-33**). First, a diet must contain sufficient amounts of each of the six categories of nutrients: water, proteins, carbohydrates, lipids, vitamins, and minerals (described in Sections 22-4–22-8). And second, a healthy diet must contain sufficient energy to support an individual's metabolic needs without containing a surplus of calories. But it is not easy to find the best strategy to satisfy these requirements.

Laboratory rodents—including those in longevity studies in which the animals have lived significantly longer than any wild rodent—have no such trouble with choosing a healthy diet. They are fed a diet that consists simply of water and special

💡 *A healthy diet should contain sufficient amounts of each of the six categories of nutrients and just enough energy to support an individual's metabolic needs.*

FIGURE 22-33 Food quality and quantity are the main factors to consider in choosing a healthy, balanced diet.

food pellets. The food pellet formulation is the result of decades of research on animal nutrition. It includes carefully controlled amounts of each nutrient and does not vary from the time an animal reaches maturity until it dies. Each day, the rodents receive a specific number of the pellets, and each day the rodents eat them. Humans (thankfully?) do not subsist on a single food item. But for that reason, one of the most important principles guiding selection of a healthy diet is *balance*.

Balance in a diet is important because no one food is completely adequate. Milk, for example, is a very good source of protein and calcium, but does not contain sufficient iron for most adults. Meats, on the other hand, are rich in iron (as well as protein) but generally are poor sources of calcium. Every type of food, in fact, while providing some nutritional value, also falls short in some other essential nutrient, whether a protein or a specific vitamin or mineral. For this reason, nutritionists recommend consuming a variety of foods from each of the basic food groups—including (1) grains, (2) vegetables, (3) fruits, (4) milk and other dairy products, and (5) meats, poultry, and beans—consuming small quantities of unsaturated fats such as olive and canola oil, and exercising daily to manage body weight (FIGURE 22-34).

The U.S. Department of Agriculture (USDA) has established dietary guidelines, which it updates every five years. These highlight the most important issues with respect to determining the ideal quantity and quality of food consumed. In addition to

urging people to take steps to ensure that their food is safe to eat, they also recommend the following.

1. Keep your weight within the recommended range.
2. Be physically active.
3. Choose a variety of fruits, vegetables, grains—particularly whole grains—and nonfat or low-fat milk and milk products.
4. Keep your diet low in saturated fat, cholesterol, and total fat.
5. Keep your diet low in sugars relative to complex carbohydrates and fiber.
6. Keep your diet low in salt.
7. If you consume alcoholic beverages, do so in moderation.

Food labels are an often overlooked tool that can help in adhering to these guidelines and selecting a balanced diet. Ingredient lists, too, are very valuable, listing every ingredient in order of amount (by weight). Ultimately, following these guidelines can help reduce the incidence and severity of chronic diseases such as stroke and other manifestations of cardiovascular disease, diabetes, and cancer.

Q Why is it increasingly difficult to maintain a healthy diet as we get older?

Complicating the USDA's dietary guidelines is the fact that we need to reduce our caloric intake as we get older. Metabolic rate falls slowly but surely, beginning around age 30. Consequently, without an increase in activity, eating the same amount of food—even if it is a healthy diet—leads to a surplus of calories, a surplus that becomes larger and larger with each passing year. On average, most adults gain about half a pound every year throughout their thirties, forties, and fifties.

It is important to note that people who do not consume meat, poultry, fish, and/or milk products can still have a balanced diet. Legumes, seeds, and nuts can provide many of the same nutrients found in meat, including protein. Dark leafy vegetables can provide iron, another nutrient plentiful in meat. And in fact, because such diets tend to be lower in fat content, they can be valuable in helping to maintain a healthy body weight.

RECOMMENDED DAILY FOOD INTAKE

GRAINS — VEGETABLES — FRUITS — OILS — DAIRY — MEAT & BEANS

Because no one food is completely adequate, nutritionists recommend consuming a variety of foods from each of the basic food groups.

FIGURE 22-34 **What nutritionists recommend.**

TAKE-HOME MESSAGE 22·15

A balanced diet contains adequate amounts of essential nutrients and energy, but not surplus amounts, and is low in substances—including saturated fats, cholesterol, sugar, salt, and alcohol—that can have adverse health effects when consumed in greater quantities.

Obesity can result from too much of a good thing.

Jerry and Louis Kahn are two brothers who really love to eat. The pair tip the scales at about 500 pounds each—and their hunger never subsides. What is unusual about the Kahns' difficulty controlling their weight is that doctors have pinpointed the exact physiological source of their problem. They both possess an altered gene that renders their bodies unable to recognize the internal measure of food intake and register "enough," much like a broken thermostat that never shuts off a heater. Jerry and Louis are eternally hungry because their brains never get the "we're full" message from their stomachs.

Like the Kahns, we all have inherited genes from our parents that significantly influence our body weights. The thing is, we don't need to carry a defective gene to become obese. All humans inherit dozens (possibly hundreds) of genes that influence body weight, and even in their "normal" condition, these genes are likely to lead to weight problems (**FIGURE 22-35**). But this raises a couple of questions. Why would it be in our genetic interests to have huge appetites? Why would natural selection favor such genes? To answer these questions, we must consider the harsher, less predictable environment in which *Homo sapiens* evolved.

Our ancestors lived off the land by hunting animals and gathering plants. Under such conditions, it was unclear where the next meal was coming from. Powerful, instinctual hunger kept our ancestors going in that tough, energetically demanding world. Imagine a time when the individuals of a population varied in their appetites. Some individuals thought of food day and night, and ate whenever they could. Others became satiated once their daily needs were met. Of these types, which included individuals with the biggest surplus of energy stored in their thighs and buttocks when food became scarce? Who weathered the famine, with calories left over for reproducing? Who is most likely to be your ancestor? In every case, it is the enthusiastic and not the restrained eaters. Recent studies using PET scans (positron emission tomography, a type of imaging) have supported this, demonstrating that just the sight of food sets off activity in the brain's pleasure centers—a mechanism that generally leads to the consumption of food when it is available.

The consequence of our perpetual hunger is not news: one of every four Americans is obese. In terms of size, plumpness gets labeled "obesity" when our body mass index hits 30. **Body mass index,** or **BMI,** equals body weight in

? *Why has natural selection favored genes for large appetites?*

FIGURE 22-35 Are your genes making it difficult for you to maintain a healthy weight?

kilograms divided by height in meters squared (kg/m^2). A BMI of 30 translates to about 209 pounds if you are 5 feet 10 inches tall, and 180 pounds if you are 5 feet 5 inches. With a BMI of 25 or higher, you are only considered "overweight." BMI isn't the only way to evaluate obesity, and it has its problems. Because the measure does not consider body composition, professional athletes and bodybuilders with unusually large muscle mass have BMIs that fall within the obese range. Still, it is a useful and easily obtained measure (**FIGURE 22-36**). Repeatedly, around the world, as societies get richer and as individuals age, they tend to become fatter. Most of us would reduce our risk of heart disease, stroke, and diabetes if we lost even as little as

BODY MASS INDEX (BMI)

	UNDER WEIGHT (<18.5)	HEALTHY WEIGHT (18.5–24.9)						OVERWEIGHT (25–29.9)					OBESE (>30)					
BMI	18	19	20	21	22	23	24	25	26	27	28	29	30	31	32	33	34	35
6′4″	148	156	164	172	180	189	197	205	213	221	230	238	246	254	263	271	279	287
6′3″	144	152	160	168	176	184	192	200	208	216	224	232	240	248	256	264	272	279
6′2″	141	148	155	163	171	179	186	194	202	210	218	225	233	241	249	256	264	272
6′1″	136	144	151	159	166	174	182	189	197	204	212	219	227	235	242	250	257	265
6′0″	132	140	147	154	162	169	177	184	191	199	206	213	221	228	235	242	250	258
5′11″	129	136	143	150	157	165	172	179	186	193	200	208	215	222	229	236	243	250
5′10″	126	132	139	146	153	160	167	174	181	188	195	202	209	216	222	229	236	243
5′9″	122	128	135	142	149	155	162	169	176	182	189	196	203	209	216	223	230	236
5′8″	118	125	131	138	144	151	158	164	171	177	184	190	197	203	210	216	223	230
5′7″	115	121	127	134	140	146	153	159	166	172	178	185	191	198	204	211	217	223
5′6″	112	118	124	130	136	142	148	155	161	167	173	179	186	192	198	204	210	216
5′5″	108	114	120	126	132	138	144	150	156	162	168	174	180	186	192	198	204	210
5′4″	105	110	116	122	128	134	140	145	151	157	163	169	174	180	186	192	197	204
5′3″	102	107	113	118	124	130	135	141	146	152	158	163	169	175	180	186	191	197
5′2″	98	104	109	115	120	126	131	136	142	147	153	158	164	169	175	180	186	191
5′1″	95	100	106	111	116	122	127	132	137	143	148	153	158	164	169	174	180	185
5′0″	92	97	102	107	112	118	123	128	133	138	143	148	153	158	163	168	174	179

Height (left axis) — **Body Weight (Pounds)**

FIGURE 22-36 One indicator of healthy body weight: body mass index. The BMI indicates the ratio between height and body weight; the chart shows healthy body-weight ranges.

10 pounds. But because of the "famine-fearing" genes we carry, this is easier said than done.

From the cellular perspective, the specific causes of obesity are an increase in the size and number of fat cells an individual carries. Excess calories can be converted to fat regardless of whether they come from fats, carbohydrates, or proteins. Whatever the source, the fat molecules are added right to the fat cells in the body's adipose tissue. Fat cells increase in number primarily during the late years of childhood and the early teens (**FIGURE 22-37**). After that, the cells tend to grow in size rather than number with excess caloric intake, although when a fat cell becomes too large it will divide. The reverse, unfortunately, is not true. When people lose weight, their fat cells become smaller but are never lost completely. Consequently, it is especially important to avoid obesity early in life.

FIGURE 22-37 It's important to maintain a healthy body weight during childhood.

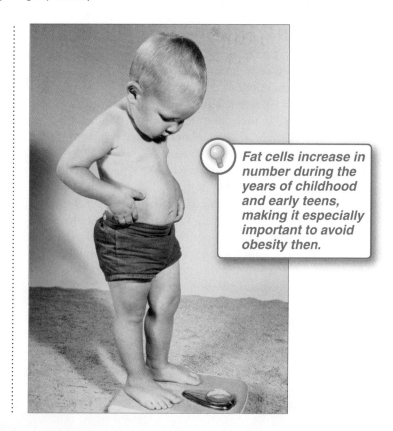

Fat cells increase in number during the years of childhood and early teens, making it especially important to avoid obesity then.

Food for Energy and Growth   Nutrients   Digestion and Absorption   Diet and Health

The problems of obesity are not restricted to humans. Most primates in zoos are also overweight, as are many pets and most laboratory research animals. In each case, the reason is the same as for humans. In their natural world, food is limited and unpredictable. Animals overeat when they do not need to expend much energy to acquire food and food is plentiful. In the next section, we explore some weight-loss diets and why they are almost universally unsuccessful.

22•17

Weight-loss diets are a losing proposition.

> I can reason down or deny everything, except this perpetual Belly: feed he must and will, and I cannot make him respectable.
>
> —Ralph Waldo Emerson, *Representative Men*, 1850

Weight loss is both a simple and a complicated problem. It is simple because there is one complete and perfect plan that guarantees success; it requires only five words of description: "Eat less. Move around more." Regardless of the genes it carries, any animal of any species will lose weight when it expends more calories than it consumes. The equation holds whether the calories are consumed in hamburgers or in fresh, organic vegetables. Similarly, it doesn't matter whether energy is expended in the weight room or on the couch.

But weight loss is also complex: while we know that eating less and moving around more are all that is necessary, and while almost all short-term "diets" work, in the long-run, with very few exceptions, they fail. (**FIGURE 22-38**). More than half of the advice books currently on the *New York Times* bestseller list promise new plans for losing weight. Five years ago that was also true—although the bestsellers were different books. It may seem as if there are plenty of new ideas about how to lose weight, yet the problem has not gone away. Rather, it has gotten worse.

Current interventions designed to facilitate weight loss range from mild to extreme. They fall into three categories: drugs, surgery, and behavior modification. Each has both promising and problematic elements (**FIGURE 22-39**).

Drugs and Other Chemical Interventions

Xenical. The most promising of recently developed weight-control drugs is Xenical, a product that interferes with fat digestion by binding to lipases (fat-digesting enzymes) and

 It may seem as if there are plenty of new ideas about how to lose weight, but any successful plan must simply help people to "eat less and move around more."

FIGURE 22-38 Weight-loss diets make for popular reading.

blocking them from doing their job. As a consequence, some of the fat in the digestive system passes through the body without absorption. In randomized, double-blind, placebo-controlled clinical studies—the gold standard for experimental design—Xenical has succeeded in helping people lose about 10 pounds over the course of one year. In the second year, these people regained some of their weight, but still ended up a bit lighter and with reduced circulating cholesterol and blood pressure. These findings are promising, but no long-term studies have been conducted to assess the permanence of the weight loss or potential side effects. Additionally, at a cost of more than $1,000 per year, Xenical is too expensive for most people to use.

Meridia. Approved for the treatment of obesity, this appetite-suppressant has shown promise as a weight-loss product. It reduces the rate at which the chemical serotonin, associated

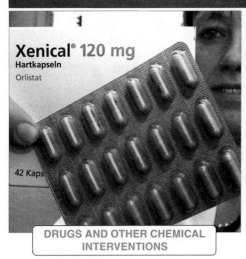

DRUGS AND OTHER CHEMICAL INTERVENTIONS

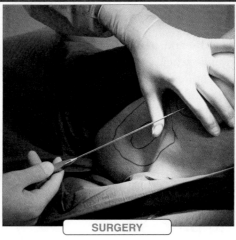

SURGERY

BEHAVIOR MODIFICATIONS: WEIGHT-LOSS DIETS

FIGURE 22-39 **What are the promises and perils of weight-loss interventions?**

with satiation, is removed from the space between nerve cells in the brain. Concerns over possible adverse effects on the cardiovascular system, however, have prompted some opposition to continued availability of this prescription drug.

Olestra and NutraSweet. Some artificially created molecules, such as Olestra and NutraSweet, can trick our taste buds into responding as if a molecule of sugar or fat, respectively, were present. Olestra, for example, is designed to have a taste and texture similar to fats, but in an indigestible molecule (see Section 2-13). After stimulating the taste buds that normally respond to fats, it ultimately is excreted, without having yielded any energy (read: without having deposited unwanted fat in your body). Still, as the NutraSweet cookie study described earlier in this chapter illustrates, our bodies have been built to detect reductions in caloric intake and to respond by increasing consumption. We're not tricked quite so easily. For this reason, low-calorie versions of food are unlikely to be successful on their own in generating permanent weight loss.

Caffeine and other stimulants. A variety of products claim to increase the expenditure of energy without an offsetting increase in appetite. This approach is theoretically sound, but there are no published data on either the safety or efficiency of these unregulated products. While clinical trials demonstrate that stimulants such as caffeine can produce short-term weight loss in the range of 5–10 pounds, long-term studies reveal that most of the short-term losses do not last.

Placebo. During clinical studies for diet pills, one observation was quite unexpected. As we learned in Chapter 1, researchers testing new compounds always have a "placebo" group. Subjects in this group go through all the same motions but get pills with none of the test drug. Because the placebo pills and

the test drug pills are identical in appearance, no one knows which patients are getting the drug candidate and which are getting blanks. The goal is to separate the effects of the test drug from the effects of the monitoring process. As expected, some new drugs work and others fail, but here's the strangest finding: people in placebo groups always lose weight. In a study on the effectiveness of Xenical, for instance, more than 25% of the people in the placebo group lost at least 10 pounds. How can this be? While those in the placebo group aren't using drugs, they are keeping track of their weight and are more aware of their food intake than usual. This mindfulness may be the only "secret" behind the success of some crazy and non-scientific diets that advocate, for example, only eating food of a certain color (but "as much as you want") on a certain day. Careful monitoring proves to be a crucial component of weight control.

Surgery

Liposuction. Liposuction is fast becoming one of the most popular surgical procedures in the United States, with close to half a million performed each year. In this procedure, doctors directly remove fat cells from various parts of the body, using a hollow tube and a suction device. Over time, however, individuals who have undergone liposuction tend to regain all the lost weight. In fact, the only follow-up study on liposuction found that within a few months, nearly half of the patients weighed more than they did before the surgery. This is because body weight is a function of caloric intake and energy expenditure; fat cells can be removed, but without a change in the inputs and outputs, eventually the body will achieve the same composition.

Bariatric surgery and stomach banding. More invasive surgical procedures are also possible. The most effective is also the most extreme. In a type of surgical procedure known as bariatric surgery, surgeons bypass a significant portion of the small intestine and seal off, by stomach banding, most of a person's stomach. This has two effects. First, it reduces the amount of food people can eat before becoming full—they actually become violently ill if they consume more than a few tablespoons at one time. And second, it reduces the ability of their small intestine to digest and absorb nutrients. Before all of the nutrients that they consume can be absorbed, the food material passes through the shortened digestive system and is excreted. The surgery carries significant risks, though, and leads to major nutritional deficiencies in almost a third of all cases. Still, something can be said for bariatric surgery that cannot be said unequivocally for any drug or diet: it works. One study of more than 600 patients found that after 14 years, the average weight loss was 100 pounds! Additionally, many health problems such as diabetes, high cholesterol, and high blood pressure went away.

Behavior Modification: Weight-Loss Diets

Portion control and general caloric restriction. Can we change our eating habits permanently? To answer this question, researchers put a group of monkeys on a very low-calorie diet. The monkeys shed pounds initially, then stabilized at much lower weights for two years. After two years they were given unlimited access to food. Did they maintain their new weights? Absolutely not. After spending close to 10% of their lives at a constant, low weight, these monkeys quickly returned to their original, pre-diet weights.

This monkey example suggests that there might be a "set point" for body weight. A variety of human and non-human studies do, in fact, reveal that just like a thermostat for a room, when weight is below the set point, the body induces calorie-seeking behavior, and when weight is above the set point, the mind and body are free to pursue other goals. In a human study equivalent to the hungry monkey study, researchers observed a group of successful dieters over time. The newly skinny people had lost an average of 70 pounds per person through a comprehensive program. Three years after completing the program, the participants had, on average, regained all of their lost weight.

Low-carbohydrate diets. These are the latest in a long series of fad diets that enjoy popularity before being discarded for failing to deliver on the claims of their proponents and the promise of their short-term success. They are based on the incorrect assumption that carbohydrates universally cause rapid increases in blood sugar, followed by large releases of insulin from the pancreas, leading to immediate and efficient conversion of the blood sugar into fats that are stored throughout the body. While this scenario is correct for some carbohydrates, other carbohydrates, such as whole wheat pasta, produce less of an insulin response than a similar amount of high-protein beef. Similarly, many high-fiber fruits and vegetables are also rich in carbohydrates yet increase blood sugar levels only very gradually

and elicit very small insulin responses. As a consequence, blanket avoidance of carbohydrates can lead to insufficient fiber intake as well as vitamin and mineral deficiencies. Unlimited consumption of fat, too, can lead to a caloric surplus and weight gain. Low-carbohydrate diets do lead reliably to impressive initial weight loss. This is because in the absence of dietary carbohydrates, glycogen (and the large amount of water bound to it) in the liver and muscles is quickly used up.

General Problems with Weight-Loss Diets The main problems with most popular weight-loss diets are that (1) they focus on reducing weight (even weight due to water) rather than reducing body fat; (2) they reduce muscle mass, the body tissue best able to burn fat; (3) because they reduce body weight too rapidly, they trigger several defense mechanisms designed to preserve the body's energy reserves; and (4) they don't focus enough on the other side of the energy equation: exercise. (**FIGURE 22-40**). This generally leads to four problems.

GENERAL PROBLEMS WITH WEIGHT-LOSS DIETS
- They focus on reducing weight (even weight due to water) rather than body fat.
- They reduce muscle mass, the body tissue best able to burn fat.
- Because they reduce body weight too rapidly, they trigger several defense mechanisms designed to preserve the body's energy reserves, generally leading to even more problems.
- They don't focus enough on the other side of the energy equation: exercise.

FIGURE 22-40 **Weight-loss diets often fail.**

1. *Nutritional deficiencies.* Consider how a family facing a financial crunch may be forced to defer important work, such as fixing the car's brakes. Similarly, when the body goes into efficiency mode to combat a shortage of calories, a variety of systems get modulated down or turned off. Hungry lab animals, for example, almost completely lose their sex drive and may be less adept at fighting infection. Nearly all popular diets are seriously deficient in vitamins, minerals, and fiber.

2. *Metabolic rate reduction.* Sudden caloric restriction leads to a rapid reduction in basal metabolic rate, and this lower rate remains for several weeks after resuming normal caloric intake. With a reduced BMR, your body burns fat at a slower rate.

3. *Loss of muscle mass and body fluids rather than body fat.* Low-calorie diets lead to weight loss, but as much as 45% of the weight loss comes from the loss of muscle mass. Muscle tissue is significantly more metabolically active than the relatively inert fat cells. As a consequence, the body's fat-burning capacity is significantly reduced along with its muscle mass. Weight loss, as we've noted, is also commonly due to loss of the water bound to glycogen in muscles and the liver.

4. *Increased lipoprotein lipase activity.* With a reduction in caloric intake, your body increases the activity of an enzyme called lipoprotein lipase. This enzyme is responsible for converting nutrients in the bloodstream to fats for storage.

As with the metabolic rate reduction, the increased activity of lipoprotein lipase continues for weeks following resumption of a normal diet.

An evaluation by the National Institutes of Health of *all* the major diet programs concluded that there was no good evidence that any of the programs reliably led to long-term weight loss. A large study published in the *New England Journal of Medicine* came to a similar conclusion in 2009. The claims made by weight-loss programs rely on anecdotal accounts of individuals that are not at all representative of the average outcome. Unfortunately, this means that there are no easy solutions to the problem of weight control. As long as we live in our modern, zoo-like environment of plenty, we're going to struggle with natural systems that relentlessly seek out and efficiently store calories.

TAKE-HOME MESSAGE 22•17

Weight loss is both a simple and a complicated problem. There is only one complete and perfect plan that guarantees success: reduced caloric intake and increased caloric expenditure. Interventions designed to facilitate weight loss involve drugs, surgery, or behavior modification, none of which is reliably successful.

22•18

Diabetes is caused by the body's inability to regulate blood sugar effectively.

A finely tuned, responsive machine. When it functions properly, the human body can resemble such a machine. Nowhere is this more true that in the processing of food. After you digest and absorb food, there's an increase in the amount of glucose circulating in your bloodstream. This triggers the release of insulin by your pancreas. Insulin is a storage-stimulating hormone that causes your body's cells, especially muscle cells and fat cells, to pull the glucose in. They can then either use it for energy or convert it to glycogen or fat for storage until the energy is needed some other time. This leads to a reduction in glucose in the bloodstream and brings your blood sugar level back down to normal.

Foods differ in the extent to which they cause a surge in blood sugar and subsequent release of insulin. Foods that cause a rapid and large surge—such as orange juice, honey, and white potatoes—are classified as having a high **glycemic**

index and are less desirable in the diet. More desirable are foods that cause only a slow, moderate increase, having a low glycemic index. These include whole grains and beans. With a reduced insulin response comes more efficient utilization of the sugar and lipids in the bloodstream and a reduction in fat storage. Insulin surges can also be reduced by eating smaller meals or, if you consume foods that have a high glycemic index, eating them with other foods as part of a meal.

Even finely tuned machines can malfunction. More than 10 million Americans (and 100 million people worldwide) have problems with their insulin-response systems, referred to as **diabetes.** These problems are chiefly of two types (**FIGURE 22-41**): either (1) the pancreas doesn't secrete enough insulin in response to an increase in blood sugar, or (2) the pancreas secretes plenty of insulin, but the cells of the body don't respond to it, usually due to a deficiency in glucose receptors on their

Food for Energy and Growth   Nutrients   Digestion and Absorption   Diet and Health

DIABETES: TYPE 1 vs. TYPE 2

Insulin—a hormone produced by the pancreas in response to increased blood sugar—causes your body's cells to pull glucose in from blood vessels.

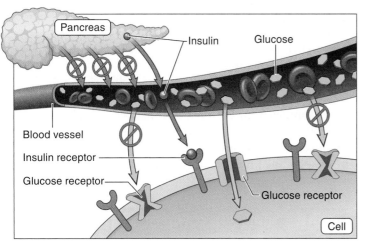

TYPE 1 DIABETES
The pancreas doesn't secrete enough insulin in response to an increase in blood sugar.

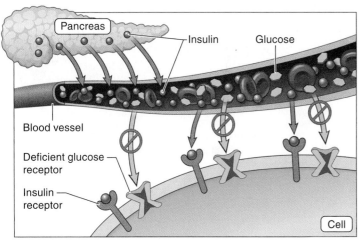

TYPE 2 DIABETES
The pancreas secretes plenty of insulin, but the cells of the body don't respond to it, usually due to a deficiency in glucose receptors on the cell membranes.

FIGURE 22-41 Diabetes is a disruption in the body's regulation of blood sugar.

Q Why must diabetics inject insulin rather than taking it in pill form?

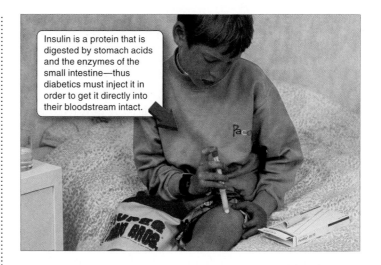

FIGURE 22-42 Type 1 diabetes is treated with insulin injections.

cell membranes. In both cases, blood sugar remains high, and a host of problems can occur as a result of such persistence of glucose in the bloodstream.

The first type of diabetes (called type 1) is hereditary and usually occurs in children. Generally, people with type 1 diabetes have a pancreas that doesn't secrete enough insulin, thus they can be treated by insulin injections (**FIGURE 22-42**). (Unfortunately, because insulin is a protein, it is digested by stomach acids and the enzymes of the small intestine, so diabetics must inject the insulin in order to get it into their bloodstream intact.) The second type of diabetes (type 2) is about 10 times more common. It generally develops after the age of 40, and in about 90% of cases is a consequence of obesity. It appears that chronic and excessive amounts of sugar in the diet (and, later, in the bloodstream) reduce the sensitivity and/or number of cellular insulin receptors that help control blood sugar. This causes even greater releases of insulin, which can, ultimately, wear out the insulin-producing cells of the pancreas. Type 2 diabetes is treated by minimizing the glucose fluctuations in the bloodstream. Weight loss is also encouraged, as it reduces insulin resistance.

Because chronically high levels of blood sugar affect nearly all the cells of the body, the health effects can be far-reaching and severe. Cells in the eye lens can become deformed, causing blurry vision; blood vessels can be damaged, causing circulatory system and kidney malfunction; and nerves can also be damaged. Taken together, the varied problems resulting from diabetes make it the sixth leading cause of death in the United States.

TAKE-HOME MESSAGE 22·18

Digesting and absorbing food leads to an increase in the amount of glucose circulating in the bloodstream, which triggers the release of insulin by the pancreas, causing the body's cells, especially muscle cells and fat cells, to pull the glucose in for energy or storage. Problems with regulation of blood sugar, called diabetes, affect millions of people and are caused by heredity and poor diet.

Food and infection: spicy foods are natural antibiotics.

Have you ever tasted salsa so spicy that it brought tears to your eyes? After you gulped down a beverage to extinguish the fire in your mouth, did you ignore the distress signals from your taste buds and head right back for more? Why would anyone seek out such culinary torture? The answer is surprisingly simple, although not immediately apparent. We'll start by asking the question: what *are* spicy foods?

Spices come from plants. Plants are rooted in the ground, and their immobility makes them easy targets for their natural enemies. But although they can't run away, they don't just give in to those organisms that want to eat them. They fight back chemically. Plants have evolved to produce a large number of toxic compounds to help in this fight. The presence of these noxious chemicals makes the plant toxic to would-be predators, either killing them outright or being so unpleasant-tasting that predators search elsewhere for a meal.

Humans, somewhat unexpectedly, actually seek out these toxins. We don't think of them as toxins, though. We call them spices, and as long as they're not too toxic, they make our food taste better. There is also a deeper, more evolutionarily relevant reason we find our food to be more appealing with spices added. They help us in our own battles with natural enemies. "Food poisoning," it turns out—which affects about 1 out of 10 people in the United States each year—is a misleading term. It isn't the food that poisons us. Instead, it is the microorganisms, particularly bacteria, that poison us. Humans and plants must perpetually fight against infection from microorganisms. This task is difficult because bacteria find easy entry into our bodies via the food we eat. After sitting out at room temperature for just a few hours, food can acquire huge amounts of bacteria. But by adding spices to our food, we take advantage of the plant defenses to strike back at the microbes, killing them before they make it to our digestive systems.

The "spices kill bugs" theory emerged from extensive observations and analyses. It has generated several predictions that have been tested.

Prediction 1: The magnitude of spice use in any part of the world should be related to the amount of microbial growth in that part of the world.

Observations: Put another way, this is a prediction that in warm, wet countries (where microbial growth occurs more readily), spice use should be greatest, while in cooler climates, spice use should be less. In an analysis of more than 4,500 meat-based recipes and 2,100 vegetable-

based recipes from 36 countries, this prediction was overwhelmingly supported. There is a strong correlation between regions with high average temperatures and their use of spices with antimicrobial effects (**FIGURE 22-43**). Spices were included in every single recipe, for example, from Ethiopia, Kenya, Greece, India, Indonesia, Iran, Malaysia, Morocco, Nigeria, and Thailand. Conversely, two-thirds of all recipes from Finland and Norway called for no spices at all.

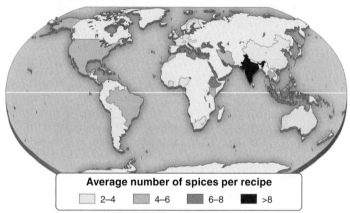

SPICE USE AND CLIMATE

Average number of spices per recipe

| 2–4 | 4–6 | 6–8 | >8 |

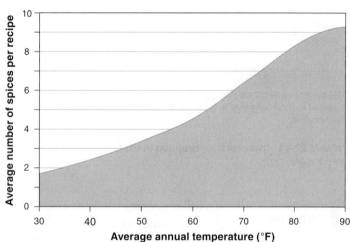

There is a strong correlation between regions having high average temperatures (where microbial growth occurs more readily) and their use of spices with antimicrobial effects.

FIGURE 22-43 Fighting natural enemies. Antimicrobial spices are used much more where temperatures are high.

Food for Energy and Growth   Nutrients   Digestion and Absorption   Diet and Health

SPICE USE AND ANTIMICROBIAL PROPERTIES

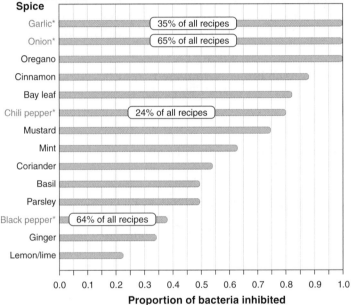

Spice

Garlic* — 35% of all recipes
Onion* — 65% of all recipes
Oregano
Cinnamon
Bay leaf
Chili pepper* — 24% of all recipes
Mustard
Mint
Coriander
Basil
Parsley
Black pepper* — 64% of all recipes
Ginger
Lemon/lime

0.0 0.1 0.2 0.3 0.4 0.5 0.6 0.7 0.8 0.9 1.0
Proportion of bacteria inhibited

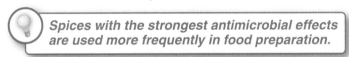

Spices with the strongest antimicrobial effects are used more frequently in food preparation.

* The four most commonly used spices are shown in red.

FIGURE 22-44 Recipe ingredients with antimicrobial properties. (Photo shows woman with drying chili peppers.)

Two observations suggest that this relationship between spice use and climate cannot be attributed to the fact that more spices grow in the countries with hotter, wetter climates. First, onion and garlic, two of the most potent antimicrobial spices, grow in all of the countries studied but are used more frequently in the warmer countries. And second, although the warmer countries do have larger numbers of local spices to choose from, they use a greater proportion of the available spices than do the cooler countries.

Prediction 2: Spices with the strongest antimicrobial effects should be used most, and the weaker antimicrobial agents used less frequently.

Observations: In a test of 42 spices, in which each was added to individual plates of bacteria, nearly all exhibited antimicrobial properties—sometimes quite dramatically—when used in the amounts called for in recipes. For example, the toxic compound in cilantro was twice as effective at killing *Salmonella* bacteria as was the commonly used antibiotic drug gentamicin. Most of the spices tested were broad in their effects, too, killing most of the 30 different types of common food-borne bacteria tested. Overall, onions and black pepper, which had the best antimicrobial effects (they killed all species of bacteria they came into contact with), were used most frequently, appearing in more than 60% of all recipes. They were followed by garlic (in 35% of all recipes), chili peppers (24%), and lemon and lime juice (23%). Other commonly used spices include parsley, ginger, bay leaf, coriander, and cinnamon (**FIGURE 22-44**).

Prediction 3: Because bacterial growth is faster and more common on meat than on vegetables, meat recipes should call for more spices than vegetable recipes.

Observations: The vegetable recipes called for, on average, 2.4 spices, while the meat recipes called for almost twice as many, with an average of 3.9.

Research on the connection between the use of spices and their antimicrobial properties continues. Nonetheless, it seems to be quite likely that humans did initially incorporate spices into food preparation because of their antimicrobial properties. Given that refrigeration is a very recent invention, consumption of food that had been "sanitized" by spices ensured the spice-consumers greater survival and reproduction. This example shows how seemingly arbitrary behaviors may reflect evolutionary adaptations.

TAKE-HOME MESSAGE 22·19

Plants produce toxic compounds that make the plant distasteful to would-be predators, either killing them outright or being so unpleasant-tasting that predators search elsewhere for a meal. Humans seek out these toxins, using them as spices that help us fight off illness-inducing microorganisms.

Knowledge You Can Use

When digestion breaks down. Microbes, stress, and stomach ulcers.

Q: If the digestive system is so good at breaking down all the molecules sent through it, why doesn't it digest itself? The cells lining the stomach are protected by a layer of highly alkaline (i.e., the opposite of acidic) mucus that keeps them from coming in direct contact with the strong stomach acids.

Q: What happens if the stomach lining is damaged? Breaches in the protective layer of mucus in the stomach render the stomach vulnerable to ulcers—from small erosions in the digestive tract lining to life-threatening holes all the way through to the abdominal cavity. Ulcers can also form in the first part of the small intestine.

Q: What causes these ulcers? Ulcers are caused by infections of bacteria living in the stomach and the first part of the small intestine. Called *Helicobacter pylori,* these bacteria live in the tiny spaces between the stomach- and intestine-lining cells, where they create cocoon-like areas around themselves that are less acidic than their surroundings. The bacteria then damage the mucus and the top layer of cells, while stimulating increased secretions of acids. This exposes the underlying cells to harsh gastric juices, hydrochloric acid, and digestive enzymes. The result is a minor irritation at first, but over time, the harsh chemicals can eat right through the cells, at which point they damage the underlying capillaries—causing the ulcer to bleed—and can damage the nerves in the area, too, causing extreme pain.

Q: But isn't it stress that causes stomach ulcers? Until about 1990, it was not clear that ulcers were caused by bacterial infection. Instead, it was believed that psychological stress played a much more important role in causing stomach ulcers. Because antibiotics can kill *H. pylori* and cure most ulcers within two weeks, however, it now seems clear that the role of stress in causing stomach ulcers is relatively small.

Q: What can you conclude? While stress is off the hook as the culprit, ulcers are still not completely understood. Consider, for instance, that as many as 50% of people in the world have *H. pylori* living in their digestive systems, yet only about 10% of people will develop an ulcer at some point in their lives. Clearly, there are additional factors beyond infection. And research increasingly reveals that stress does reduce the immune system's effectiveness and can increase susceptibility to illness. We explore this link in Chapter 26.

1 Food provides the raw materials for growth and the fuel to make it happen.

Animals must eat for two reasons: to acquire the energy needed for all growth and activity, and to acquire the raw materials required for life. Carnivores consume only other animals. Herbivores consume only plants. And omnivores consume both plants and animals. The minimal energetic needs of an individual not engaged in any activity are called the basal metabolic rate, or BMR.

2 Nutrients are grouped into six categories.

Water is probably the single most important component of a balanced diet, while proteins, carbohydrates, and fats provide calories and raw materials. Vitamins and minerals are organic and inorganic molecules (respectively) in the diet that are used in the production and action of enzymes and other molecules. Humans and other animals show an evolved preference for fatty foods over carbohydrate- or protein-laden foods.

3 We extract energy and nutrients from food.

The digestive process in humans includes four distinct phases. (1) Ingestion involves tearing and grinding food in preparation for passing it to the stomach. (2) Digestion, the process of dismantling large pieces of food, physically and chemically breaking them down into absorbable molecules, occurs primarily in the stomach and small intestine. (3) Absorption, in the small intestine, is the process by which energy-rich food particles are taken into the cells of the body. (4) Water and ions are absorbed before the indigestible portions of consumed food are defecated. Most animals don't produce enzymes that break down cellulose, although many have symbiotic bacteria that do this for them.

4 What we eat profoundly affects our health.

Ancestral humans experienced unpredictable food supplies, leading to the evolution of strong appetites. In the modern industrial world, such instincts have problematic consequences for weight control. Although there is, in theory, one complete and perfect plan that guarantees successful weight control—reduced caloric intake and increased caloric expenditure—the many interventions designed to help people lose weight are rarely successful. Problems with regulation of blood sugar, called diabetes, affect millions of people and are often caused by poor diet. Somewhat ironically, but for good evolutionary reasons, humans seek out toxic compounds that are produced by plants to ward off predators. Such compounds, used as spices, help us fight off illness-inducing microorganisms.

KEY TERMS

1. Based on the types of diet they consume, spiders and owls are considered:
   a) carnivores.
   b) omnivores.
   c) herbivores.
   d) primary producers.
   e) fluid-feeders.

2. Basal metabolic rate:
   a) depends to a large degree on how active an individual is.
   b) does not vary across mammalian species.
   c) is a measure of the minimal energetic needs of an individual not engaged in any activity.
   d) is the same for males and females of any given species.
   e) All of the above are correct.

3. Water has many functions in animal bodies. These include all of the following except:
   a) lubricating many joints, the spinal cord, and the eyes.
   b) serving as a solvent for many vitamins and minerals.
   c) transporting nutrients and waste materials throughout the body.
   d) regulating growth and development.
   e) All of the above are functions of water in animal bodies.

4. Why do dieters lose large amounts of "water weight" during the first few days of a diet?
   a) The first, most accessible, molecules that can be broken down for energy are glycogen molecules in muscles and liver. And because large amounts of water are bound to glycogen, as the glycogen is removed from tissues, so too is the water.
   b) Dieters tend to reduce their consumption of all food and beverages—including their consumption of water—during the first days of a diet.
   c) Dieting causes a slight increase in body temperature, which leads to increased evaporative cooling and the loss of water.
   d) The fat cells of the body are primarily filled with water. As these cells are utilized for energy, the water is also lost.
   e) Actually, dieters do not lose "water weight" during the first few days of a diet. This is a myth.

5. On food packages, "fiber" refers to plant material that we can't fully digest but is important for maintaining a healthy digestive tract. "Fiber" refers to a type of:
   a) carbohydrate.   d) amino acid.
   b) nucleic acid.   e) protein.
   c) lipid.

6. Proteins are an essential component of a healthy diet for humans (and other animals). Their most common purpose is to serve as:
   a) fuel for running the body.
   b) raw material for growth.
   c) inorganic precursors for enzyme construction.
   d) organic precursors for membrane construction.
   e) long-term energy storage.

7. Vitamin and mineral supplements are generally necessary for individuals in all of the following categories except:
   a) post-menopausal women.
   b) healthy people with good diets.
   c) people on extremely low-calorie diets.
   d) pregnant women.
   e) people with limited milk consumption or sun exposure.

8. Most mammals (including humans) prefer the taste of fats to carbohydrates and proteins. Why?
   a) Fats are more easily digested than proteins or carbohydrates.
   b) Fats were much less available than proteins and carbohydrates in most ecosystems in which humans and other mammals evolved.
   c) The caloric content of a gram of fat is more than double that of a gram of protein or carbohydrate.
   d) The vitamin and mineral content of a gram of fat is more than double that of a gram of protein or carbohydrate.
   e) Many individuals lack the enzymes (such as lactase) to break down polysaccharides into their component sugars.

9. Why do birds eat gravel?
   a) Gravel contains most of the essential minerals for a bird's diet.
   b) Birds have poor vision and have difficulty distinguishing gravel from small seeds.
   c) By chewing on gravel, birds are able to sharpen their teeth, increasing their ability to crack open hard nuts or catch their prey.
   d) The gravel collects in the stomach, where it helps to grind up the food they eat.
   e) Because they have such a small brain relative to body size, birds tend to be the least intelligent of all vertebrates.

10. Across dozens of cultures, humans have developed common ways of preparing their food, including using heat and marinating food in acidic solutions, such as vinegar or lemon juice. How might these be adaptations that help with digestion?
    a) Harsh conditions such as heat and acid help to disrupt the tissue of food items. This increases the efficiency with which digestive enzymes can make contact with the food molecules and break them down.
    b) These methods of food preparation reduce the necessity of producing chyme and so increase the caloric efficiency of food intake.
    c) Because even the weakest acids are toxic to all bacteria, these methods of food preparation reduce the incidence of dietary-induced bacterial infection.
    d) These methods increase the body's ability to extract energy from normally indigestible cellulose.
    e) These methods of food preparation reduce the need for water consumption.

11. Which of the following statements about the small intestine is incorrect?

   a) It is the primary site of digestion and absorption of nutrients into the bloodstream.

   b) It is the chief site of absorption of water by the digestive system.

   c) It is the longest part of the digestive tract.

   d) It receives secretions from the gall bladder.

   e) It is the part of the digestive tract where all food macromolecules can be broken down into absorbable monomers.

12. To leave the digestive tract and enter the cells of the body, a substance must cross a cell membrane. During which stage of digestion does this take place?

   a) peristalsis   d) chemotaxis

   b) absorption   e) ingestion

   c) elimination

13. Digestion and absorption:

   a) involve the breakdown of food into small nutrient molecules (absorption) and the passage of those molecules into the bloodstream (digestion).

   b) both occur primarily in the large intestine, or colon.

   c) are terms that describe the same process.

   d) both occur primarily in the stomach.

   e) involve the breakdown of food into small nutrient molecules (digestion) and the passage of those molecules into the bloodstream (absorption).

14. In the mammalian digestive system, vitamin-synthesizing symbiotic bacteria live primarily in the:

   a) small intestine.

   b) esophagus.

   c) mouth.

   d) large intestine.

   e) stomach.

15. Though essentially the same organ, the human appendix is much smaller than a koala's cecum. This is because:

   a) humans take supplements to obtain enough vitamins and do not need the extra vitamins produced by the bacteria housed in the appendix.

   b) humans aid the digestive process by marinating and cooking foods, so they do not require a large appendix to aid food digestion.

   c) humans maintain bacteria in their intestine rather than in their appendix, so the organ does not need to be as large as a koala's cecum.

   d) humans use the appendix to digest proteins rather than cellulose.

   e) humans get a greater proportion of their nutrients from meat than do koalas, so they do not need as large an organ to digest the plant matter they eat.

16. Cows have large populations of bacteria in their digestive systems. Which of the following best explains why?

   a) The mutualistic microbes combat the harmful microbes that may enter a cow's body on its food.

   b) Cows are able to use cellulose-producing bacteria to help them digest their food.

   c) Most cows actually do not have large populations of bacteria in their digestive systems. Only infected cows have these microbes.

   d) Scientists put the microbes there, so that they can study how the microbes affect cows' digestion.

   e) The microbes metabolize the cellulose in the plants that cows eat.

17. The spices that many humans use to season their food:

   a) are generally compounds produced by plants to reduce their risk of being eaten.

   b) are actually dead microorganisms.

   c) consist primarily of amino acids.

   d) are the chief cause of ulcers.

   e) can only be grown in tropical regions of the world.

SHORT-ANSWER QUESTIONS

1. What are the six groups of nutrients? What is their primary role in human health?

2. What are the four distinct phases used by humans to extract nutrients from food? For each phase, what significant activity takes place that contributes to nutrient harvesting and absorption?

3. Describe how some mammals, which do not have enzymes to break down cellulose, are able to extract nutrients from cellulose-containing food.

4. Describe the two forms of diabetes. What are the risk factors and treatments?

See Appendix for answers. For additional study questions, go to www.prep-u.com.

25

Reproduction and Development

From two parents
to one embryo
to one baby

❶ How do animals reproduce?

The endangered black rhinoceros and calf.

25•1 –

Reproductive options (and ethical issues) are on the rise.

Thirty-year-old Diane Blood wanted to have a child with her husband, Stephen. And then the High Court in England ruled that she could not. The problem: her husband was dead.

Stephen Blood had died of bacterial meningitis two years earlier, but when he was in a coma the day before he died, his wife asked the doctors to take sperm from him, and the sperm sample was frozen and stored. The Human Fertilisation and Embryology Authority, however, ruled that because he hadn't given written consent, his sperm could not be used.

This case illustrates a type of ethical and legal quandary that is becoming increasingly common (**FIGURE 25-1**). Technology is making conception and pregnancy possible in many situations where they previously were not possible. But along with many happy outcomes, there are also numerous complex legal battles and, as yet, few consistent legal decisions on such matters. Here are some examples.

Q *Are frozen embryos divided up like other marital assets at divorce?*

• Do couples have the right to make contracts with a surrogate mother, a woman who carries and gives birth to their child? And, if so, can they pay her a salary to do so? In North Dakota, the surrogate actually becomes

the legal parent of the child. In Washington, DC, and in many states, a couple can pay the surrogate's expenses, but nothing more.

• Do egg donors have any rights (and responsibilities) with respect to the children conceived with their eggs? Is the situation the same for sperm donors? Several states have ruled differently on these issues.

• Do children conceived from sperm or egg donors have a right to know who the donor was?

• If a couple has embryos created and frozen for later implantation but then gets divorced, who retains custody of the embryos? In one Tennessee case, custody was given to the mother, against the wishes of the father. A Texas court, on the other hand, refused to give frozen embryos to the mother. With almost half a million frozen embryos in the United States, this is likely to be an increasingly common issue for courts to decide.

In this chapter, we describe how men produce sperm and women produce eggs, as well as the process by which fertilization occurs (or does not occur). We also explore the early stages of development, following fertilization, including

25-2 CHAPTER 25 • REPRODUCTION AND DEVELOPMENT

▼
How Do Animals Reproduce? Male and Female Reproductive Systems Sex Can Lead to Fertilization Human Development

Advances in assisted reproductive technology are giving rise to complex legal battles and ethical dilemmas.

FIGURE 25-1 In the headlines: ethical issues and reproductive technologies.

the steps by which an embryo is triggered to develop as a male or a female. We also investigate the perils and promise of a variety of assisted reproductive technologies.

But first, a happy resolution to the case we opened with. Diane Blood was eventually allowed to take the sperm to another country where she could be inseminated (after re-mortgaging her house to pay for the expensive legal battles). The law in England still prevents storage of sperm from a man without his written consent, but an appeals court made an exception in her case, and Diane Blood was able to conceive a child (and, three and a half years later, another child) with her husband's sperm.

TAKE-HOME MESSAGE 25·1

Technology is making conception and pregnancy possible in many situations where they previously were not possible. But it is simultaneously giving rise to complex legal battles and ethical dilemmas

25·2

There are costs and benefits to having a partner: asexual versus sexual reproduction.

The term reproduction, the biological process by which new organisms are produced from existing organisms, usually conjures images of a male and a female, contributing equal amounts of genetic material and producing offspring together. And for most animals, this is how it's done. But recall from Section 6-14 that there are two fundamentally different ways in which organisms can reproduce. While the vast majority of plants and animals reproduce sexually, prokaryotes and many plant and animal species reproduce asexually—and some can reproduce in both ways.

Asexual reproduction involves the production of offspring by a single individual without a contribution of genetic material from another individual. There are several types of

Q Do female turkeys need males to reproduce?

asexual reproduction in animals, including parthenogenesis, budding, and fragmentation (FIGURE 25-2).

Parthenogenesis. In **parthenogenesis,** a female's egg develops into a new organism without ever having to be fertilized by a sperm cell. Some species can reproduce asexually or sexually, depending on

TYPES OF ASEXUAL REPRODUCTION

Asexual reproduction involves the production of offspring by a single individual without contribution of genetic material from another individual.

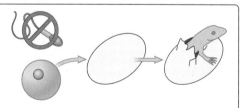

PARTHENOGENESIS
A female's egg develops into a new organism without ever having to be fertilized by a sperm cell.

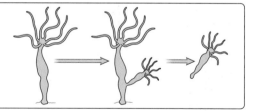

BUDDING
An offspring grows right out of the body of the parent.

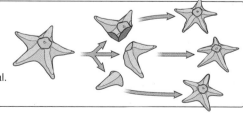

FRAGMENTATION
A parent breaks into multiple pieces, and each develops into a fully functioning, independent individual.

FIGURE 25-2 Asexual reproduction: parthenogenesis, budding, and fragmentation.

environmental conditions; parthenogenesis allows them to utilize resources as quickly as possible. Aphids, for example, produce eggs that develop into normal adults without fertilization in the spring, when food is plentiful. When food is more limited, the eggs are fertilized before development. Hammerhead sharks and, occasionally, turkeys also have the capability to reproduce by parthenogenesis (although turkeys resulting from asexual reproduction tend to be less healthy). Other animal species, including the desert grassland whiptail lizard, are exclusively asexual, and all of the individuals in the species are female. Among these lizards, though, ovulation rates are increased by female-female courtship rituals and behavior called "pseudocopulation" that resembles the male-female mating seen in related species.

Budding. In budding, an offspring grows directly out of the body of the parent. Hydras, predatory cnidarians, reproduce by budding.

Fragmentation. In fragmentation, a parent breaks into multiple pieces, each of which develops into a fully functioning, independent individual. Fragmentation is seen among many species of flatworms, as well as some sea stars. Among some sea stars, for example, if even a tiny part of one arm breaks off, it can develop into a complete individual.

In contrast to asexual reproduction, **sexual reproduction** involves two individuals contributing genetic material to produce offspring (**FIGURE 25-3**). The genetic material is

SEXUAL REPRODUCTION

Sexual reproduction involves two individuals contributing genetic material to produce offspring. The genetic material is contained in gametes, the reproductive cells.

EGG
• Female gamete
• Haploid (one copy of each chromosome)

SPERM
• Male gamete
• Haploid (one copy of each chromosome)

FERTILIZATION

FERTILIZED EGG
• Diploid (two copies of each chromosome)

FIGURE 25-3 In sexual reproduction, two parents contribute genetic material to the offspring. The fusion of female gamete (egg) and male gamete (sperm) forms a zygote that potentially develops into offspring.

contained in gametes, the reproductive cells. The male gamete is called a **sperm** (or sperm cell) and the female gamete is called an egg or **ovum** (*pl.* **ova**). Recall from

SEXUAL vs. ASEXUAL REPRODUCTION

SEXUAL REPRODUCTION

ADVANTAGES
• Offspring are genetically different from each other and from either parent.
• Genetic diversity among offspring can be an evolutionary adaptation, increasing fitness in changing environments.

DISADVANTAGES
• Finding a partner and mating can be difficult and time-consuming.
• Only half of an individual's alleles will be passed to its offspring.

ASEXUAL REPRODUCTION

ADVANTAGES
• Reproduction is fast and efficient.
• All of an individual's alleles are passed on to its offspring.

DISADVANTAGES
• With a changing environment, individuals producing genetically diverse offspring are more likely to have offspring suited to the environment.

FIGURE 25-4 Genetic variation versus efficiency: advantages and disadvantages of sexual and asexual reproduction.

25-4 CHAPTER 25 • REPRODUCTION AND DEVELOPMENT

How Do Animals Reproduce?   Male and Female Reproductive Systems   Sex Can Lead to Fertilization   Human Development

Section 6-11 that the cellular division process of meiosis produces gametes, cells that contain only half as many sets of chromosomes as other body cells (the somatic cells). When the male and female gametes fuse in **fertilization,** the full chromosome number is restored to the diploid condition. Both the production of the gametes and the combination of genetic material from two individuals at fertilization tend to increase the genetic diversity among offspring. We explore sexual reproduction in greater detail in the remainder of this chapter.

An important feature of sexual reproduction is that it leads to offspring that differ genetically from each other and from either parent (see Figures 6-21 and 6-23). This genetic diversity among an individual's offspring can be an evolutionary adaptation, increasing fitness in changing environments. If an environment is gradually changing, individuals producing diverse offspring increase the likelihood that one of their offspring will be suited, genetically, to the new environment. There are, however, disadvantages to sexual reproduction. The two main drawbacks are that (1) finding a partner and mating can be time-consuming and dangerous, and (2) an individual

contributes only half of the alleles that its offspring carry (**FIGURE 25-4**).

With asexual reproduction, the advantages and disadvantages are more or less reversed. It can be fast and easy, because it involves only a single individual. And if an organism's environment is stable, it is beneficial for offspring to carry all of the genes that their parent carried. If an environment is changing, however, asexually reproducing organisms may be at a disadvantage.

TAKE-HOME MESSAGE 25·2

Organisms can reproduce in two ways: asexually or sexually—or both. Asexual reproduction, which can be fast and efficient, leads to offspring genetically identical to the parent; it occurs in all prokaryotes and in many plant and animal species. Sexual reproduction, which leads to offspring that are genetically different from each other and from either parent, occurs in the vast majority of plant and animal species.

25·3

Fertilization can occur inside or outside a female's body.

Sexual reproduction, as we've seen, leads to the production of genetically diverse offspring and so can have evolutionary advantages. But because sexual reproduction requires male and female gametes to come together at fertilization, it also presents a challenge: the male and female gametes must somehow get to each other. Two general strategies have evolved as a consequence of this challenge: **external fertilization,** in which the sperm and egg unite outside the male's and female's bodies, and **internal fertilization,** in which the sperm are deposited directly in the female's reproductive tract and meet and unite with eggs inside the female's body (**FIGURE 25-5**).

The first vertebrates evolved in the oceans. In this environment, it was possible for females to produce and release batches of eggs right into the water. Males could then release sperm into the water, where fertilization could take place. Many aquatic invertebrates—including sea urchins and

clams—along with most fishes and amphibians use external fertilization to bring sperm and eggs together.

Although seawater is not harmful to sperm or eggs, one potential problem for organisms using external fertilization is that the tiny gametes of one sex can be very quickly washed away from those of the other sex when the gametes are released into water. For this reason, males and females of a species tend to produce very large numbers of gametes and release their gametes at the same time and very near each other. A variety of cues help to synchronize the release of gametes by males and females, including water temperature, the phase of the moon, day length, chemicals released by one or the other sex, and courtship rituals.

Q Male frogs clutch onto female frogs for months at a time without letting go. Why?

Among the most extreme tactics employed for ensuring that sperm and eggs are released at the same time and in the same place is something called

Reproductive Technology

EXTERNAL FERTILIZATION
The sperm and egg unite outside of the male's and the female's body.

INTERNAL FERTILIZATION
Sperm are deposited directly in the female's reproductive tract and unite with the eggs inside the female's body.

FIGURE 25-5 Methods of fertilization. Frogs deposit large quantities of sperm and eggs into the water, where some are fertilized. In mammals, such as bears, fertilization takes place within the reproductive tract of the female.

amplexus, used by most species of frogs. In amplexus, the male embraces the female frog from behind, wrapping his front legs around her body. He then holds on until the female releases her eggs, at which point he releases his sperm and fertilizes them. This doesn't sound all that remarkable, except that males will sometimes hold on to a female for weeks or even months at a time!

As we learned in Chapter 11, the colonization of land by vertebrates opened up a huge number of new niches, but presented one huge problem for animals. External fertilization just doesn't work well on land. First, gametes cannot be moved around (and thus toward each other) without water. Secondly, and even more important, gametes quickly dry out on land. For these reasons, there was strong selective pressure on land-colonizing vertebrates for a new method to evolve: internal fertilization.

Used by nearly all terrestrial animals, internal fertilization solves the problem of gamete desiccation (drying out) by having males deposit their sperm directly in the reproductive tract of females. This deposit is usually accomplished by the male placing his reproductive organ within the female's reproductive tract, in the act of **copulation.** Inside the female's body, there is sufficient moisture for the sperm to remain viable until one or more are able to fertilize her eggs.

Once an egg is fertilized by a sperm, the fertilized egg is called a zygote. Following the first division into two cells (and

The kangaroo is a viviparous animal. The embryo develops inside the womb of the mother for approximately 33 days when it emerges blind, hairless and just a few centimeters long. It finishes development in its mother's protective pouch—staying in the protective environment for many months.

How Do Animals Reproduce? | Male and Female Reproductive Systems | Sex Can Lead to Fertilization | Human Development

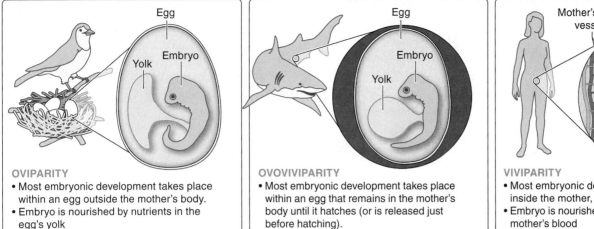

OVIPARITY
- Most embryonic development takes place within an egg outside the mother's body.
- Embryo is nourished by nutrients in the egg's yolk
- Examples: all birds; also some fishes, amphibians, reptiles, insects, and spiders

OVOVIVIPARITY
- Most embryonic development takes place within an egg that remains in the mother's body until it hatches (or is released just before hatching).
- Embryo is nourished by nutrients in the egg's yolk
- Examples: some sharks, fishes, amphibians, reptiles, and invertebrates

VIVIPARITY
- Most embryonic development takes place inside the mother, and live offspring are born.
- Embryo is nourished by nutrients in the mother's blood
- Examples: nearly all mammals; also some fishes, amphibians, and reptiles

FIGURE 25-6 **Three strategies for protecting and nourishing a developing embryo.**

continuing to approximately 8 weeks of development in humans), it is called an **embryo.** The embryo must, at some point in its development, leave the female's body. There are three different strategies for this (**FIGURE 25-6**).

1. Oviparity, a strategy in which the fertilized egg moves outside the body and most embryonic development continues there. The embryos are nourished by nutrients contained in the egg's yolk, and live offspring emerge or hatch from the egg. This developmental strategy is most familiar to us among birds (all bird species are oviparous), but it also occurs among most fishes, amphibians, reptiles, insects, and spiders.

2. Ovoviviparity, a less common strategy, in which most embryonic development takes place inside an egg, with the embryo nourished by the egg's yolk, but the egg itself remains in the female's body until it hatches (or is released just before hatching). This strategy is used by many aquatic organisms, including sharks and some other fishes, and some species of amphibians, reptiles, and invertebrates.

3. Viviparity, a strategy in which the embryo develops inside the mother, nourished by nutrients carried in her blood, and live offspring are born. This strategy is perhaps most familiar to us because it is used by humans and nearly all other mammals, but it is also occurs among some reptiles, amphibians, and fishes.

TAKE-HOME MESSAGE 25·3

Sexual reproduction requires fertilization, which occurs externally in most fishes and amphibians, and internally in most other vertebrates, including humans. Among those species having internal fertilization, development of the embryo can be nourished by yolk within an egg (that may or may not be retained within the female's body during development) or, remaining in the mother's body, by nutrients carried in her blood.

Reproductive Technology

❷ Male and female reproductive systems have important similarities and differences.

"From Here to Eternity," 1953

25•4

Sperm are made in the testes.

Beginning at puberty and continuing for their entire lives, men produce sperm, often more than 100 million per day. The process of sperm production, called **spermatogenesis,** is similar among most mammals and requires 9-10 weeks in humans. In this section, we examine the structures of the male reproductive system and the production of sperm and **semen,** a fluid expelled at ejaculation that usually contains sperm. We begin with an examination of the male reproductive structures and the role each plays in the process of sperm formation and fertilization (**FIGURE 25-7**).

Male Reproductive Structures Externally, a male has just two reproductive structures, the penis and the scrotum. The **penis** has three columns of tissue—one on either side and a third on the bottom side—that can become engorged with blood, causing erection and making copulation possible. In most animal species, including dogs, walruses, and most primates other than humans, a bone (known as a baculum) is present in the penis and contributes to its stiffness. The **scrotum,** generally on the outside of the body in the pelvis region, is a sac containing the two **testes** (*sing.* **testis;** also called testicles), the site of sperm production. Each testis is made up of highly coiled **seminiferous tubules,** lined with cells, called spermatogonia, that are the site of sperm

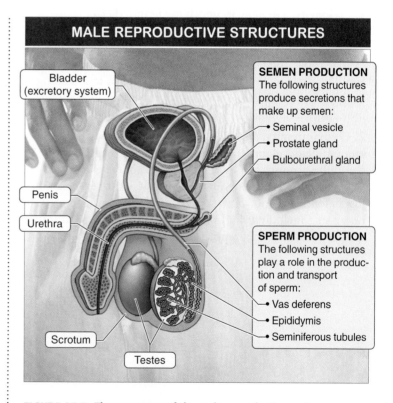

MALE REPRODUCTIVE STRUCTURES

Bladder (excretory system)

Penis

Urethra

Scrotum

Testes

SEMEN PRODUCTION
The following structures produce secretions that make up semen:
• Seminal vesicle
• Prostate gland
• Bulbourethral gland

SPERM PRODUCTION
The following structures play a role in the production and transport of sperm:
• Vas deferens
• Epididymis
• Seminiferous tubules

FIGURE 25-7 The structures of the male reproductive system.

25-8   CHAPTER 25 • REPRODUCTION AND DEVELOPMENT

How Do Animals Reproduce?   Male and Female Reproductive Systems   Sex Can Lead to Fertilization   Human Development

production. It is in cells between the seminiferous tubules where **testosterone,** the principal male sex hormone, and other androgens are produced. Testosterone stimulates sperm production.

Connected to the seminiferous tubules is the **epididymis,** a 15- to 20-foot-long coiled tube, in each testis, where sperm mature. The epididymis in each testis is linked to a **vas deferens,** a tube of smooth muscle tissue that passes from the testis into the body. The vas deferens from each testis connects to a single ejaculatory duct, which continues into the urethra, a duct passing through the penis and through which semen and urine are expelled.

Three other important male reproductive structures produce secretions that make up semen. These include the **prostate gland,** located just below the urinary bladder, which secretes into the urethra a milky, basic (as opposed to acidic) fluid containing enzymes and sperm nutrients that makes up just under one-third of the volume of the ejaculate. A pair of **seminal vesicles,** secrete into the semen nutrients for the sperm, as well as substances that increase sperm motility and make the female reproductive tract more hospitable to sperm. And finally, a pair of **bulbourethral glands,** located just below the urethra near the base of the penis, contribute the remaining 1% or so of the ejaculate, as well as a mixture of mucus and sugar that lubricates the tip of the penis prior to copulation.

Gametogenesis in Males

Recall from Sections 6-10 through 6-14 that gametes are produced by cells that undergo meiosis. Diploid cells, the spermatogonia, are present in the highly coiled seminiferous tubules of the testes (**FIGURE 25-8**). Each spermatogonium divides by mitosis to produce two cells.

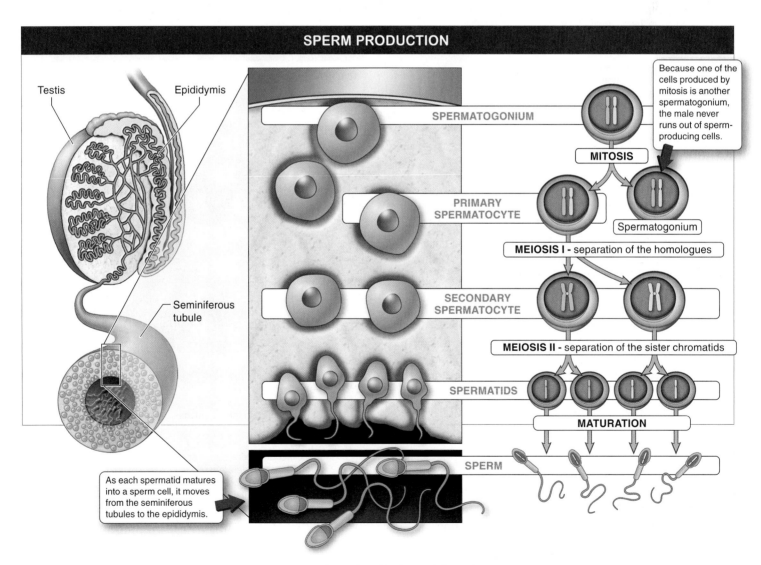

FIGURE 25-8 Gametogenesis in males. Sperm are continuously produced in the testis by meiosis.

Reproductive Technology

STRUCTURE OF SPERM

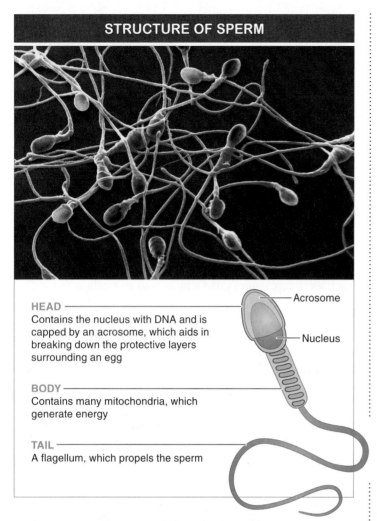

HEAD —
Contains the nucleus with DNA and is capped by an acrosome, which aids in breaking down the protective layers surrounding an egg

BODY —
Contains many mitochondria, which generate energy

TAIL —
A flagellum, which propels the sperm

— Acrosome

— Nucleus

FIGURE 25-9 **Sperm structure reflects its function.**

One of these cells is another spermatogonium, so the male never runs out of a store of sperm-producing cells; the other is a **primary spermatocyte,** which undergoes meiosis, in the first step of sperm production. Each primary spermatocyte produces two cells in the first meiotic division. These two cells are called **secondary spermatocytes,** and they then complete the second meiotic division, each producing two spermatids. The four spermatids produced by each spermatogonium, as products of meiosis, are haploid. As each spermatid matures into a sperm cell, it moves from the seminiferous tubules to the epididymis, where, over the course of approximately 18 hours, the sperm become motile—that is, they become able to move.

Each sperm cell consists of three primary parts: (1) the head region, containing the sperm cell's nucleus with its DNA, plus a cap-like **acrosome** containing enzymes that can break down the protective layers surrounding an egg; (2) the body region, which contains many energy-generating mitochondria; and (3) the tail, a flagellum that propels the sperm through the fluid in the female reproductive tract (**FIGURE 25-9**).

Sperm production is tremendously sensitive to numerous factors. Two of the most important factors are hormones and temperature. The optimum temperature for sperm production is approximately two degrees lower than body temperature. This accounts for why, in most mammals, the testes hang outside the body, where their temperature can be controlled by moving them closer to or farther from the heat of the body. It also accounts for the fact that men exposed to hot tubs or hot baths for 30 minutes or more each week generally show signs of infertility, with fewer numbers of sperm as well as lower motility of the sperm they do have. Fortunately, the condition almost always can be reversed by reducing exposure to the hot tubs or baths.

Q Do hot tubs reduce a man's fertility?

The path that sperm take from the male to the female is as follows (**FIGURE 25-10**):

THE PATH OF SPERM

During ejaculation, sperm move from the male body as follows:

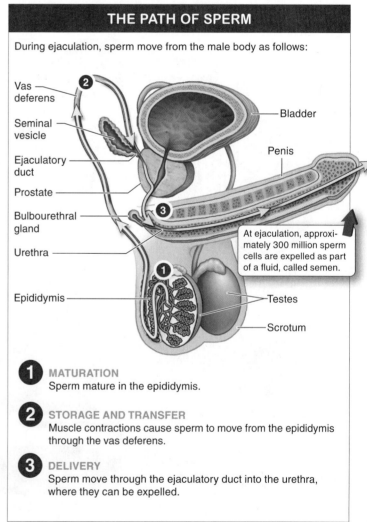

Vas deferens

Seminal vesicle

Ejaculatory duct

Prostate

Bulbourethral gland

Urethra

Epididymis

Bladder

Penis

At ejaculation, approximately 300 million sperm cells are expelled as part of a fluid, called semen.

Testes

Scrotum

1 MATURATION
Sperm mature in the epididymis.

2 STORAGE AND TRANSFER
Muscle contractions cause sperm to move from the epididymis through the vas deferens.

3 DELIVERY
Sperm move through the ejaculatory duct into the urethra, where they can be expelled.

FIGURE 25-10 **The pathway taken by sperm during ejaculation.**

How Do Animals Reproduce? Male and Female Reproductive Systems Sex Can Lead to Fertilization Human Development

1. *Maturation:* sperm mature in the epididymis, within each testis.

2. *Storage and transfer:* during ejaculation, sperm move from the epididymis (in each testis) through the vas deferens. Their movement is generated by contractions of the muscular tissue that makes up the vas deferens.

3. *Delivery:* sperm moving from each vas deferens then pass through the ejaculatory duct and into the urethra. During copulation, sperm are expelled from the urethra into the female reproductive tract.

At ejaculation, the sperm are expelled as part of the semen. Although there are approximately 300 million sperm cells in the fluid of a single ejaculation, the sperm make up only about 1% to 5% of the total volume of ejaculated fluid. In the next section, we explore the question of why so many sperm are present in an ejaculation and the observation that a significant proportion of sperm is not actually capable of fertilizing an egg.

TAKE-HOME MESSAGE 25·4

In adult men, sperm are continuously produced in the testes by meiosis. Semen—consisting of sperm cells and fluids that nurture and aid the sperm in fertilization—is ejaculated during copulation.

25·5

There is unseen conflict among sperm cells.

In her book *The Chimpanzees of Gombe: Patterns of Behavior,* published in 1986, Jane Goodall reported female copulatory rates of "an average of between five and six copulations per female per hour in the early morning, after which the rate dropped gradually to about two per hour in the midmorning, rose very slightly during the afternoon, and tapered off to one per hour in the evening." These observations were consistent with the realization that researchers had come to in the 1970s that if females (of any species, not just chimps) mate with more than one male, there may be competition among the males' sperm.

Q A chimp's testicles are 15 times bigger than a gorilla's! Why?

The idea of sperm competition, or "sperm wars" as they have been called, gives rise to several testable predictions. One simple prediction is this: when a female is likely to mate with more than one male, the males that produce more sperm are likely to be more successful at fertilizing the female's eggs. Some interesting observations support this prediction. For example, gorillas have golf-ball-sized testes, while chimpanzees' testes are closer in size to baseballs. Gorilla testicles account for only 0.02% of body weight, while chimp testes account for 0.30%, 15 times as much. Why the huge difference? Gorilla groups are relatively small, and all females within a group mate with just one male, the dominant silverback. In contrast, as Jane Goodall noted, fertile chimpanzee females may have sex dozens of times a day with many different males. Consequently, the tiny testes of the gorilla are perfectly adequate, but for a chimp male to win these sperm competitions, he must produce significantly more sperm (**FIGURE 25-11**). Similarly, among fruit bats, males of species that

Q A female's mating with more than one male leads to sperm competition and the evolution of increased sperm production and testis size.

FIGURE 25-11 The evolutionary consequences of sperm competition among males. Female mating behavior influences the size of males' testes and sperm production. The inset shows the size of a male chimp's brain (top) relative to one of its testicles.

Reproductive Technology

live in large social groups have significantly larger testes than males of species that live in smaller groups.

Sperm competition has given rise to several other adaptations.

- Physical barriers to copulation, such as the mating plugs produced by the coagulation of semen in many species that prevent sperm from other males entering the female's reproductive tract.

Q *Why do male fruit flies produce toxic semen?*

- Toxic semen components, such as the protein in fruit fly semen that suppresses further mating by the female for several days (ensuring a male's paternity), as well as the fruit fly semen components that can incapacitate the sperm of other males (and even decrease the female's lifespan by about 10%).

- Large numbers of sperm (20% to 30% of the sperm in each ejaculate in humans) differing structurally from the sperm that are able to move along the female reproductive tract and fertilize an egg. These sperm have been described as "kamikaze sperm," adapted to preventing other males' sperm from reaching and fertilizing an egg. More recent research suggests, however, that these non-fertilizing sperm may simply be abnormal sperm that reflect errors during meiosis.

- Genital morphology, such as the claspers and scrapers of dung flies, as well as the "shovel penis" of some dragonfly species that make it possible for males to dislodge the sperm of previous males that have mated with a female (**FIGURE 25-12**).

This unseen conflict between males is an area of considerable investigation as researchers try to understand the physical and behavioral consequences of such competition. It seems that females are not passive players in these battles and that, in many cases, the female will eject the sperm from undesirable males.

💡 *Sperm competition can influence the evolution of genital morphology that aids in displacing other males' sperm.*

FIGURE 25-12 **Sperm wars.** This dragonfly, *Calopteryx virgo,* has a "shovel penis" that can scrape away the sperm deposited by a rival.

TAKE-HOME MESSAGE 25·5

When females mate with more than one male, sperm competition occurs and can lead to a variety of adaptations, including increased sperm production and testis size, semen that can create a physical barrier to subsequent mating, toxic semen components, and penis morphology that aids in the displacement of rival males' sperm.

25-12 CHAPTER 25 • REPRODUCTION AND DEVELOPMENT

How Do Animals Reproduce?   Male and Female Reproductive Systems   Sex Can Lead to Fertilization   Human Development

Eggs are made in the ovaries (and the process can take decades).

From a genetic perspective, making eggs barely differs from making sperm. In the female gonads—the **ovaries** rather than the testes—diploid cells undergo meiosis to produce haploid eggs, and in the process, a great deal of variation is generated so that each haploid egg has a unique genetic makeup. When the haploid egg is fertilized by a sperm, the diploid condition is restored.

But the process of egg production differs from sperm production in several key ways. Eggs are produced in much smaller numbers; each egg is considerably larger than a sperm cell; and the production process can take decades rather than days, even though it begins at a much younger age. Let's explore the specifics, beginning with a description of the female reproductive system (**FIGURE 25-13**).

Female Reproductive Structures Externally, a female has just two structures, the **clitoris** and the **labia,** which develop from the same embryonic tissue that in males produces the penis and scrotum. There is also a vaginal opening. Internally, the **vagina** is a tube-like chamber into which sperm are released during copulation. The vagina connects with the **uterus,** also called the womb, which resembles an upside-down pear. The lower, narrowest portion of the uterus is called the **cervix.** The lining of the uterus, rich with blood vessels, is the **endometrium,** and this is where a fertilized

egg implants and is nourished. The uterus is also where an embryo develops throughout pregnancy.

Connecting to the top of the uterus on the left and right sides are the **Fallopian tubes,** or **oviducts.** Each Fallopian tube extends outward and is funnel-shaped near its end where the ovaries lie, held in place by thin membranes. Each ovary is about the size of a large olive.

Gametogenesis in Females The process of gametogenesis in females, called **oogenesis** (pronounced oo-oh-GEN-eh-sis), starts in the ovaries prior to birth—that is, while the female is still a fetus (**FIGURE 25-14**). Here, diploid cells called **oogonia** (*sing.* **oogonium**) multiply by mitosis. Each oogonium then begins meiosis, but stops at prophase I, at which point the cell is called a **primary oocyte** and is contained within a **follicle**—the small structure in which an egg will form. At birth, there are approximately one million follicles present in a female's ovaries, each follicle containing a primary oocyte.

The primary oocytes remain in their hibernation-like state until puberty. At that point, periodic bursts of **follicle-stimulating hormone (FSH)** cause several primary oocytes to complete meiosis I. Unlike in the production of sperm, however, when the primary oocyte divides into two cells, although the pairs of homologous chromosomes split evenly,

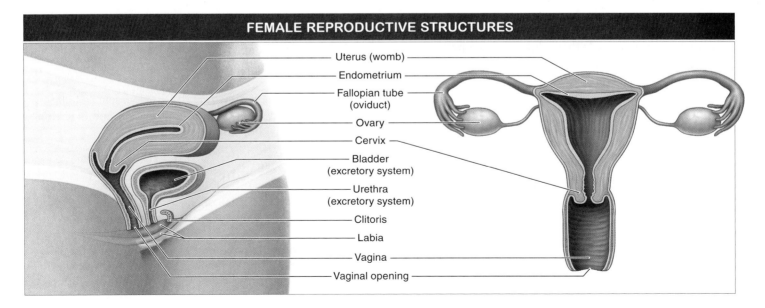

FEMALE REPRODUCTIVE STRUCTURES

- Uterus (womb)
- Endometrium
- Fallopian tube (oviduct)
- Ovary
- Cervix
- Bladder (excretory system)
- Urethra (excretory system)
- Clitoris
- Labia
- Vagina
- Vaginal opening

FIGURE 25-13 The structures of the female reproductive system.

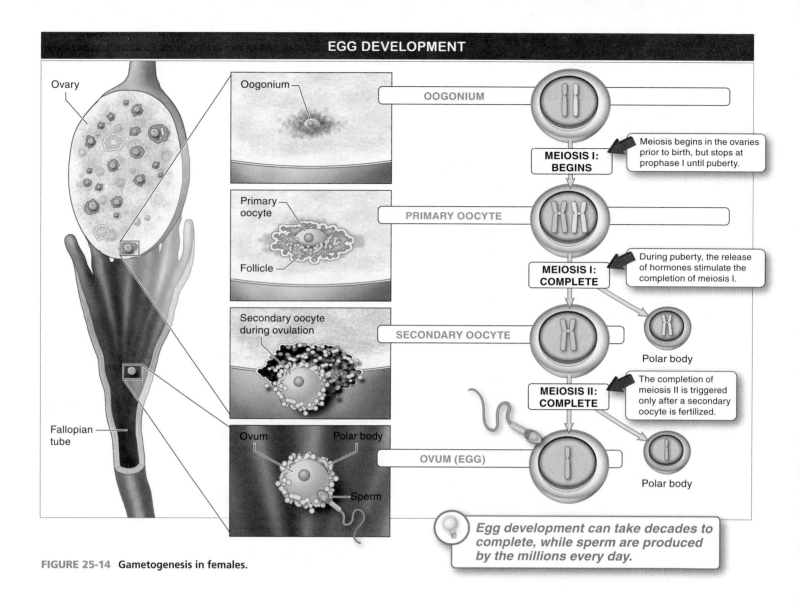

FIGURE 25-14 **Gametogenesis in females.**

nearly all of the cytoplasm goes to one of the cells, now called a **secondary oocyte.** The other cell, known as a **polar body,** gets almost no cytoplasm and eventually disintegrates. At this point, meiosis again stops.

When females **ovulate,** generally a single follicle in one ovary ruptures, releasing the secondary oocyte—which still has not completed meiosis. The secondary oocyte, which at this point can be called an egg, is swept by cilia into the Fallopian tube and carried down toward the uterus. If sperm have been deposited in the vagina during copulation, it is in the Fallopian tube that the sperm, swimming up from the vagina and through the uterus, are most likely to fertilize the egg. It is only *after* fertilization that a secondary oocyte is triggered to finally complete meiosis—once again with an unequal division of cytoplasm. One of the resulting cells, the ovum, receives most of the cytoplasm, while the other receives almost none. This second polar body disintegrates just as the

first polar body did. The haploid ovum now fuses with the haploid nucleus of the sperm, forming a diploid fertilized egg, called a zygote.

In the next section, we see how the development of follicles, the preparation of the uterus for implantation, and ovulation are coordinated by hormone secretions.

TAKE-HOME MESSAGE 25•6

Genetically, the production of eggs barely differs from sperm production. In the ovaries, diploid cells begin to undergo meiosis, a process that continues in the Fallopian tubes following ovulation, and produces genetically varied haploid gametes. A much smaller number of eggs than sperm are produced, however, and each egg is considerably larger than a sperm cell.

Hormones direct the process of ovulation and the preparation for gestation.

If you are female, here's something you may have noticed if you are living in a dormitory (or are in prison): when women live in close proximity, over time their reproductive cycles become synchronized so that they menstruate at approximately the same time and, perhaps less obviously, ovulate at the same time. This issue was first addressed in a scientific publication in 1971, when Martha McClintock reported findings—inspired by her own experiences—based on data from 135 female students living in a dormitory at Wellesley College in Massachusetts. Similar observations have been reported in other animal species, and subsequent studies implicate airborne chemicals, called **pheromones** (probably released from women's underarms), that can shorten or lengthen the reproductive cycle in other women. It's not clear why such synchrony of reproductive cycles would occur, however. And other researchers have argued that the different lengths of women's cycles make it impossible for them to become truly synchronized. The jury is still out on this hotly contested issue.

Hormones regulate the timing and development of egg production, called the **ovarian cycle,** which occurs approximately every 28 days. Hormones also regulate another aspect of the reproductive cycle, the **menstrual cycle,** during which the uterus prepares for the possible implantation and nurturing of a fertilized egg, and sheds its lining when fertilization does not occur. We describe each of these cycles and the ways in which each influences the other (**FIGURE 25-15**).

Q What does the process of being an egg donor entail?

Females have about one million follicles, or potential eggs, when they are born, but most women ovulate fewer than 500 times over the course of their life. This leaves a lot of potential eggs lying around. In the normal course of events, these follicles just disintegrate, but in recent decades, modern medicine has taken to tinkering with the reproductive cycle to make it possible for a woman to donate her eggs to another woman. The process involves several steps.

First, if you choose to be a donor, each day for about a week, you have an injection of a drug called Lupron, which suppresses your own reproductive cycle. The suppression is followed by a week of injections of a fertility drug that contains large amounts of two hormones, LH (luteinizing

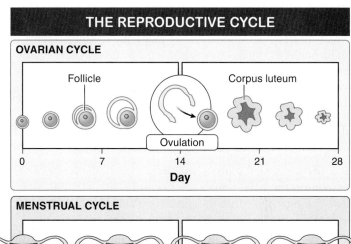

THE REPRODUCTIVE CYCLE

OVARIAN CYCLE

Follicle · Corpus luteum · Ovulation

0 · 7 · 14 · 21 · 28

Day

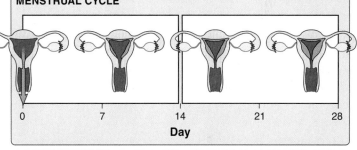

MENSTRUAL CYCLE

0 · 7 · 14 · 21 · 28

Day

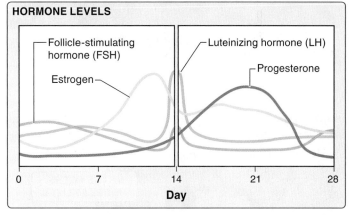

HORMONE LEVELS

Follicle-stimulating hormone (FSH) · Luteinizing hormone (LH) · Progesterone · Estrogen

0 · 7 · 14 · 21 · 28

Day

FIGURE 25-15 The stages of the female reproductive cycle and associated hormonal changes.

hormone) and FSH, which induces one to two dozen follicles to develop in your ovaries. A doctor examines your ovaries by ultrasound to count the number of developing follicles and to estimate their size. Finally, you are given an injection of human chorionic gonadotropin, which stimulates ovulation, the night before the egg "retrieval." The following morning, before the eggs have been released from the follicles, the doctor inserts a tiny needle into each follicle within the ovaries and sucks out the eggs, one by one. This process takes about half an hour. The donor's role is now over. The eggs are placed in a Petri dish, mixed with sperm to fertilize them, and the fertilized eggs are allowed to divide for 2-6 days before several are transferred to the recipient's uterus—with the hope that they will implant and a successful pregnancy will occur.

In the normal monthly cycle, without injections, hormones direct the development of a follicle and the release of an egg (ovulation), while simultaneously preparing the uterus for implantation. Let's follow the changes in hormone levels and their effects during the 28-day cycle (see Figure 25-15).

1. *Menstruation.* Traditionally, the first day of menstrual bleeding, a woman's "period," or **menstruation,** is considered the first day of the menstrual cycle. Three to five days of bleeding occur as the lining of the uterus is sloughed off.

2. *FSH produced.* As the uterine lining sheds, the levels of **estrogen,** the chief female sex hormone, drop. Reduced levels of estrogen cause the pituitary gland to release follicle-stimulating hormone (FSH).

3. *Follicle develops.* FSH, just as its name indicates, causes a few follicles in the ovaries to grow and develop, although only one follicle reaches full maturity. Within this one follicle, the primary oocyte completes its first meiotic division and becomes a secondary oocyte.

4. *Estrogen produced.* As the follicles develop, they produce estrogen, gradually increasing the level of estrogen in the blood.

5. *LH released.* The high levels of estrogen trigger the release of a burst of luteinizing hormone (LH) and of more FSH.

6. *Ovulation.* The burst of LH triggers ovulation, causing the ovum to erupt from the follicle and out of the ovary. This release occurs approximately halfway through the cycle, around day 14, and signals the end of what is called the **follicular phase** of the reproductive cycle.

7. *Progesterone produced.* As the second half, or **luteal phase,** of the reproductive cycle begins, the follicle cells that had surrounded the ovum develop into a structure called the **corpus luteum** (Latin for "yellow body"). These cells begin secreting smaller amounts of estrogen, but increasing amounts of progesterone.

8. *Endometrium thickens.* **Progesterone,** just as its name suggests (*pro* = for; *gestare* = to bear), causes the body to prepare for gestation of an embryo, in case fertilization occurs. Progesterone's primary effect is to cause a thickening of the endometrium, or lining of the uterus. The endometrium becomes increasingly rich with blood vessels and deposits of glycogen that can nourish a developing embryo.

At this point, the process can go in one of two directions, depending on whether or not the egg is fertilized (**FIGURE 25-16**).

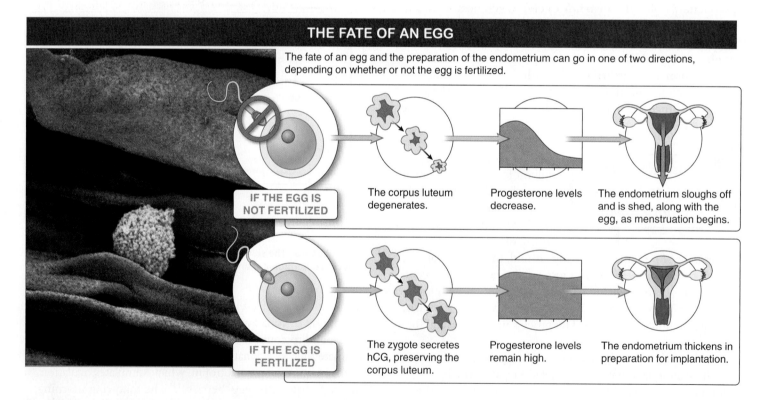

THE FATE OF AN EGG

The fate of an egg and the preparation of the endometrium can go in one of two directions, depending on whether or not the egg is fertilized.

IF THE EGG IS NOT FERTILIZED

The corpus luteum degenerates.

Progesterone levels decrease.

The endometrium sloughs off and is shed, along with the egg, as menstruation begins.

IF THE EGG IS FERTILIZED

The zygote secretes hCG, preserving the corpus luteum.

Progesterone levels remain high.

The endometrium thickens in preparation for implantation.

FIGURE 25-16 Two possible fates for an egg. Shown here: an egg moving down the oviduct.

How Do Animals Reproduce?　　Male and Female Reproductive Systems　　Sex Can Lead to Fertilization　　Human Development

Jury is still out. In 1971 Martha McClintock reported that women living together in a dormitory at Wellesley College experienced synchronized menstrual cycles. It is not clear why such synchrony would occur, and some researchers disagree that synchronization is possible.

If the egg is not fertilized, the egg disintegrates and the corpus luteum degenerates about 12 days after ovulation, sloughs off, and it is shed, along with the disintegrating egg, as menstruation begins. Abruptly removing this source of estrogen and progesterone causes the lining of the uterus to slough off, and menstruation begins. With continuing reduction in estrogen levels, the pituitary gland is spurred to release FSH and the process begins again.

If the egg is fertilized, which usually occurs in the Fallopian tube, the zygote begins development and after several days begins to secrete **human chorionic gonadotropin (hCG).** This hormone prevents degredation of the corpus luteum, which continues to secrete progesterone, thereby maintaining the endometrium. In the next section, we investigate what happens next in development of the embryo.

Reproductive cycling continues from puberty, usually in the early teens, until **menopause**—the cessation of ovulation and menstruation—usually between ages 45 and 55. It is not clear whether there is any evolutionarily adaptive value to menopause. In most species other than humans, females remain fertile throughout their entire adult life. Menopause may be a consequence of the relatively recent (on an evolutionary time scale) increase in human longevity. Regardless of the evolutionary explanation, oocyte depletion seems to influence the onset of menopause.

TAKE-HOME MESSAGE 25•7

In the ovaries, a cell within a follicle is stimulated to develop into a fertile egg by coordinated secretions of the hormones estrogen, FSH, and LH. The preparation of the uterus for implantation of a fertilized egg is coordinated by progesterone.

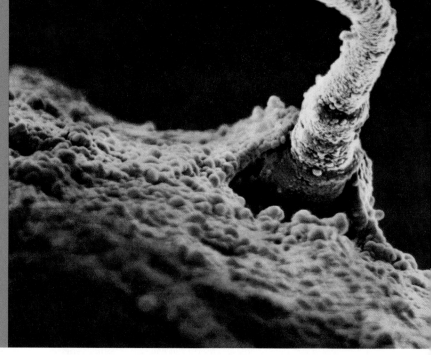

❸ Sex can lead to fertilization, but can also spread sexually transmitted diseases.

Sperm fertilizing an egg.

25·8

In fertilization, two cells become one.

For fertilization to occur, it's not enough for sperm cells to be in the same general location as an egg—there are some specific events that must occur. The process of fertilization in vertebrates involves three separate steps: penetration, activation, and fusion of the nuclei (**FIGURE 25-17**). And before a sperm can take that first step and penetrate an egg, it must find it.

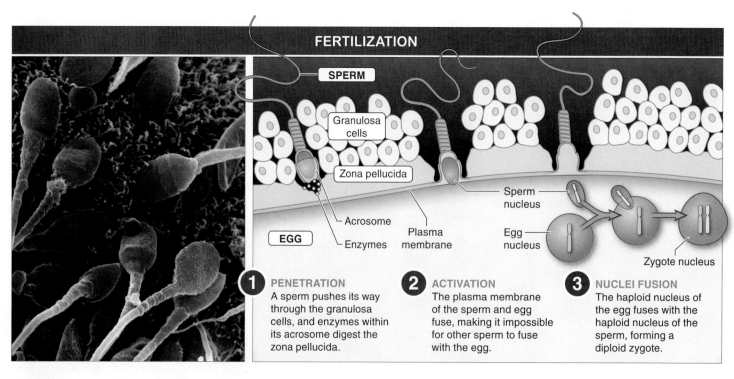

FERTILIZATION

SPERM

Granulosa cells

Zona pellucida

Sperm nucleus

Acrosome

EGG — Enzymes

Plasma membrane

Egg nucleus

Zygote nucleus

① PENETRATION
A sperm pushes its way through the granulosa cells, and enzymes within its acrosome digest the zona pellucida.

② ACTIVATION
The plasma membrane of the sperm and egg fuse, making it impossible for other sperm to fuse with the egg.

③ NUCLEI FUSION
The haploid nucleus of the egg fuses with the haploid nucleus of the sperm, forming a diploid zygote.

FIGURE 25-17 Fertilization is the fusion of one sperm with an egg.

25-18 CHAPTER 25 • REPRODUCTION AND DEVELOPMENT

How Do Animals Reproduce?   Male and Female Reproductive Systems   Sex Can Lead to Fertilization   Human Development

Recently, researchers discovered that sperm have receptors, like chemical sensors, that cause the sperm cells to swim toward a chemical attractant that is released by the egg. This attractant, in essence, says, "I'm over here!"

After ovulation, the egg is still surrounded by some smaller cells, called granulosa cells. These cells stand between the sperm and the egg, but they're not the only barrier. Between the granulosa cells and the egg's membrane, there is a glycoprotein layer called the **zona pellucida** (pronounced puh-LOO-sih-duh). As sperm approach the egg, release of calcium by cells surrounding the egg appears to increase the swimming speed and tail movements of the sperm, in a process known as sperm activation. A second phase of sperm activation occurs as a sperm cell pushes its way through the granulosa cells, and the acrosome (at the head of the sperm) dissolves and releases digestive enzymes that help the sperm digest its way through the zona pellucida.

Once the sperm gets through the zona pellucida, the oocyte is activated, and the plasma membranes of the sperm and egg fuse. This fusion has a couple of important consequences. First, it changes the egg membrane in such a way that it is impossible for any other sperm to also fertilize the egg. After all, it would be a genetic disaster for the fertilized egg to have more than two sets of chromosomes. Second, the fusion of the plasma membranes of sperm and egg induces the egg to complete its second meiotic division. On doing so, one haploid egg is formed, along with one smaller polar body. The latter disintegrates or is ejected from the egg.

In many species, stripping away the zona pellucida makes it possible for the egg to be fertilized by sperm from different species. This suggests that something in the zona pellucida, perhaps recognition sites, makes it possible for the egg to be fertilized only by sperm from the same species.

And, finally, the haploid nucleus of the egg fuses with the haploid nucleus of the sperm, creating a diploid cell—the zygote.

TAKE-HOME MESSAGE 25·8

At fertilization, a sperm penetrates the protective zone around the egg, the egg blocks additional sperm entry, and the sperm and egg membranes fuse. The egg then completes its second meiotic division, and the haploid nuclei of the egg and sperm fuse, forming a diploid zygote.

25·9

Numerous strategies can help prevent fertilization.

Pregnancy depends on the occurrence of a great many events, relating to the production of sperm and eggs, their coming together in fertilization, and implantation of the zygote in the uterus. **Contraception,** or birth control, is the attempt to prevent pregnancy. Although a wide variety of contraception methods are used—with varying degrees of effectiveness—each method generally represents one of three general strategies: (1) preventing ovulation, (2) preventing fertilization, or (3) preventing implantation. **FIGURE 25-18** summarizes various methods of contraception, how they work, and their failure rates.

Preventing Ovulation
Birth control pills. Available since 1960, birth control pills are among the most effective of all methods of contraception, with a failure rate of 1% to 8%; that is, among 100 women using birth control pills over the course of one year, there would be 1-8 pregnancies. (If taken every day at exactly the same time, they are 99+% effective; the

Q How do birth control pills work?

problem is that not all women are consistent in taking them.) Among 100 women using no contraception, there would be about 85 pregnancies during one year.

Two chief varieties of birth control pills are available, one that contains synthetic versions of the hormones estrogen and progesterone, and one that contains only a synthetic progesterone. The estrogen-progesterone pill prevents ovulation by keeping estrogen levels just high enough so that the release of FSH by the pituitary gland is never triggered. As long as FSH is never released, eggs never develop and ovulation does not occur. The progesterone component of the pill causes just enough development of the lining of the uterus that a plug of mucus forms at the connection between the vagina and uterus, blocking sperm from getting through.

Taking the birth control pill at the same time every day is essential. If more than 24 hours go by between

METHODS OF CONTRACEPTION

METHOD	HOW IT WORKS
PREVENTING OVULATION	
• Birth control pills	A pill containing synthetic hormones prevents the release of FSH by the pituitary gland, thus preventing egg development and ovulation (effectiveness: 92–99%).
• Hormone implants or injections	Synthetic hormones are inserted under the skin to prevent the release of FSH by the pituitary gland, thus preventing egg development and ovulation (effectiveness: 97–99%).
PREVENTING FERTILIZATION	
• Condoms	A thin rubber or natural membrane sheath placed on the penis or inside the vagina, covering the cervix, prevents sperm from coming in contact with an egg (effectiveness: male condoms: 85–98%; female condoms: 79–95%).
• Diaphragm/ cervical cap	A dome-shaped piece of rubber placed in the vagina blocks the cervix and prevents sperm from coming in contact with an egg (effectiveness: 84–94%).
• Sterilization	A medical procedure permanently alters the reproductive system to prevent the release of sperm or block the movement of eggs down the Fallopian tubes (effectiveness: >99%).
• Abstinence	Individuals refrain from sexual intercourse (effectiveness: complete abstinence: 100%; abstinence during days when fertility is likely, based on analysis of female's menstrual cycle pattern: 75–99%).
PREVENTING IMPLANTATION	
• Intrauterine device (IUD)	A small plastic or metal device inserted into the uterus by a doctor prevents a fertilized egg from implanting (effectiveness: >99%).
• "Morning-after" pills	A pill containing a dose of estrogen 50 times higher than that found in birth control pills can stop ovum development or implantation (effectiveness: >75%).

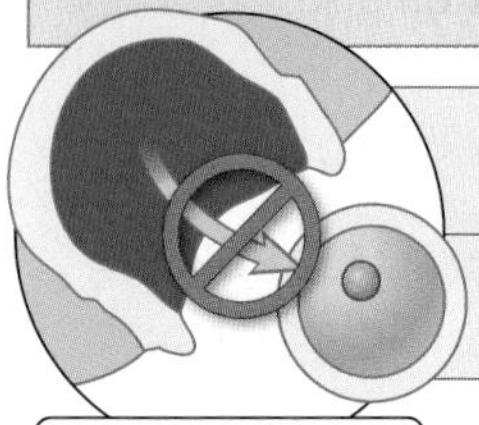

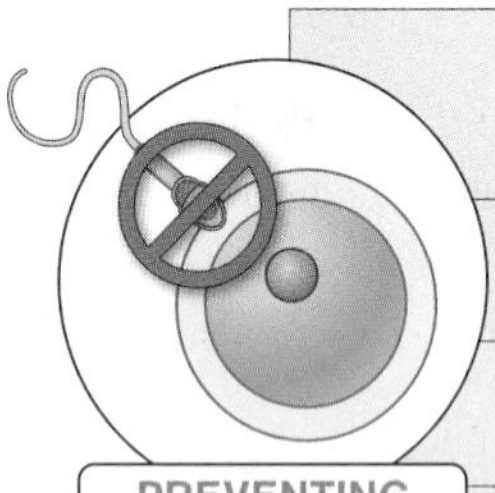

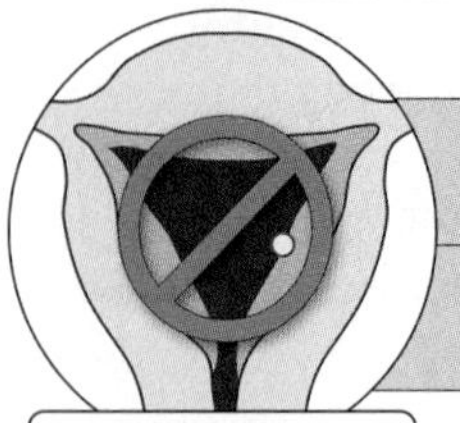

FIGURE 25-18 Preventing pregnancy.

taking pills, the estrogen level in the body begins to drop; if it gets below a critical level, FSH release by the pituitary is triggered, which can lead to ovulation and the risk of pregnancy.

The long-term health consequences of using birth control pills include a slightly elevated risk of cardiovascular disease, particularly among women who smoke. However, because birth control users have a reduced risk of pregnancy—a condition that carries with it some significant health risks—and a reduced risk of ovarian and endometrial cancers, women's overall mortality risk is reduced while on the pill.

Although the birth control pill is one of the most commonly used methods of contraception, recent research has revealed that the hormones may actually alter women's attraction to men. When not taking birth control pills, most women prefer the odor of men possessing certain genetic combinations that are most different from their own. When taking the pill,

however, their preference switches and they prefer the odor of men with genetic combinations most similar to their own. It remains to be seen how significant any effect of birth control pills is on women's mate preferences, and much additional research in this area is under way.

Hormone injections or implants. Injections or capsule implants, just under the skin, of synthetic estrogen and progesterone, or progesterone only, represent a slight variation on birth control pills. The prevention of pregnancy works in the same way, but with the added convenience of not having to take a pill every day. Some implants, in fact, need to be implanted and removed only once every three years. Consequently, these methods are slightly more effective than birth control pills, because much of the user error is eliminated.

Preventing Fertilization
Condoms. The condom—a thin rubber or natural membrane sheath placed on the penis or inside the vagina, covering the cervix, that prevents sperm from coming in contact with an

How Do Animals Reproduce?   Male and Female Reproductive Systems   Sex Can Lead to Fertilization   Human Development

egg—is one of several barrier methods of contraception, which keep sperm from coming in contact with an egg. Condoms have the added benefit of being one of the only methods of contraception that offer effective protection against sexually transmitted diseases, including HIV/AIDS. (See the next section for further discussion of this topic.)

Diaphragm or cervical cap. A diaphragm or cervical cap—a dome-shaped piece of rubber placed in the vagina, blocking the cervix—also prevents pregnancy by blocking sperm from reaching an egg. The use of spermicidal creams with a diaphragm or cervical cap (and with a condom as well) can increase their effectiveness, resulting in a failure rate of 6% to 16%.

Sterilization. Sterilization is the permanent alteration of the reproductive system to prevent the release of sperm or the movement of eggs down the Fallopian tubes. In a tubal ligation, the woman's oviducts are cut and tied off so that eggs cannot reach the uterus. In a vasectomy, the vas deferens on each side is cut and tied off so that sperm cannot reach the urethra, thereby causing a man's semen to carry no sperm. There are no side effects in either case. Each of these procedures, however, should be considered permanent (although in rare cases, the procedure can be successfully reversed).

Abstinence. Abstinence—not having sexual intercourse—is the most effective method of preventing pregnancy. In practice, however, abstaining from intercourse can prove difficult, particularly in the context of a long-term relationship. And temporary abstinence during the times when conception is most likely (often called the "rhythm method"), while theoretically effective, has a failure rate as high as 25%, probably due to variation in the time of ovulation and the fact that sperm can live for 72 hours (and possibly longer) in the female reproductive system.

Preventing Implantation
Intrauterine device (IUD). The intrauterine device, or IUD, is a small plastic or metal device that is inserted by a doctor into the uterus. The IUD (which can be left in for 3-4 years) does not prevent fertilization from occurring but instead prevents a fertilized egg from implanting in the uterus. IUDs have a failure rate of just under 1%. Some women experience side effects from IUDs (including cramps and other pain) and may need to have the device removed.

Q What is the "morning-after" pill?

"Morning-after" pills. Although not recommended as a long-term strategy for contraception, the morning-after pill, a dose of estrogen 50 times greater than that found in birth control pills, can stop ovum development or implantation. The morning-after pill has a failure rate of up to 25% and is recommended only for cases of rape and emergency situations in which other methods of contraception have failed. In contrast to the large hormone content of morning-after drugs, another drug, known as RU486, is considered an anti-hormone drug. It blocks progesterone receptors in the uterus, thereby causing the lining of the uterus to be sloughed off. This can end a pregnancy any time during the first seven weeks. In addition to causing abdominal pain and cramping, RU486 can also have other adverse effects, including nausea, vomiting, and fever.

TAKE-HOME MESSAGE 25·9

Pregnancy can be prevented by numerous methods, each of which acts in one or more ways to prevent ovulation, fertilization, or implantation.

25·10

Sexually transmitted diseases reveal battles between microbes and humans.

To many microbes, the human genitals and reproductive tract represent a desirable place to find shelter, nourishment, and opportunities for reproducing and dispersing. Unfortunately, these microbes can cause problems for humans in the form of **sexually transmitted diseases (STDs).** STDs produce symptoms of varying severity, from mild to extreme discomfort to sterility or even death. It is estimated that more than 300 million new cases of STDs occur each year worldwide.

Sexually transmitted diseases are caused by bacteria, viruses, fungi, protists, and even some arthropods. The organisms are passed from the mucous membranes (of the genitals, as well as of the anus and mouth) of one individual to those of another

SEXUALLY TRANSMITTED DISEASES

CAUSE	EXAMPLES	SYMPTOMS	TREATMENT
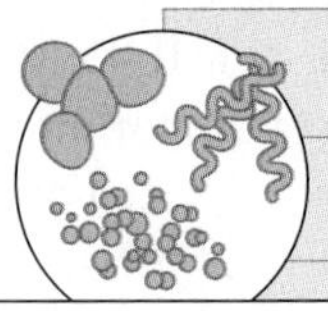 **BACTERIUM**	• Gonorrhea	Often none; sometimes painful urination, genital discharge, or irregular menstruation	Several antibiotics can successfully cure gonorrhea; however, drug-resistant strains are increasing.
	• Syphilis	Often no symptoms for years; eventual sores, skin rash, and if untreated, organ damage	Penicillin, an antibiotic, can cure a person in the early stages of syphilis.
	• Chlamydia	Often none; sometimes painful urination, genital discharge	Chlamydia can be easily treated and cured with antibiotics.
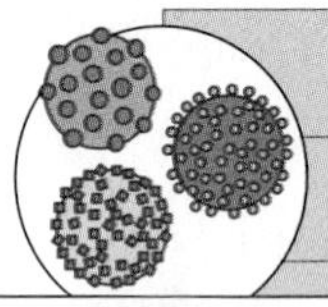 **VIRUS**	• HIV/AIDS	Initial symptoms range from none to flu-like; late stages involve severe infections and death	Currently no cure. Antiretroviral treatment can slow progression. Drug-resistant strains occur.
	• Genital herpes	Often none; outbreaks include sores on genitals, flu-like symptoms	Currently no cure. Antiviral medications can shorten and prevent outbreaks.
	• Human papilloma virus (HPV)	Often none; some types can lead to genital warts, others can cause cervical cancer	A vaccine prevents HPV, and is recommended for girls age 11–12. Warts and cancerous lesions can be removed.
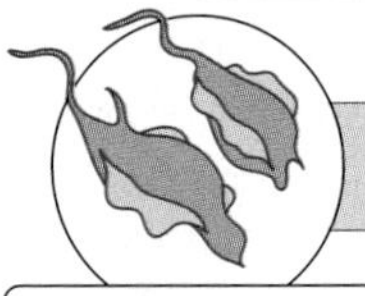 **PROTIST**	• Trichomoniasis	Painful urination and/or vaginal discharge in women; often no symptoms in men	Trichomoniasis can usually be cured with prescription drugs.
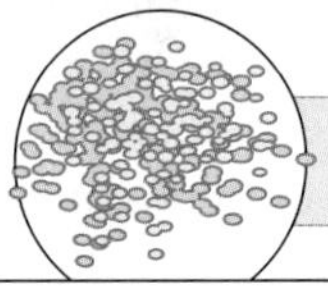 **FUNGUS**	• Yeast infections	Genital itching or burning, and/or vaginal discharge in women; genital itching in men	Yeast infections can usually be cured with antifungal suppositories or creams.
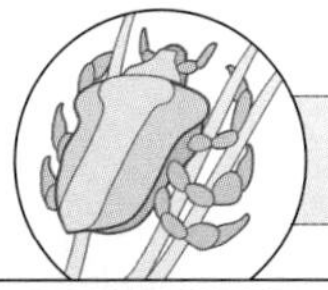 **ARTHROPOD**	• Crab lice	Visible lice eggs or lice crawling or attached to pubic hair, itching in the pubic and groin area	Crab lice can be treated with over-the-counter lotions.

FIGURE 25-19 The most common STDs.

during sexual contact; sometimes they are transmitted by needles used for drug injections.

Some of the most common STDs, their symptoms, and treatments are listed in **FIGURE 25-19**. Although most are curable with antibiotics, antifungal drugs, or anti-protozoan drugs, two characteristics of STDs make them nearly impossible to completely eradicate from a population: (1) their symptoms may be mild or completely absent at times, causing many people to unwittingly pass an infection to their partners, and (2) to prevent reinfection, both partners must be treated simultaneously. Furthermore, because most microbes have such high reproductive rates, populations of a microbe can evolve quickly and become resistant to existing drugs, reducing the long-term effectiveness of treatments. Consequently, the treatment of STDs represents one of the most pressing public health issues in the world today.

TAKE-HOME MESSAGE 25·10

Sexually transmitted diseases (STDs) are caused by a variety of organisms, including bacteria, viruses, protists, fungi, and arthropods. Worldwide, more than 300 million people are infected each year. The effects of being infected with an STD range from non-existent, to mild to extreme discomfort, sterility, or even death.

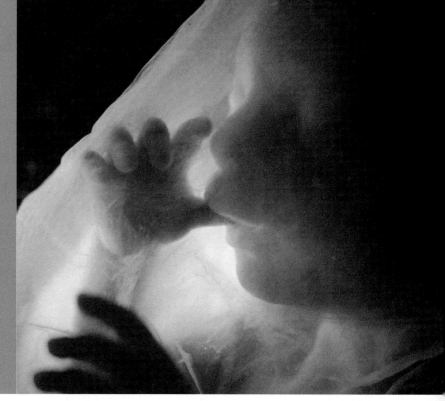

4 Human development occurs in specific stages.

Developing human fetus five months after fertilization.

25·11 --

Early embryonic development occurs during cleavage, gastrulation, and neurulation.

How do you build a complete human, with specialized cells, tissues, and organs, when at fertilization there is just a zygote, a single cell that doesn't resemble a human at all? This question is studied and answered by developmental biology, the branch of science that seeks to understand and explain how a complex organism develops from a single cell. To be sure, the genes in that initial cell are important, and the environmental conditions in which the cell develops are also critically important. These factors interact as the development of humans and most other vertebrates proceeds in a carefully coordinated sequence of three stages: cleavage, gastrulation, and neurulation.

Cleavage The first phase, **cleavage,** is the early cell division, by mitosis, of the zygote, beginning shortly after fertilization (**FIGURE 25-20**). It starts when, about 30 hours after fertilization, the zygote divides into two cells. Then, about 30 hours later, it divides again, becoming four cells. This continues through numerous divisions. Although the number of cells increases significantly during cleavage, there is little or no growth in overall size. Rather, the fertilized egg is partitioned into more

and more cells that are smaller and smaller. These multiple cell divisions are fueled by nutrients that were in the egg. At the cleavage stage, it is difficult to distinguish between species as dissimilar as sea urchins and humans.

After about six days of continuous cell division, the cells form a hollow ball, called a **blastula**—the mammalian version is called a **blastocyst**—of approximately a thousand cells. The cells secrete fluid into the center, where there is an inner mass of cells that will form the embryo. The outer cells also produce human chorionic gonadotropin (hCG), which keeps the corpus luteum from disintegrating, so that it continues to produce progesterone and thereby maintain the lining of the uterus for implantation.

The blastocyst grows rapidly and forms membranes that surround and protect it. These include the **amnion,** which surrounds the embryo, and the **chorion,** which, along with the endometrium, forms the **placenta,** the structure that connects the developing embryo to the wall of the uterus

25-23

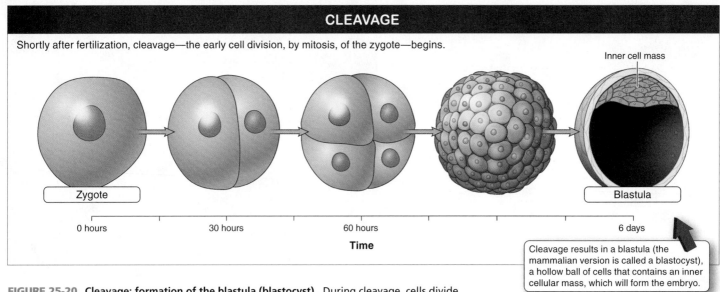

CLEAVAGE

Shortly after fertilization, cleavage—the early cell division, by mitosis, of the zygote—begins.

Inner cell mass

Zygote

Blastula

0 hours   30 hours   60 hours   6 days

Time

Cleavage results in a blastula (the mammalian version is called a blastocyst), a hollow ball of cells that contains an inner cellular mass, which will form the embryo.

FIGURE 25-20 Cleavage: formation of the blastula (blastocyst). During cleavage, cells divide continuously, eventually forming a hollow ball filled with fluid.

(see Figure 25-25). The placenta is packed with blood vessels that bring nourishment to the embryo and remove wastes generated by the embryo.

Gastrulation In the second phase of development, **gastrulation,** three distinct **germ layers** of tissue form. Picture a beach ball—a hollow sphere. Now imagine making a fist and slowly pushing inward on the beach ball. This resembles the

process of gastrulation. The indentation is called the blastopore and is located almost opposite from the point at which the sperm entered the egg. The blastopore will become the anus in vertebrates. At this point the entire mass of cells is called a gastrula (**FIGURE 25-21**).

Three distinct layers of tissue form during gastrulation. The cells in these layers have not yet differentiated (that is, they all

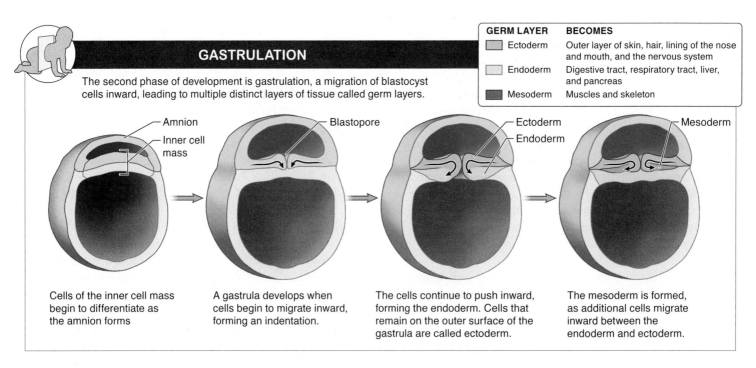

GASTRULATION

The second phase of development is gastrulation, a migration of blastocyst cells inward, leading to multiple distinct layers of tissue called germ layers.

GERM LAYER	BECOMES
Ectoderm	Outer layer of skin, hair, lining of the nose and mouth, and the nervous system
Endoderm	Digestive tract, respiratory tract, liver, and pancreas
Mesoderm	Muscles and skeleton

Amnion
Inner cell mass
Blastopore
Ectoderm
Endoderm
Mesoderm

Cells of the inner cell mass begin to differentiate as the amnion forms

A gastrula develops when cells begin to migrate inward, forming an indentation.

The cells continue to push inward, forming the endoderm. Cells that remain on the outer surface of the gastrula are called ectoderm.

The mesoderm is formed, as additional cells migrate inward between the endoderm and ectoderm.

FIGURE 25-21 Gastrulation: formation of three germ layers. During gastrulation, three distinct layers of tissue form that will eventually make up the structures of the body.

How Do Animals Reproduce?   Male and Female Reproductive Systems   Sex Can Lead to Fertilization   Human Development

look similar to one another), but they have become determined, which means that the type of tissue they will become, their ultimate developmental fate, is irreversibly decided. Prior to determination, cells are referred to as "totipotent" and have the capacity to develop into any type of tissue in the body.

Here's a summary of what happens during gastrulation.

1. First, the blastocyst begins to fold inward forming an indentation, the blastopore. The blastopore is located almost opposite the point at which the sperm entered the egg.

2. As the cells continue to push inward, they are called **endoderm,** and they form the lining of what will eventually become the digestive tract; the blastopore will become the anus. Endoderm cells will also form the liver, the pancreas, and the lining of the respiratory tract. At this point, the entire mass of cells is called a **gastrula.**

3. The cells that remain on the outer surface of the gastrula are called **ectoderm** and will ultimately form the outer layer of skin, the hair, the nervous system, and the lining of the nose and mouth.

4. Some additional cells migrate inward, between the endoderm and ectoderm, forming a third type of tissue, called **mesoderm,** which will ultimately give rise to muscles and the skeleton.

The specific details of gastrulation vary slightly from one species to the next. The general outcome, however—the formation of endoderm, mesoderm, and ectoderm—occurs throughout the vertebrates.

Neurulation and the Formation of Adult Structures

As an embryo begins its third week of development, the three types of tissue formed during gastrulation begin to develop into the various organs and tissues. At this time, within the mesoderm and running the length of the embryo, just above the digestive tract, a structure called the notochord forms. The **notochord** is a flexible rod that develops in all chordates and gives support to surrounding tissue. In vertebrates, the notochord's function is ultimately taken over by the backbone.

Just above the notochord, ectoderm folds in for the entire length of the embryo, first forming a groove and then becoming a long hollow tube, called the **neural tube.** The process is referred to as **neurulation** and the resulting neural tube ultimately develops into the entire nervous system, including the brain (located opposite the original position of the blastopore) and the spinal cord (**FIGURE 25-22**).

As the neural tube is developing, blocks of mesoderm tissue, called somites, begin to form down the length of the embryo. These somites will form the vertebrae and the muscles of the body. Next to the somites, spaces form that will become the

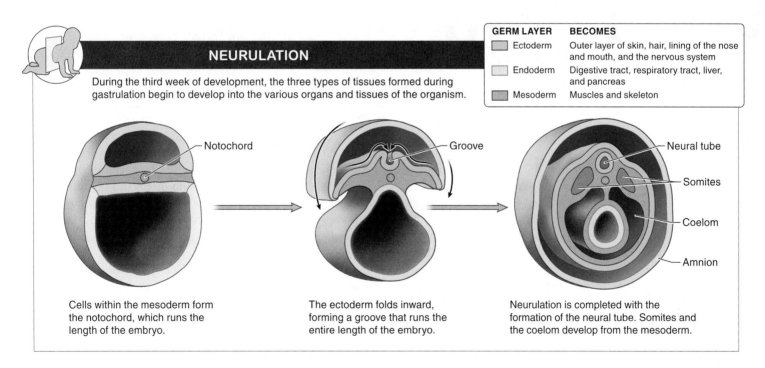

GERM LAYER	BECOMES
Ectoderm	Outer layer of skin, hair, lining of the nose and mouth, and the nervous system
Endoderm	Digestive tract, respiratory tract, liver, and pancreas
Mesoderm	Muscles and skeleton

NEURULATION

During the third week of development, the three types of tissues formed during gastrulation begin to develop into the various organs and tissues of the organism.

Cells within the mesoderm form the notochord, which runs the length of the embryo.

The ectoderm folds inward, forming a groove that runs the entire length of the embryo.

Neurulation is completed with the formation of the neural tube. Somites and the coelom develop from the mesoderm.

FIGURE 25-22 Neurulation: formation of organs and tissues from the germ layers. During neurulation, the germ layers begin to develop into the organs and tissues of the body.

Reproductive Technology

body cavity, or **coelom** (pronounced SEE-lum). Within the coelom, many of the organs will form. At this point, toward the end of the third week of development, the embryo is only 2 millimeters (less than one-tenth of an inch) in length. Further development and specialization occur as some cells are programmed to die, in essence "sculpting" the body the way that a sculptor would create a statue.

Other cells may be induced to develop into one particular cell type or another by neighboring cells that send signals, possibly proteins, to turn certain genes on or off. This process was demonstrated dramatically by researchers who transplanted cells from the top of a newt blastopore in one embryo to another developing embryo. In the recipient embryo, the

blastopore cells induced the development of nearby cells to form a second neural tube!

25·12

How does an embryo become male or female?

During the first few weeks after fertilization, surprisingly little distinguishes boys from girls. Then, about four weeks into embryo development in mammals, a gene carried on the Y chromosome, called SRY (for **s**ex-determining **r**egion on the **Y**-chromosome), can initiate development of the embryo as a male (**FIGURE 25-23**). The gene is expressed in the tissue that will form the gonads, and in most cases in which SRY is expressed, the gonads develop as testes. (There is a gene on the X chromosome that also influences sex determination and, in rare cases, can alter typical sex development.) If SRY is not present, as in females who do not carry a Y chromosome, ovaries develop instead. Once activated, SRY also stimulates numerous other genes involved in testes formation.

Once the fetal gonads develop, they start producing steroid hormones. If testes, they produce testosterone. If ovaries, they produce estrogen. The presence of high levels of testosterone causes the ducts connecting the gonads and the outside of the body to develop into the male internal reproductive organs, including the vas deferens (on each side), ejaculatory duct, and prostate. In the absence of testosterone, these ducts become the female reproductive organs, including the uterus, cervix, and Fallopian tubes.

Following development of the internal reproductive organs, undifferentiated external genitals develop. If testosterone is present and is modified slightly (by an enzyme called 5-alpha-reductase) into dihydrotestosterone (DHT), it causes the external genitals to become the penis and scrotum. In the

Q Can someone with a Y chromosome still develop as a female?

absence of DHT, female external genitals develop, including the clitoris, labia, and vagina. Sex differentiation is generally complete by about the 12th week of development in humans.

At several points in development, the development of an embryo as male or female can be disrupted. Disruptions of this type occur in several genetic disorders.

Androgen insensitivity syndrome. Some XY individuals (approximately 1 in 20,000) carry a non-functioning copy of the androgen receptor. Although the SRY gene on the Y chromosome triggers the development of testes, this X-linked recessive trait causes the tissues of the body to be unresponsive to the normal effects of testosterone. Consequently, individuals with this syndrome develop what appears to be a typical female body. Internally, however, there is no uterus and no ovaries, but rather testes that remain inside the abdomen. Individuals with this condition are identified as female, and the condition is usually not detected until the girl fails to menstruate.

5-Alpha-reductase deficiency. Some XY individuals carry a non-functioning version of the gene for the enzyme that converts testosterone into DHT. Without DHT to direct the development of external male genitals, these individuals possess testes, but the external genitals develop as they would in a female. Consequently, individuals with this condition are generally identified as female at birth and in early childhood. At puberty, however, in response to the significantly increased testosterone production by the testes,

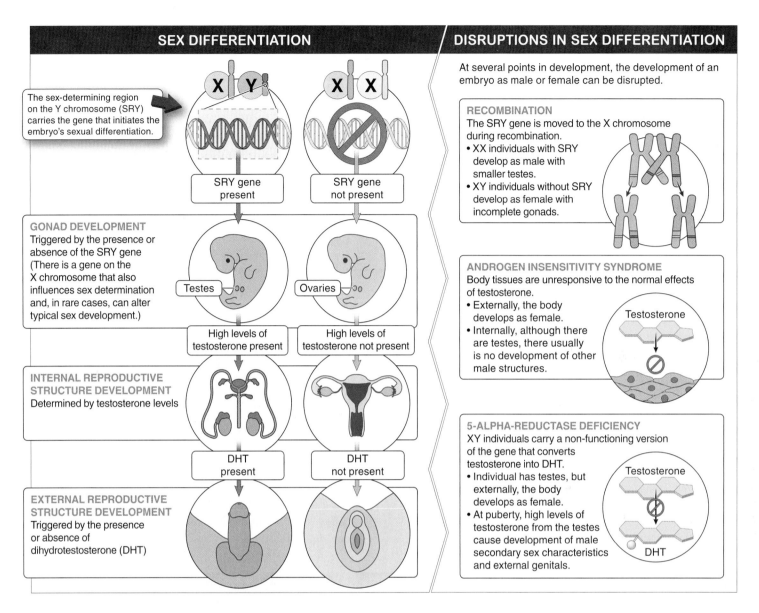

SEX DIFFERENTIATION

The sex-determining region on the Y chromosome (SRY) carries the gene that initiates the embryo's sexual differentiation.

X Y — SRY gene present

X X — SRY gene not present

GONAD DEVELOPMENT
Triggered by the presence or absence of the SRY gene (There is a gene on the X chromosome that also influences sex determination and, in rare cases, can alter typical sex development.)

Testes — High levels of testosterone present

Ovaries — High levels of testosterone not present

INTERNAL REPRODUCTIVE STRUCTURE DEVELOPMENT
Determined by testosterone levels

DHT present

DHT not present

EXTERNAL REPRODUCTIVE STRUCTURE DEVELOPMENT
Triggered by the presence or absence of dihydrotestosterone (DHT)

DISRUPTIONS IN SEX DIFFERENTIATION

At several points in development, the development of an embryo as male or female can be disrupted.

RECOMBINATION
The SRY gene is moved to the X chromosome during recombination.
- XX individuals with SRY develop as male with smaller testes.
- XY individuals without SRY develop as female with incomplete gonads.

ANDROGEN INSENSITIVITY SYNDROME
Body tissues are unresponsive to the normal effects of testosterone.
- Externally, the body develops as female.
- Internally, although there are testes, there usually is no development of other male structures.

Testosterone

5-ALPHA-REDUCTASE DEFICIENCY
XY individuals carry a non-functioning version of the gene that converts testosterone into DHT.
- Individual has testes, but externally, the body develops as female.
- At puberty, high levels of testosterone from the testes cause development of male secondary sex characteristics and external genitals.

Testosterone — DHT

FIGURE 25-23 Typical and atypical sex development.

these individuals develop male secondary sex characteristics, including a deeper voice, facial hair, and increased muscle mass. The external genitals grow and often come to resemble a penis and scrotum more than a clitoris and labia.

Recombination leading to XX individuals with the SRY gene or XY individuals lacking SRY. It is possible, during the production of sperm by males, for crossing over to occur between the X and Y chromosomes. If this crossover causes the SRY gene to be moved to the X chromosome, and if the sperm cell carrying the X with SRY or the Y without SRY fertilizes an egg, irregular development occurs in the resulting individual. In XX individuals with the SRY gene, the individual appears to develop as a typical male. Although testes develop, however, they are smaller than average. These individuals are infertile (cannot produce sperm that can

fertilize an egg or eggs that can be fertilized) and also tend to be shorter than XY males. In XY individuals without the SRY gene, the gonads develop incompletely, resembling streaks of connective tissue, but these individuals appear to develop as a typical female. At puberty, however, they are taller than average, do not develop secondary sex characteristics, and do not menstruate.

TAKE-HOME MESSAGE 25·12

Mammalian embryos develop female internal and external reproductive organs unless a gene on the Y chromosome stimulates fetal gonads to develop as testes, leading to testosterone production, which then stimulates the development of male reproductive organs.

There are three stages of pregnancy.

The development of a human embryo and fetus is usually divided into three equal periods, of approximately three months each. (The **fetus** stage begins about 8 weeks after fertilization, when the organs and other major structures first form.) Each of these **trimesters** is characterized by specific features and developmental milestones (**FIGURE 25-24**).

The First Trimester We have already discussed several of the most significant events of the first trimester. This period is characterized by relatively little growth: at the end of the first three months, the fetus is only about two or three inches long and weighs about an ounce. Much more important than growth during the first trimester is development and the differentiation of cells into specialized types of tissues. Here are some of the chief milestones (times indicate how much time has passed since fertilization).

First month

30 hours: The first cleavage occurs.

60 hours: The second cleavage occurs. In both cleavages, there is no overall growth, just cell division.

6–7 days: The zygote reaches the uterus for implantation. At this time, the zygote has become a hollow ball of cells (a blastocyst) with a small inner mass of cells that will become the embryo.

2nd week: Gastrulation occurs, and three distinct tissue layers develop. At this point, the placenta also forms. This occurs as the two membranes around the blastocyst—the amnion around the embryo and the chorion around the amnion—grow. The chorion ultimately branches out and surrounds the lining of the uterus. Together, the chorion and endometrium form the placenta (**FIGURE 25-25**), a mass of tissue in which nutrients, respiratory gases, and waste products are transferred between the mother and the developing embryo. (Although there is a yolk sac in placental mammals, its size is reduced and the placenta takes over the yolk sac's role of nourishing the embryo.) The embryo is connected to the chorion by the body stalk, which will become the **umbilical cord.**

Although the mother's blood and embryo's blood do not mix, they come in very close contact at the placenta, and oxygen diffuses from mother to embryo as carbon dioxide diffuses from embryo to mother. The placenta also nourishes the embryo and secretes hormones, including hCG, which maintains the corpus luteum, ensuring continued secretions of progesterone and, consequently, maintenance of the endometrium.

3rd week: Neurulation, the formation of the neural tube—which will develop into the nervous system—from ectoderm, follows soon after gastrulation.

HUMAN EMBRYO DEVELOPMENT

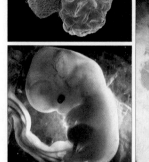 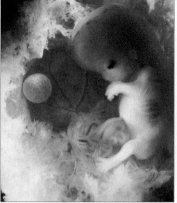 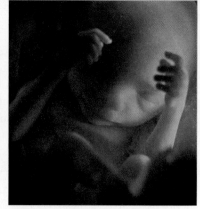 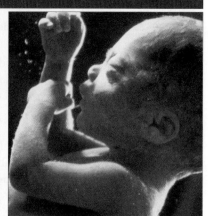

FIRST TRIMESTER: MONTHS 1–3
• Cells begin to differentiate into specialized types of tissues.
• Major organs and structures begin to form, including the eyes, heart, liver, pancreas, and gall bladder, as well as the limbs.

SECOND TRIMESTER: MONTHS 4–6
• Significant muscle and bone growth occurs, with less new development relative to the first trimester.

THIRD TRIMESTER: MONTHS 7–9
• Significant development of the nervous system.

FIGURE 25-24 Development of the human embryo and fetus. The nine months of human fetal development are divided into three-month trimesters.

How Do Animals Reproduce?   Male and Female Reproductive Systems   Sex Can Lead to Fertilization   Human Development

THE PLACENTA

The placenta is a mass of highly vascularized tissue in which nutrients, respiratory gases, and waste products are transferred between the mother and the developing embryo.

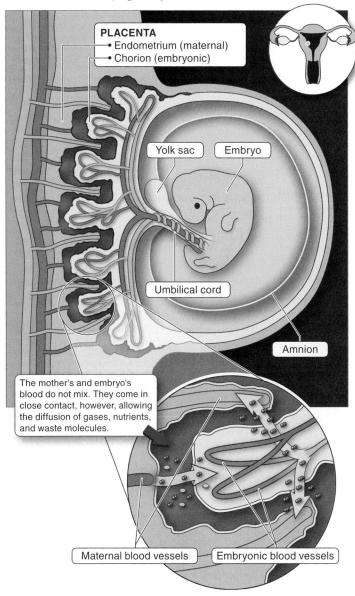

FIGURE 25-25 **Structure and function of the placenta.**

4th week: The formation of major structures and organs, including the eyes and heart, begins. At this point, it is also possible to see the arm and leg buds.

Second month

During this time, the limbs take shape. The major organs, including the liver, pancreas, and gall bladder, can also be seen. In spite of such dramatic development and differentiation, though, very little growth has occurred yet, and the weight of the embryo is about one gram, less than one-tenth of an ounce!

Third month

During the third month, the nervous system develops, as do some of the first reflexes, such as suckling. At this point, the corpus luteum finally degenerates. In the absence of the progesterone it has been producing, a new ovulatory cycle would typically (i.e., without pregnancy) occur, but because the placenta produces significant levels of estrogen and progesterone (which inhibit the production of FSH and LH), no ovulation occurs. The fetus's heartbeat usually becomes audible around the 10th week. The development of mammary glands in the mother's breasts is also stimulated at this time, in preparation for later milk production (**lactation**).

The Second Trimester The second trimester, months 4, 5, and 6 of a pregnancy, is a time of significant growth and less new development relative to the first trimester. During this time, as the bones get bigger and the muscles develop, the fetus moves around and the mother can often feel it kick. The heartbeat becomes much louder and can be heard easily with a stethoscope. Its amplified "whooshing" sounds like a freight train. Although the fetus cannot survive outside the womb at the end of the second trimester, its size has increased to about 600 grams (1.3 pounds) and 12 inches in length.

The Third Trimester The third trimester is all about growth, as the fetus ultimately becomes large enough to survive outside the mother—the minimum size for survival is generally about a pound and a half (3-4 kg). In addition to growth, during the third trimester there is significant development of the nervous system. The addition of new neurons occurs at the explosive rate of 15 million per hour, a rate that continues even after birth.

TAKE-HOME MESSAGE 25·13

The nine-month development of a human embryo and fetus is divided into three equal periods, or trimesters. The first trimester is primarily a time of development and differentiation of cells into specialized types of tissues, as the embryo implants in the uterus and the placenta forms. The second and third trimesters are characterized mostly by significant growth and rapid development of the fetus's nervous system.

Pregnancy culminates in childbirth and the start of lactation.

Birth, also called parturition, is the culmination of pregnancy, and it occurs in three phases. The first is the initiation of contractions and the dilation, or opening, of the cervix. Toward the end of the third trimester, the fetus usually becomes positioned with its head down and its skull resting on the cervix. This positioning, along with the increasing size of the fetus, stretches the uterus. Although the exact process is not fully understood, fetal hormones then cause the placenta to produce hormones, including estrogen and prostaglandin, that stimulate contractions in the uterus. The stretching of the uterus causes the pituitary gland to release oxytocin, another hormone that causes contractions. The contractions are referred to as **labor.** The rate of contractions increases from one or two per hour over many hours or even days before the birth, to about one every two to three minutes when birth is about to occur. The contractions cause a gradual dilation of the cervix, with the opening increasing from just over an inch (about 3 cm) at the beginning of labor to 4 inches (about 10 cm) or more at the end (**FIGURE 25-26**).

The second phase of birth is the delivery of the baby. This generally occurs with the head passing first through the

Q How long does breastfeeding last?

vagina, which is also called the birth canal. After delivery of the baby, there is a brief relaxation of the contractions before the third and final phase of the birth process. The contractions then resume and, after the placenta is sheared from the wall of the uterus, the contractions expel it through the birth canal. The umbilical cord is then clamped and cut, and clotting quickly stops any bleeding.

During pregnancy, mammary gland development is stimulated by estrogen, progesterone, and other hormones. After birth, the pituitary hormone prolactin stimulates milk production. Suckling by the infant, too, causes the release of prolactin and the hormone oxytocin, which further increases milk production. During the first few days, a yellowish fluid, called colostrum, is released. Colostrum is high in protein and contains numerous antibodies from the mother that protect the infant from some diseases (**FIGURE 25-27**). Gradually, the colostrum is replaced by milk, which is higher in fat and sugar, with less protein than colostrum. The average duration of breastfeeding varies a lot from one country, and one culture, to another—it is 12 weeks in the United States and as long as two to two and a half years in Bangladesh and Nepal, respectively. Among

THE PHASES OF BIRTH

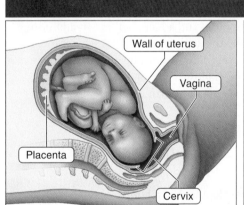
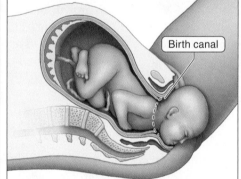
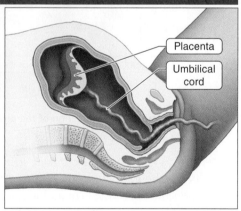

1 INITIATION OF CONTRACTIONS AND DILATION OF THE CERVIX
Hormones, including estrogen and prosta-glandins, stimulate contractions in the uterus that cause a gradual opening of the cervix.

2 DELIVERY OF THE BABY
The baby's head passes through the vagina, or birth canal, followed by the rest of the body.

3 EXPULSION OF THE PLACENTA
Final contractions shear the placenta from the uterus wall and expel it through the birth canal.

FIGURE 25-26 Labor and birth.

25-30   CHAPTER 25 • REPRODUCTION AND DEVELOPMENT

How Do Animals Reproduce?   Male and Female Reproductive Systems   Sex Can Lead to Fertilization   Human Development

Lactation, stimulated by prolactin and other hormones, nourishes the baby with protein, carbohydrates, and lipids, as well as with protective antibodies.

FIGURE 25-27 Complete nutrition. Breastfeeding provides an infant with all the nourishment it needs, along with antibody protection from some diseases.

hunter-gatherer societies of humans, breastfeeding continued for as long as four years.

During lactation, the suckling of the infant prevents the pituitary from releasing a sufficient surge of LH to cause ovulation. For this reason, during lactation, a woman's fertility is significantly reduced. As a method of birth control this method (called "lactational amenorrhea") depends on several conditions being satisfied, including that the mother is exclusively breastfeeding (i.e., the baby is not getting nourishment in any other way), the baby is less than six months old, and no more than six hours pass between any two feedings.

Q Can breastfeeding be effective as birth control?

TAKE-HOME MESSAGE 25·14

Birth is the culmination of pregnancy and occurs in three phases. The first is the initiation of contractions and the dilation of the cervix. The second is delivery of the baby. The third is expulsion of the placenta. Lactation, stimulated by prolactin and other hormones, nourishes the baby with proteins, carbohydrates, and lipids and provides the infant with protective antibodies.

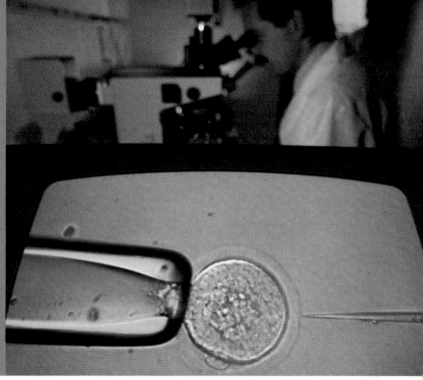

❺ Reproductive technology has benefits and dangers.

A single sperm is injected into the cytoplasm of an egg.

25·15

Assisted reproductive technologies are promising and perilous.

Just as technological advances have led to numerous developments in methods of preventing pregnancy, so, too, have they led to the development of techniques that help couples have children in situations where previously they might have remained infertile. In this section we examine some of these techniques, beginning more than a hundred years ago with the somewhat low-tech procedure that started it all.

In 1884, a woman came to see Dr. William Pancoast because she had not been able to conceive a child. After examining the couple, Dr. Pancoast determined that the husband was infertile. In the course of a discussion about the case by Dr. Pancoast and his students, someone suggested that semen should be collected from "the best-looking" member of the class and used to inseminate the woman. Dr. Pancoast agreed and arranged to see the patient again, under the pretense of another examination, at which point he injected the semen into the woman's uterus. Only when it became clear that the woman was pregnant did the doctor inform the husband of what he had done. The husband, however, was happy and requested only that the doctor not tell his wife how she had become pregnant. Eventually, a healthy son was born, the first recorded child born as the result of artificial insemination with a donor's sperm. From these inauspicious beginnings, there have been tremendous advances in the technologies available to couples experiencing difficulty having children.

Infertility is defined as a couple not being able to get pregnant after one year of trying—a definition that includes approximately 7% of married couples in the United States in any given year. There are many reasons for and causes of infertility—evenly divided between males and females—including low sperm counts and insufficient sperm motility, Fallopian tube damage or blockage, and ovulation problems. In 10% of cases, no cause can be found.

The technologies available are varied and include such interventions as surgery to repair blocked Fallopian tubes and hormone treatments to increase sperm counts or egg production. They also include a range of options called **assisted reproductive technology (ART),** the use of fertility treatments in which both sperm and egg are handled. These procedures typically involve removing eggs from a woman's ovaries, combining them with sperm to achieve fertilization in a Petri dish, and subsequently reinserting the now fertilized eggs into the reproductive tract of that woman, or another woman. In many cases—such as the case described at the beginning of this chapter—the eggs, sperm, or fertilized eggs may be frozen for some period of time before completing the process (**FIGURE 25-28**). The methods used in ART include the following.

IVF-ET. This stands for in vitro fertilization–embryo transfer. It is the most common of all ART methods. Several secondary

How Do Animals Reproduce?   Male and Female Reproductive Systems   Sex Can Lead to Fertilization   Human Development

oocytes are collected from a woman's ovaries and combined with sperm in a Petri dish. After several days, the fertilized eggs, at the eight-cell stage, are inserted into the woman's uterus, with the hope that they will implant and a pregnancy will result.

ZIFT. The technique of zygote intra-Fallopian transfer differs from IVF-ET in only two respects. After fertilization in a Petri dish, the fertilized eggs are transferred not to the uterus but to one of the Fallopian tubes instead. They also are transferred earlier, at the one-cell stage. Perhaps because surgery is needed to place the fertilized egg within the Fallopian tube, ZIFT is used by only 1% of couples seeking ART. In some cases, transfer to the Fallopian tube is not made until the fertilized egg is in the two- to four-cell stage (this is referred to as tubal embryo transfer). Some studies have shown ZIFT to have a higher implantation rate than IVF-ET.

GIFT. The method known as gamete intra-Fallopian transfer differs from ZIFT only in that the oocytes are immediately mixed with sperm and transferred to a Fallopian tube so that fertilization occurs in the body, rather than in a Petri dish.

In some cases, if the male's sperm counts are particularly low or if his sperm have low motility, a procedure called ICSI, or intracytoplasmic sperm injection, may be used in conjunction with IVF-ET or ZIFT. In this procedure, a single sperm is injected directly into an egg. While this method can be effective as a treatment for male infertility, there are concerns because

sperm selection is bypassed. That is, instead of one sperm "winning" in the competition to fertilize the egg, a sperm is selected by the individual doing the procedure. This may be why there's an increased incidence of genetically carried birth defects with ICSI.

Outside the definition of ART, but still intriguing, is the increasingly effective process for selecting the sex of a baby, known as "sperm sorting." In this method, a fluorescent dye that binds to the DNA is applied to a sperm sample. Because the X chromosome is larger than the Y chromosome (by about 3%), the X-chromosome-bearing sperm bind more dye. The dyed sperm are then given a small electric charge, based on which chromosome they carry, and as they are passed through a tube in single file, the sperm cells are deflected to a collecting tube on one side or the other, depending on their charge. The selected sperm carrying an X or Y sex chromosome can then be used in any of the ART methods described above. The purities of the X versus Y samples of sperm range from 70% to 90%.

TAKE-HOME MESSAGE 25·15

Assisted reproductive technology (ART) procedures typically involve removing eggs from a woman's ovaries, combining them with sperm to achieve fertilization, and reinserting the fertilized eggs into the woman's uterus or Fallopian tube. These technologies can enable previously infertile couples to have babies.

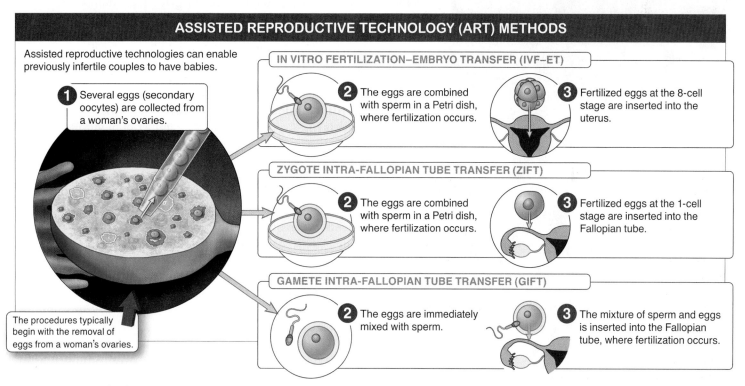

ASSISTED REPRODUCTIVE TECHNOLOGY (ART) METHODS

Assisted reproductive technologies can enable previously infertile couples to have babies.

1 Several eggs (secondary oocytes) are collected from a woman's ovaries.

The procedures typically begin with the removal of eggs from a woman's ovaries.

IN VITRO FERTILIZATION–EMBRYO TRANSFER (IVF–ET)

2 The eggs are combined with sperm in a Petri dish, where fertilization occurs.

3 Fertilized eggs at the 8-cell stage are inserted into the uterus.

ZYGOTE INTRA-FALLOPIAN TUBE TRANSFER (ZIFT)

2 The eggs are combined with sperm in a Petri dish, where fertilization occurs.

3 Fertilized eggs at the 1-cell stage are inserted into the Fallopian tube.

GAMETE INTRA-FALLOPIAN TUBE TRANSFER (GIFT)

2 The eggs are immediately mixed with sperm.

3 The mixture of sperm and eggs is inserted into the Fallopian tube, where fertilization occurs.

FIGURE 25-28 Technologies used in assisted reproductive technology.

Knowledge You Can Use

Business and science in conflict. Why is the number of multiple births—twins, triplets, and more—on the rise?

Q: **Multiple births are in the news a lot. Are they on the rise?**
Yes! Between 1980 and 2008, the incidence of twins in the United States increased by 70%. The rate of triplets and higher increased even more.

Q: **Why are there so many more multiple births?** Consider this: if you are running a fertility clinic, one of the most important pieces of information that will lead to the success or failure of your clinic is the percentage of treated couples who become pregnant. Unfortunately, in most assisted reproductive technology procedures, this number is influenced by the number of embryos transferred into the woman: 5–10 transferred embryos are more likely to result in pregnancy than 1–4 transferred embryos. The problem is, though, that with 5–10 embryos transferred, the risk of "multiples"—twins, triplets, or more—also increases, as does the health risk to the mother and the babies. And so the decision regarding the number of embryos to transfer involves a trade-off between the perceived effectiveness of the clinic and the risk to the mother. This point was vividly illustrated in 2009 by the case of Nadya Suleman (called "Octomom" by the media), a California woman who gave birth to octuplets affter eight embryos were implanted.

Q: **Are fertility clinics bringing the rate back down to safer levels?** In the past 10 years, the number of in vitro fertilization cycles in which four or more embryos were transferred dropped from 62% to 21%. This has significantly reduced the incidence of triplets, but the rate of twins has remained high. And although, for women under 35, the American Society of Reproductive Medicine now recommends the transfer of just a single embryo during ART procedures, for women above 35, it still recommends three to five embryos be transferred.

❶ How do animals reproduce?

Animals can reproduce asexually or sexually. Asexual reproduction can be fast and efficient, but leads to offspring genetically identical to the parent. Sexual reproduction occurs in the vast majority of animal species and leads to offspring that are genetically different from one another and from either parent.

❷ Male and female reproductive systems have important similarities and differences.

In adult men, sperm are continuously produced in the testes by meiosis. Semen, consisting of sperm cells and accessory fluids that nurture the sperm and aid in fertilization, is ejaculated during copulation. In adult women, diploid cells in the ovaries undergo meiosis to produce genetically varied haploid eggs. Fewer eggs than sperm are produced, and eggs are much larger than sperm.

❸ Sex can lead to fertilization, but can also spread sexually transmitted diseases.

At fertilization, a sperm penetrates the egg. The egg blocks additional sperm entry, and the sperm and egg membranes fuse. The haploid nuclei of the egg and sperm then fuse, forming a diploid zygote. Pregnancy can be prevented by preventing ovulation, fertilization, or implantation.

❹ Human development occurs in specific stages.

Fertilization is followed by cleavage of the zygote, with many rapid cell divisions but without growth. Next, in gastrulation, a gut begins to form, along with three distinct germ layers with specific developmental fates. In neurulation, mesoderm forms the notochord, and ectoderm forms a neural tube, which will become the brain and spinal cord. Mammalian embryos develop female reproductive organs unless a gene on the Y chromosome stimulates the fetal gonads to develop as testes, leading to the further development of male reproductive organs. The development of human embryos is divided into three trimesters. The first is primarily a time of development and differentiation; the second and third are characterized mostly by significant growth. Birth is the culmination of pregnancy, and lactation, stimulated by prolactin and other hormones, nourishes the baby and provides protective antibodies

❺ Reproductive technology has benefits and dangers.

Assisted reproductive technology procedures typically involve removing eggs from a woman's ovaries, combining them with sperm to achieve fertilization in a Petri dish, and reinserting the fertilized eggs into the woman. They can enable couples to have babies who previously would have been infertile.

KEY TERMS

1. Some animals are primarily asexual in their reproduction, but have the ability to switch to sexual reproduction under certain conditions. What adaptive advantage might an animal that generally reproduces asexually have by also being able to reproduce sexually?
   a) to increase the genetic diversity of its offspring during periods of stress
   b) to confuse its predators
   c) to give the animal some variety in its life
   d to increase its own likelihood of survival
   e) Only a) and d) are correct

2. Amplexus is a tactic that occurs in most species of frogs. The most likely reason that this tactic has evolved is:
   a) the gametes of terrestrial animals can quickly dry out in non-aquatic environments.
   b) it enables internal fertilization to occur without the necessity of viviparity.
   c) it ensures that the sperm and eggs are released at the same time and in the same place, increasing the likelihood of fertilization.
   d) it reduces the negative effect of salt water on gametes.
   e) All of the above are correct.

3. Meiosis occurs in the _____ in female humans and in the _____ in male humans.
   a) follicles; seminiferous tubules
   b) somatic cells; germ cells
   c) uterus; prostate gland
   d) follicles; prostate gland
   e) Fallopian tube; vas deferens.

4. Which three sets of accessory glands add secretions to the semen in human males?
   a) the seminal vesicles, the prostate gland, and the bulbourethral glands
   b) the ejaculatory duct, the prostate gland, and the vas deferens
   c) the seminal vesicles, the prostate gland, and the urethra
   d) the seminal vesicles, the prostate gland, and the epididymis
   e) the ejaculatory duct, the prostate gland, and the bulbourethral glands

5. When individual females mate with multiple males within short periods of time:
   a) a male that produces more sperm than other males has an increased probability of reproductive success.
   b) internal fertilization cannot occur.
   c) there is selection for a reduction in the size of the male testes.
   d) the male gametes experience reduced desiccation.
   e) All of the above are correct.

6. The tissue that develops into the penis in males, develops into _____ in females.
   a) the vagina   d) the oviduct
   b) the labia   e) the ovary
   c) the clitoris

7. The completion of meiosis II in the oocyte of human females occurs:
   a) before birth.   d) a few hours before ovulation.
   b) during menstruation.   e) at ovulation.
   c) after the oocyte is fertilized by a sperm.

8. The corpus luteum:
   a) secretes chorionic gonadotropin.
   b) is reabsorbed when fertilization occurs.
   c) is the only source of the hormones that maintain pregnancy.
   d) secretes progesterone but not estrogen.
   e) is the initial source of progesterone during pregnancy.

9. In mammalian fertilization, the extracellular layer of the egg that functions, in part, as a sperm receptor is called the:
   a) endoderm.   d) egg plasma membrane.
   b) jelly coat.   e) zona pellucida.
   c) acrosome.

10. The hormones present in birth control pills typically prevent pregnancy by:
    a) preventing formation of the endometrial lining of the uterus.
    b) preventing ovarian follicles from maturing.
    c) preventing sperm from fertilizing the ovulated egg.
    d) causing the endometrium to be shed once a fertilized egg has implanted.
    e) preventing implantation of fertilized eggs in the endometrium.

11. Tying off the vas deferens leading from each testis will:
    a) prevent formation of sperm.
    b) decrease testosterone secretion.
    c) reduce secretion from the seminal vesicles.
    d) reduce secretions from the prostate gland.
    e) None of the above.

12. When do cells begin to lose their totipotency?
    a) anaphase of mitosis   d) cleavage
    b) gastrulation   e) neurulation
    c) late prophase I of meiosis

13. The phenotype of an individual who is genetically XY but is lacking the sex-determining region on the Y chromosome would be:
    a) a person who does not have testes but does have male external sex organs.
    b) completely male, because of low estrogen levels.
    c) either male or female, depending on whether the person carries the gene for DHT, which directs development of the penis.
    d) a person with ovaries and female secondary sex characteristics.
    e) completely male, because the person will produce testosterone, which masculinizes the internal and external reproductive organs.

14. In humans, fetal growth is slowest during which trimester?

   a) first
   b) second
   c) third
   d) fourth
   e) It occurs at the same rate in all trimesters.

15. In which of the following methods of assisted reproductive technology does fertilization occur within the woman's body?

   a) intracytoplasmic sperm injection
   b) in vitro fertilization–embryo transfer (IVF-ET)
   c) zygote intra-Fallopian transfer (ZIFT)
   d) gamete intra-Fallopian transfer (GIFT)
   e) All of the above.

SHORT-ANSWER QUESTIONS

1. In humans, how are male gametes formed? Where in the male reproductive system does this process occur?

2. What are germ layers? How many layers are there, what are they called, and what structures ultimately form from them?

3. Summarize the three stages of pregnancy and the major events that occur in each.

See Appendix for answers. For additional study questions, go to www.prep-u.com.

PHOTO CREDITS --

Photo Legend: *L*: left, *C*: center, *R*: right, *T*: top, *M*: middle, *B*: bottom

CHAPTER 20 **p. 20-1:** *photo* Visuals Unlimited/Corbis. **p. 20-2:** *photo* Alexander Demianchuk/Reuters/Corbis. **p. 20-3:** *Figure 20-1* AP Photo/ Sue Ogrocki. **p. 20-4:** *Figure 20-2 (L)* Emilio Suetone/Hemis/Corbis, *(R)* AP Photo/Sergei Chuzavkov. **p. 20-5:** *photo* Anup Shah/npl/Minden Pictures. **p. 20-8:** *Figure 20-6 (T)* Paul Nicklen/Getty Images, *(B)* Doug Allan/Getty Images; *Figure 20-7 (L)* Tim Farrell/Star Ledger/Corbis, *(R)* Chris Johns/Getty Images. **p. 20-9:** *Figure 20-9 (from left)* Doug Allan/npl/ Minden Pictures, Michael & Patricia Fogden/Minden Pictures, Simon King/npl/Minden Pictures, John-Francis Bourke/Corbis. **p. 20-10:** *Figure 20-10* TS Corrigan/Alamy. **p. 20-14:** *Figure 20-14* Peter Dasilva/epa/ Corbis. **p. 20-15:** *photo* Keren Su/Corbis; *Figure 20-15* Hiroya Minakuchi/ Minden Pictures. **p. 20-16:** *photo* Frans Lanting/Frans Lanting Photography. **p. 20-17:** *Figure 20-17 (T)* Image Quest Marine/Alamy, *(bottom, from left)* Dennis Kunkel Microscopy, Inc.,Visuals Unlimited/Corbis *(all)*. **p. 20-19:** *Figure 20-19 (TL)* Quest/Photo Researchers, *(BL)* Photo Quest Ltd/ Science Photo Library/Corbis, *(C)* George J. Sanker/DRK photo, *(TR)* Dennis Kunkel Microscopy, Inc, *(MR & BR)* Visuals Unlimited/Corbis; *photo* Clifford White/Corbis. **p. 20-21:** *Figure 20-22 (T)* Joe McDonald/ Corbis, *(bottom, from left)* Photo Quest Ltd/Science Photo Library/Corbis, *(both)* Visuals Unlimited/Corbis. **p. 20-23:** *Figure 20-24* D. Robert & Lorri Franz/Corbis; *photo* Eric Grave/Photo Researchers. **p. 20-24:** *Figure 20-25 (top row, from left)* MIXA/Alamy, Stuart O'Sullivan/Getty Images, Jose Luis Pelaez, Inc./Blend Images/Corbis *(bottom row, from left)* Mike Kemp/Getty Images, Hola Images/Getty Images, Radius Images/Alamy. **p. 20-25:** *Figure 20-26 (top row, from left)* Andersen Ross/Blend Images/Corbis, Mark Andersen/Getty Images, Radius Images/Alamy, *(bottom row, from left)* Caroline Schiff/Getty Images, Andersen Ross/Getty Images, RubberBall/ Alamy. **p. 20-26:** *photo* Jupiterimages/Brand X/Alamy.

CHAPTER 21 **p. 21-1:** *photo* Susumu Nishinaga/Photo Researchers. **p. 21-2:** *photo* Christopher Furlong/Getty Images. **p. 21-4:** *Figure 21-2* Chris Newbert/Minden Pictures; *Figure 21-3 (T)* Daniel J. McCauley IV, *(B)* Ruoso Cyril/Peter Arnold. **p. 21-5:** *Figure 21-4* Ralph Hutchings/Visuals Unlimited, *(inset)* David M. Phillips/Photo Researchers. **p. 21-8:** *photo* Dennis Kunkel Microscopy, Inc.; *Figure 21-6* Dietmar Busse/Getty Images. **p. 21-11:** *Figure 21-9 (L)* Eyecandy Images/IPNstock.com, *(R)* BSIP/ Phototake. **p. 21-12:** *Figure 21-10* Alix/Photo Researchers. **p. 21-13:** *Figure 21-11* Fancy Photography/Veer. **p. 21-14:** *Figure 21-12 (L)* Dr. Fred Hossler/Visuals Unlimited, *(C)* Dennis Kunkel Microscopy, Inc/Phototake, *(R)* CNRI/Photo Researchers; *Figure 21-13* AP Photo/Eckehard Schulz. **p. 21-15:** *photo* Luca Trovato/Jupiterimages. **p. 21-16:** *Figure 21-14* Popperfoto/Getty Images, *(inset)* imagebroker/Alamy. **p. 21-17:** *Figure 21-15* Frans Lanting/Frans Lanting Photography. **p. 21-18:** *Figure 21-16 (L)* Science Photo Library, *(R)* SPL/Photo Researchers. **p. 21-19:** *Figure 21-17 (T)* Banana Stock/Jupiterimages, *(B)* DigitalVision/Superstock. **p. 21-21:** *Figure 21-18* Dietmar Busse/Getty Images, *(inset)* Michael Abbey/ Photo Researchers. **p. 21-22:** *Figure 21-20* Phototex/NEWSCOM. **p. 21-23:** *Figure 21-21* Everett Collection; *photo* Corbis. **p. 21-24:** *photo* Paul Souders/Corbis. **p. 21-28:** *Figure 21-26* Fancy/Veer/Corbis. **p. 21-29:** *Figure 21-27 (L)* Dennis Kunkel Microscopy, Inc., *(R)* Dr. Bahman Guyuron. **p. 21-30:** *Figure 21-29* Yva Momatiuk & John Eastcott/Minden Pictures. **p. 21-31:** *photo* Frans Lanting/Frans Lanting Photography.

p. 21-32: *photo* Image Source/Getty Images; *Figure 21-31 (L & R)* Pr. M. Brauner/Photo Researchers. **p. 21-33:** *Figure 21-32* IMAX/Photofest. **p. 21-34:** *photo* Julian Herbert/Getty Images. **p. 21-36:** *Figure 21-36 (T)* Loungepark/Getty Images, *(B)* Image Source Ltd/age fotostock; *Figure 21-37* Lennart Nilsson. **p. 21-37:** *Figure 21-38 (L)* Dorling Kindersley; *(R)* Foodfolio /Jupiterimages. **p. 21-38:** *photo* Danita Delimont/Alamy; *Figure 21-39* Design Pics Inc./Alamy. **p. 21-39:** *Figure 21-40* Alison Wright/ Corbis. **p. 21-40:** *Figure 21-41* imagebroker/Alamy. **p. 21-41:** *Figure 21-42* Doug Allan/Minden Pictures. **p. 21-42:** *photo* Mark M. Lawrence/Corbis.

CHAPTER 22 **p. 22-1:** *photo* Marcus Wilson-Smith/age fotostock. **p. 22-2:** *photo* Michael Freeman/Corbis. **p. 22-4:** *Figure 22-2 (T)* Gunter Zlesler/Peter Arnold, *(M)* Fred Bavendam/Minden Pictures, *(B)* Alan & Sandy Carey/zefa/Corbis; *Figure 22-3* Adrian Hepworth/NHPA, *(inset)* Alex Wild. **p. 22-5:** *Figure 22-4* CDO Ranching and Development L.P., *(inset)* Joseph Sohm/Visions of America/Corbis. **p. 22-6:** *Figure 22-5 (T) & (BL)* Loungepark/Getty Images, *(BR)* Image Source Ltd/age fotostock; *Figure 22-6* Heinrich van den Berg/Getty Images. **p. 22-7:** *photo* Frans Lanting/Corbis; *Figure 22-7* Thomas Mangelsen/Minden Pictures. **p. 22-9:** *Figure 22-8* Judith Haeusler/Getty Images; *Figure 22-9 (T)* FoodCollection/ age fotostock, *(B)* Riou/PhotoCuisine/Corbis. **p. 22-11:** *Figure 22-10* Image Source/Corbis; *Figure 22-11 (L)* Lew Robertson/Corbis, *(C)* John E. Kelly /Jupiterimages, *(R)* LWA-Stephen Welstead/Corbis. **p. 22-12:** *Figure 22-12* Owen Franken/Corbis. **p. 22-13:** *Figure 22-13 (L)* Bobbi Fabian/ Getty Images, *(R)* Tim Hill/Photolibrary. **p. 22-16:** *Figure 22-16* Callum Bennetts/Alamy; *photo* Rubberball/Jupiterimages. **p. 22-17:** *Figure 22-17* Tommy Moorman. **p. 22-18:** *Figure 22-18* Oxford Scientific (OSF)/ Photolibrary; *photo* Peter Menzel www.menzelphoto.com. **p. 22-19:** *photo* Steve Allen/Getty Images. **p. 22-20:** *Figure 22-20* Image Source/Veer. **p. 22-22:** *Figure 22-22* Science Photo Library/Alamy. **p. 22-23:** *photo* S. Picavet/Jupiterimages. **p. 22-24:** *Figure 22-24* Wayne G. Lawler/Photo Researchers; *Figure 22-25* Deshakalyan Chowdhury/AFP/Getty Images. **p. 22-25:** *Figure 22-26 (L)* Dr. Richard Kessel & Dr. Gene Shih/Visuals Unlimited, *(both)* SPL/Photo Researchers. **p. 22-27:** *Figure 22-29* SPL/ Photo Researchers. **p. 22-29:** *Figure 22-30* Ladislav Janicek/zefa/Corbis, *(inset)* Dr Kari Lounatmaa/Photo Researchers; *Figure 22-31* Wayne Lynch/ age fotostock. **p. 22-30:** *Figure 22-32* Annie Griffiths Belt/Getty Images. **p. 22-31:** *photo* Sean Justice/Corbis; *Figure 22-33* Envision/Corbis, *(inset)* Mango Productions/Corbis. **p. 22-33:** *Figure 22-35* Robert Daly/Getty Images. **p. 22-34:** *Figure 22-37* Ewing Galloway. **p. 22-35:** *Figure 22-38* Tony Freeman/Photo Edit. **p. 22-36:** *Figure 22-39 (L)* AP Photo/Karl-Heinz Kreifelts, *(C)* Image Source/Corbis, *(R)* Ted Thai//Time Life Pictures/Getty Images. **p. 22-39:** *Figure 22-40* Purestock/Getty Images; *Figure 22-42* Mark Clarke/Photo Researchers. **p. 22-41:** *Figure 22-44* John Isaac/Peter Arnold. **p. 22-42:** *(T)* Tom Le Goff/Getty Images, *(B)* SPL/ Photo Researchers.

CHAPTER 25 **p. 25-1:** *photo* Michael Mährlein/age footstock. **p. 25-2:** *photo* Frans Lanting/Corbis. **p. 25-3:** *Figure 25-1* Rex USA. **p. 25-4:** *Figure 25-4 (L)* Juniors Bildarchiv/Alamy, *(R)* Dennis Kunkel Microscopy, Inc./Visuals Unlimited. **p. 25-6:** *Figure 25-5 (L)* Artur Tabor/Minden Pictures, *(R)* Arco Images GmbH/Alamy; *photo* Frans Lanting/Frans Lanting

ANSWERS

Chapter 20

1. a; 2. c; 3. d; 4. a; 5. a; 6. a; 7. d; 8. e; 9. b; 10. d; 11. a

Short-Answer Questions

1. Homeostasis is the maintenance of a constant internal environment within a narrow range of conditions around a set point, for variables such as temperature, pH, and concentrations of solute, water, CO_2, O_2, and glucose, among many others. Homeostasis allows for the normal functioning of an organism's cells. Body temperature is normally controlled by a negative feedback mechanism (thermoregulation). Hyperthermia occurs when the body temperature rises above its normal range. If high enough, this can interfere with the structure and activity of the enzymes involved in the body's metabolic activities, and this can result in metabolic dysfunction, death of cells, organ failure, and, ultimately, death of the organism.

2. Cells of similar type are organized into tissues; tissues are organized into organs that perform specialized functions; and organs are organized into organ systems, arranged in an integrated manner to perform common goals. There are four types of tissue. *Connective tissues* support and help form body structures. *Epithelial tissues* form internal and external body coverings, providing protection, synthesizing and releasing chemical products, and controlling movement of substances within the body. *Muscle tissues* have the ability to contract, generating body movements and moving materials within the body. *Nervous tissue* conducts electrical impulses, allowing communication within the organism.

3. *Connective tissue proper* includes (a) *loose connective tissue,* which has cells embedded in a semi-fluid matrix, with many collagen fibers that bind and hold organs in place, as well as storing fat and insulating, cushioning, and protecting the body; and (b) *dense connective tissue,* which has many more collagen fibers than loose connective tissue and thus has greater strength, forming tendons, which connect muscles to bones, and ligaments, which connect bones to each other. *Special connective tissue* includes (a) *bone,* composed of cells within a solid matrix interspersed with many collagen fibers, forming a rigid structure that supports and protects the body; (b) *cartilage,* composed of cells within a matrix (not as hard as bone) made up of collagen, elastin, and proteins connected to carbohydrate chains; and (c) *blood,* which has a fluid matrix called plasma, with suspended red blood cells, white blood cells, and platelets.

4. *Skeletal muscles* are made up of cells (fibers) that have alternating light and dark bands (striations) and contain many nuclei; the muscles are attached to bones, generating force for their movement, and are controlled voluntarily. *Smooth muscles,* which are not striated and have smaller cells, are found in the walls of hollow organs; contractions allow movement of liquids and solids within the organs, and are involuntary. *Cardiac muscle* is found in the walls of the heart and consists of striated, small, branched cells with a single nucleus; contractions generate pressure to move blood in the cardiovascular system, and are involuntary.

Chapter 21

1. d; 2. c; 3. a; 4. b; 5. a; 6. e; 7. e; 8. b; 9. e; 10. e; 11. a; 12. b; 13. e; 14. a; 15. c; 16. a; 17. c; 18. d; 19. d; 20. a; 21. c

Short-Answer Questions

1. Single-celled organisms, such as bacteria, are in direct contact with their environment, and direct diffusion of gases, nutrients, and wastes can take place at an adequate rate to maintain these organisms physiologically. In larger organisms made up of multiple cells, many of which are not in direct contact with the outside environment, direct diffusion is no longer feasible. With the development of a circulatory system, nutrients and gases can be brought in close proximity to cells, where diffusion can take place. An open circulatory system is characterized by having only one type of extracellular fluid; a closed circulatory system has two different extracellular fluids: interstitial fluid, bathing cells, and blood, which is contained only within the blood vessels.

2. In a single-circuit cardiovascular system, the heart has two chambers, one receiving blood that has traveled through the body, and the other moving blood to the gills and then through the blood vessels of the rest of the body. As blood moves through capillaries and other blood vessels, it slows down considerably, which slows down the delivery of substances to tissues and removal of waste products. A double-circuit system has one circuit that moves blood through the lungs and another that moves blood through the rest of the body. This system allows blood to be re-pressurized after it has traveled through the lungs, and this would be the better choice to supply tissues with high energy demands: blood can be delivered and removed at a faster rate.

3. *Red blood cells (erythrocytes):* Their primary function is to carry oxygen. They are suspended in plasma and contain iron-bearing hemoglobin, which binds, carries, and releases the oxygen. *White blood cells (leukocytes):* These are part of the body's immune system; their primary function is to seek out and destroy foreign organisms, including viruses and bacteria. *Platelets:* These cellular fragments circulate in blood and take part in plugging tears and holes in blood vessels and preventing leakage of blood. They do this by sticking together to form a clot.

4. Aquatic animals move water across their gills, which have capillaries that use a countercurrent mechanism. Blood moves through the capillaries in the opposite direction to the water flow, and this allows for a more efficient gas exchange: absorption of O_2 by and release of CO_2 from blood. In animals that breathe air, fresh air enters the lungs and moves into the alveoli. Gas exchange occurs there: O_2 in the air diffuses into capillaries in the walls of the alveoli, and CO_2 diffuses out of the blood and into the air, to be exhaled from the lungs.

Chapter 22

1. a; 2. c; 3. d; 4. a; 5. a; 6. b; 7. b; 8. c; 9. d; 10. a; 11. b; 12. b; 13. e; 14. d; 15. d; 16. e; 17. a

Short-Answer Questions

1. *Water:* important in the transport of nutrients and wastes; acts as a solvent for amino acids, sugars, minerals, and many vitamins; and takes part in some chemical reactions. *Proteins:* the source of amino acids, which are the building blocks of body proteins, such as hemoglobin, muscle cells, and enzymes. Proteins also can act as an energy source.

Carbohydrates: energy-rich chemicals used by cells, through cellular respiration, as their primary energy source. Cellulose (fiber), which cannot be digested by humans, stimulates movement of food through the intestines. *Fats:* long-term energy-storage molecules, stored as fat tissue under the skin (which also provides body insulation) and elsewhere. *Vitamins and minerals:* required in very small quantities, but playing an important role in the proper functioning of enzymes and other processes.

2. *Ingestion:* intake of food through the mouth. The structures of the mouth cut food into small pieces and grind and mix it with saliva, so that it can be transported through the esophagus to the stomach by peristaltic action. *Digestion:* breakdown of food in the mouth, stomach, and small intestine into its most basic components, which can be readily absorbed and used by cells. Digestion is accomplished by a combination of physical breakdown of food into smaller pieces and chemical breakdown by enzymes. *Absorption:* uptake of usable nutrients through the wall of the small intestine and into the bloodstream, and then transport to cells of the body. *Elimination:* finally, in the large intestine, absorption of water, salts, and vitamins, storage of feces in the rectum, and elimination through defecation.

3. Animals that consume cellulose-containing foods such as grasses and leaves have, either in their stomach or in their cecum, bacteria that can break down cellulose into a usable form.

4. Type 1 diabetes, usually beginning in childhood, results from the inability of the pancreas to produce enough insulin; treatment is injection of insulin so that cells can absorb glucose. Type 2 diabetes, generally beginning later in life, occurs when cells become less responsive to insulin or the number of insulin receptors is reduced. Risk factors include obesity and chronic consumption of high amounts of sugar. Treatment includes weight loss and minimizing glucose fluctuations.

Chapter 25

1. a; 2. c; 3. a; 4. a; 5. a; 6. c; 7. c; 8. e; 9. e; 10. b; 11. e; 12. b; 13. d; 14. a; 15. d

Short-Answer Questions

1. Human males produce sperm by the process of spermatogenesis, which occurs in the testes, located in the scrotum, outside the body. Spermatogonia, cells in the seminiferous tubules, divide by mitosis, each cell producing a new spermatogonium and a primary spermatocyte. The primary spermatocyte undergoes a first meiotic division, producing two secondary spermatocytes, each of which divides by a second meiotic division to produce four haploid sperm. Sperm move to the epididymis, where they mature and become motile.

2. Germ layers are the three layers of tissue—endoderm, mesoderm, and ectoderm—that form in the embryo during gastrulation. *Endoderm* is the inner tissue layer that forms the digestive tract, liver, pancreas, and the lining of the respiratory tract. *Mesoderm* is the middle tissue layer that gives rise to muscle and the skeletal system. *Ectoderm* is the outer tissue that gives rise to the outer layer of skin, hair, the nervous system, and the lining of the nose and mouth.

3. *First trimester:* During the first three months of development, minimal growth of the embryo takes place, but vital cell differentiation and development occur. The fertilized egg (zygote) divides and eventually forms three cell layers, from which all the organs and their associated systems will develop, as well as all body structures. This is also the stage during which the zygote implants in the uterus and the placenta forms. *Second trimester:* Significant growth occurs during the fourth through six months. The bones of the skeletal system grow and muscles develop, making possible fetal movement. *Third trimester:* The fetus primarily grows during these last three months of pregnancy. Growth and development of the nervous system also take place. During this stage, the fetus becomes an individual that can survive outside the womb.

GLOSSARY

A note about notation: The word or phrase being defined is in boldface type; it is followed by the number (in parentheses) of the chapter or chapters where it is discussed. In some cases, derivations are given. Abbreviations: Gk., Greek; Lat., Latin; *sing.*, singular; *pl.*, plural; *dim.*, diminutive (a smaller version of the object named).

A

absorption (22) The process by which biological macromolecules in food particles are taken up from the cells lining the digestive tract and then move into the bloodstream.

acrosome (25) Cap-like structure covering the head region of a sperm; it contains enzymes for penetrating the outer membrane of an egg, enabling fusion of the nuclei to occur.

amnion (25) The membrane enclosing the fluid-filled sac surrounding the embryo.

arteriosclerosis (21) A disease process, following development of atherosclerosis, in which calcium deposits harden the arteries.

artery (21) A blood vessel that transports blood from the heart, at higher pressure than veins, to the capillaries of the body.

asexual reproduction (25) A type of reproduction common in prokaryotes and plants, and also occurring in many other multicellular organisms, in which the offspring inherit their DNA from a single parent.

assisted reproductive technology (ART) (25) The use of fertility treatments in which both sperm and egg are handled.

atherosclerosis (21) A disease process in which plaques develop in the arteries, reducing the flow of blood and increasing the risk of blood clots.

atrium (21) A chamber of the heart that collects blood returning from the lungs or the rest of the body.

axon (20) A projection from the nerve cell (neuron) that transmits impulses away from the cell body.

B

basal metabolic rate (BMR) (22) The amount of energy expended by a living organism at rest in a neutral temperature environment.

bile (22) A juice that aids in the breakdown of fats; it is produced by the liver, sent to the gall bladder, and passed through a small duct into the small intestine, where it initiates the first step in fat digestion.

blastocyst (25) The mammalian blastula.

blastula (25) An early stage of embryonic development produced by cleavage of a fertilized egg (zygote). A spherical layer of cells encloses a large fluid-filled space where the embryo forms. [Gk., *blastos*, sprout]

blood (20, 21) A connective tissue with a liquid extracellular matrix containing blood cells; contained in a closed circulatory system, and important in the transport of respiratory gases, vitamins and minerals, nutrients, hormones, components of the immune system, and metabolic wastes.

blood pressure (21) The force with which blood flows through the arteries.

body mass index (22) Body weight in kilograms divided by height in meters squared (kg/m^2); often used as an index of a healthy weight for an individual based on the person's height.

bone (20) A rigid connective tissue that protects and provides support.

Bowman's capsule (20) A ball-like structure surrounding the blood-filtering unit of a nephron in the kidney. It is connected to a single, long, urine-collecting tube that excretes its filtered fluid into a collecting duct.

bulbourethral gland (25) A male reproductive gland, one on each side of the body, that contributes mucus and sugar to the ejaculate and lubricant to the tip of the penis prior to copulation.

C

calorie (22) The energy required to raise the temperature of 1 gram of water by 1° C; commonly used as a measure of the amount of energy in a particular food.

capillaries (21) Tiny blood vessels that bring blood close enough to cells to allow the diffusion of molecules into and out of the blood.

cardiac muscle (20) A type of muscle tissue, located only in the heart, that causes the heart to pump blood through the body. Cardiac muscle cells, which are fused together and connected by gap junctions, contain many more mitochondria than other types of muscle cells.

cardiovascular disease (21) Progressive deterioration of the arteries and other degradations of the circulatory system; the leading cause of death and disability in the United States.

carnivores (22) Predatory animals (and some plants) that consume only animals. [Lat., *carnis*, of flesh + *vorare, to* devour]

cartilage (20) A dense connective tissue with an extracellular matrix rich in collagen, elastin, and proteins bound to long carbohydrate chains, with a hardness between that of bone and of tendons; strong, but also flexible, cartilage is found in the ears and tip of the nose in humans, and it cushions the bones in joints throughout the body.

cell body (20) The part of the nerve cell (neuron) that contains the nucleus and other organelles.

central nervous system (20) The part of an organism's nervous system that includes the brain and spinal cord and coordinates all nervous activity.

cervix (25) The low, narrow portion of the uterus leading to the vagina. [Lat., *cervix*, neck]

chorion (25) The outer membrane surrounding the embryo, which, with the endometrium, forms the placenta.

chyme (22) A liquid mass of partially digested food that passes from the stomach through the small intestine.

cleavage (25) In embryonic development, the early cell division of the zygote, which begins shortly after fertilization.

clitoris (25) Erectile sexual organ of female mammals; develops from the same embryonic tissue that produces the penis.

closed circulatory system (21) A circulatory system in which blood is contained in vessels and is separate from the interstitial fluid that bathes cells.

coelom (25) The body cavity; it forms from the mesoderm in embryonic development.

collagen (20) A protein in the matrix of connective tissue, synthesized and secreted by connective tissue cells (fibroblasts).

colon (22) See **large intestine.**

conformer (20) An organism that, for a given physiological variable, has no set point for the variable and allows it to fluctuate with external changes in the environment.

connective tissue (20) A type of animal tissue that consists of cells embedded in a large amount of extracellular material, called matrix, which together contribute to body structure and support; includes tendons, ligaments, fat, blood, bone, and cartilage.

connective tissue proper (20) A type of connective tissue, including fat tissue, tendons, and ligaments, that has a semi-fluid, flexible matrix and functions like packing material.

contraception (25) The attempt to prevent pregnancy by preventing ovulation, fertilization, or implantation. Also called *birth control*.

coprophagy (22) A nutritional strategy, common in rabbits and rodents, in which animals consume some of their feces, thereby increasing their ability to extract energy from food by passing it through their digestive system twice.

copulation (25) The act of placing the male reproductive organ within the female's reproductive tract.

coronary arteries (21) The blood vessels that deliver oxygen and nutrients to the heart.

corpus luteum (25) A structure that develops from a follicle after ovulation; it secretes hormones to maintain pregnancy. [Lat., *corpus*, body + *luteum*, yellow]

D

dendrite (20) A branched projection from a neuron that receives signals from the external environment or from other neurons. [Gk., *dendron*, tree]

diabetes (22) A condition in which an individual does not adequately regulate their blood sugar levels; usually results from insufficient insulin secretion from the pancreas in response to an increase in blood sugar, or inadequate response of the cells of the body to insulin in the bloodstream.

diaphragm (contraceptive) (25) A dome-shaped piece of rubber placed in the vagina that blocks the cervix and prevents sperm from coming in contact with an egg. Also called *cervical cap*.

diastolic pressure (21) The second blood pressure reading; a measure of the force that blood exerts on the artery walls while the heart is between beats.

differentiated (25) Describing cells that, during development, begin to take on specific structures or functions.

digestion (22) The physical and chemical breakdown of food into its fundamental macromolecular components for absorption or elimination.

E

ectoderm (25) The outermost embryonic cell layer during gastrulation; it eventually forms skin, hair, the nervous system, and the lining of the nose and mouth. [Gk., *ektos*, outside + *derma*, skin]

ectotherms (20) Organisms that rely on the heat from an external source to raise their body temperature. [Gk., *ektos*, outside + *therme*, heat]

effector (20) A structure that can be triggered in response to a stimulus; aids in the maintenance of homeostasis by opposing or reducing changes in the internal environment in response to changes in the external environment.

egg (25) A female gamete. Also called *ovum* (pl. *ova*).

elastin (20) A protein in the matrix of connective tissue, synthesized and secreted by connective tissue cells (fibroblasts), that gives the tissue flexibility.

elimination (22) The last phase in the breakdown of food; the absorption of water, salts, and some vitamins in the large intestine, followed by defecation of remaining waste material.

embryo (25) The multicellular, developing, fertilized egg of a eukaryote. In humans, at about eight weeks following fertilization the embryo is called a fetus.

endocrine gland (20) A collection of epithelial cells that produces hormones and releases them into the bloodstream or other fluids of the body

endoderm (25) The innermost embryonic cell layer during gastrulation; it eventually forms the lining of the respiratory and digestive tracts, the liver, and the pancreas. [Gk., *endon*, within + *derma*, skin]

endometrium (25) The lining of the uterus where a fertilized egg implants and is nourished.

endotherms (20) Organisms that use the heat produced by their cellular respiration to raise and maintain their body temperature. [Gk., *endon*, within + *therme*, heat]

epididymis (25) A tube in each testis where the sperm mature.

epithelial tissue (20) A thin tissue that covers and protects the surfaces of an animal's body. Also called *epithelium*.

epithelium (20) See **epithelial tissue.**

erythrocytes (21) See **red blood cells.**

esophagus (22) The passageway from the throat to the stomach through which food travels.

essential amino acid (22) An amino acid that is not made by the body and so must be consumed in food.

estrogen (25) One of the primary female sex hormone; important in female development and the female reproductive cycle.

exocrine gland (20) A collection of epithelial cells that secretes products onto the surface of the epithelium.

external fertilization (25) The process in which sperm and egg unite outside the bodies of the male and female.

extracellular fluid (20) A body fluid that is outside the cells; as distinct from intracellular fluid. See also **blood; interstitial fluid.**

F

Fallopian tube (25) The tube that conveys eggs from an ovary to the uterus. Also called *oviduct*.

fertilization (25) The fusion of two reproductive cells.

fetus (25) Developmental stage in humans, from the end of the embryonic period, approximately eight weeks after fertilization, until birth.

filtrate (20) Fluid that accumulates in Bowman's capsule in the vertebrate kidney; it contains salts, sugars, amino acids, vitamins, and many other molecules, all at the same concentration as in the blood.

follicle (25) In an ovary, the small structure in which an egg forms.

follicle-stimulating hormone (FSH) (25) A hormone that stimulates the production of eggs.

follicular phase (25) The first half of the reproductive cycle in women, culminating in ovulation.

G

gastrula (25) The mass of cells, made up of three layers, formed during the gastrulation phase of embryonic development.

gastrulation (25) The second phase of embryonic development in which cells form distinct layers.

germ layers (25) The three distinct layers of cells formed during gastrulation.

gills (21) Organs in fishes and other aquatic animals in which gases are exchanged between water and blood capillaries.

gland (20) A collection of epithelial cells that produces secretions for use elsewhere in the body.

glial cells (20) Cells of nervous tissue that support and provide nutrients to neurons. Also called *neuroglia*.

glomerulus (20) The blood-filtering unit of the nephron; a mass of capillaries, surrounded by Bowman's capsule and connected to a single, long, urine-collecting tube that excretes its filtered fluid into a collecting duct.

glycemic index (22) A measure of the extent to which foods cause a surge in blood sugar and subsequent release of insulin.

H

heart (21) A muscular pump that, with each contraction, propels blood at high pressure to lungs, gills, or other body organs and tissues.

heat stroke (20) A potentially life-threatening medical condition caused by extreme hyperthermia, characterized by an inability of the organism to maintain homeostasis.

hematocrit (21) The proportion of blood that is made up from red blood cells; determined by spinning a blood sample in a centrifuge.

hemoglobin (21) An oxygen-carrying protein molecule in red blood cells. [Gk., *haima*, blood + Lat., *globus*, ball]

hemolymph (21) The single fluid of an open circulatory system that surrounds all cells and transports nutrients, gases, and waste products.

herbivores (22) Animals that eat plants; also known as primary consumers. [Lat., *herba*, grass + *vorare*, to devour]

heterotherm (20) An animal that has a body temperature that fluctuates as the environmental temperature changes. [Gk., *heteros*, other + *therme*, heat]

hibernate (20) To go into a state of reduced metabolic activity for days or weeks, during which the animal's body temperature can drop considerably.

homeostasis (20) The body's use of physical and chemical processes to maintain a consistent internal environment. [Gk., *homos*, same + *stasis*, standing]

homeotherm (20) An animal that maintains a relatively constant body temperature. [Gk., *homos*, same + *therme*, heat]

human chorionic gonadotropin (hCG) (25) A hormone secreted by the embryo that keeps the lining of the uterus thickened for implantation.

hyperthermia (20) A condition in which high external environmental temperature and humidity overwhelm the body's ability to dissipate heat, and body temperature becomes abnormally high; can lead to death. [Gk., *hyper*, above + *therme*, heat]

hypothermia (20) A condition in which body temperature becomes abnormally low; can lead to death. [Gk., *hypo*, under + *therme*, heat]

I

infertility (25) The inability of a couple to get pregnant after one year of trying.

ingestion (22) The intake of food via the mouth, teeth, tongue, and esophagus.

internal fertilization (25) The process in which sperm are deposited in the female's reproductive tract and unite with one or more eggs.

interstitial fluid (20) An extracellular fluid that surrounds and bathes cells; consists mainly of water and also contains nutrients, raw materials, and waste products.

K

kilocalorie (kcal) (22) One thousand calories.

L

labia (*sing.* **labium**) (25) Protective folds of skin surrounding the female genitals; develops from the same embryonic tissue that produces the scrotum.

labor (25) During childbirth, a series of contractions of the uterus.

lactation (25) Milk production in the mammary glands.

lamella (*pl.* **lamellae**) (21) Disk-like structure in gills, with elaborately branched capillaries.

large intestine (22) The last part of the vertebrate digestive system, larger in diameter but shorter in length than the small intestine. It serves to absorb water, salts, and some vitamins and, in its final compartment (the rectum), to store the indigestible parts of consumed food and symbiotic bacteria (the feces), which can then be defecated. Also called *colon*.

leukocytes (21) See **white blood cells.**

ligament (20) A connective tissue that binds bone to bone.

liver (22) An organ in vertebrates and some other animals that is important in the detoxification of toxic molecules, storage of glycogen, and synthesis of bile, hormones, and digestive enzymes.

lungs (21) Internal organs in most land vertebrates, with highly branched, moist respiratory surfaces where gases are exchanged between air and blood.

luteal phase (25) The second half of the reproductive cycle in women in which the follicle cell that had surrounded the ovum develops into the corpus luteum; culminates in pregnancy or the sloughing off of the uterine lining.

lymph (21) A clear fluid formed from interstitial fluid as it is filtered into the lymphatic vessels in vertebrates.

lymph nodes (21) In the lymphatic system, patches of connective tissue filled with pathogen-fighting white blood cells, through which lymph passes.

M

matrix (connective tissue) (20) A mass of non-living, extracellular material in which connective tissue cells are embedded.

menopause (25) The permanent cessation of ovulation and menstruation, prior to the end of an individual's life.

menstrual cycle (25) The cycle in which the uterus prepares for the implantation and nurturing of a fertilized egg, and sheds its lining if fertilization does not occur.

menstruation (25) The shedding of the uterine lining.

mesoderm (25) The middle embryonic cell layer during gastrulation; it eventually forms the muscles and skeleton. [Gk., *mesos*, middle + *derma*, skin]

mineral (22) A chemical element other than those commonly found in organic molecules (carbon, hydrogen, oxygen, and nitrogen); some minerals are required in the diet in small amounts.

muscle fiber (20) An individual muscle cell; typically contains multiple nuclei.

muscle tissue (20) A body tissue consisting of contractile cells (muscle fibers) that generate force and can facilitate movement.

myoglobin (21) An oxygen-binding protein in muscle that releases oxygen when demand is high and the partial pressure of oxygen is low.

N

negative feedback (20) A control mechanism in which sensors detect changes in the internal environment and trigger effectors to counteract the change; one of the chief strategies by which organisms maintain homeostasis.

nephron (20) The chief functional unit in the vertebrate kidney, consisting of a tubule and a mass of blood vessels that work together to accomplish the tasks of filtration, reabsorption, and excretion

nervous tissue (20) A body tissue that specializes in storing and transmitting information.

neural tube (25) A long hollow tube formed during neurulation that ultimately develops into the nervous system.

neuroglia (20) See **glial cells.**

neuron (20) The "excitable" cell within the nervous system that receives and transmits signals; made up of three distinctive elements: dendrites, a cell body, and an axon.

neurulation (25) During embryonic development, the process of the folding in of the ectoderm for the entire length of the embryo, first forming a groove and then becoming the neural tube.

non-essential amino acid (22) An amino acid that can be produced by the body and so is not needed in the diet.

notochord (25) A flexible rod in chordates whose function in vertebrates is ultimately taken over by the backbone.

nutrient (22) A substance used for energy, raw materials, and maintenance of the body's systems.

O

omnivores (22) Animals that eat both plants and other animals and thus can occupy more than one position in the food chain. [Lat., *omnis*, all + *vorare*, to devour]

oogenesis (25) The process of egg production in females.

oogonium (*pl.* **oogonia**) (25) Diploid cell in the ovary that multiplies by mitosis. Each oogonium begins meiosis but pauses at prophase I, at which point the cell is called a primary oocyte.

open circulatory system (21) A circulatory system in which a single fluid, hemolymph, circulates to transport nutrients, gases, and waste products and also surrounds all cells.

organ (20) A structure that serves specialized functions and contains several types of tissue.

organ system (20) A group of organs that work together to accomplish physiological functions.

osmoconformer (20) An organism that regulates water loss and gain by maintaining the solute concentration of its body fluids at the solute concentration of its environment.

osmoregulation (20) The regulation of water content and of the concentrations of dissolved solutes that influence osmosis; an important component of homeostasis in animals.

osmoregulator (20) An organism that regulates water loss and gain by maintaining the sollute concentration of its body fluids within a narrow range that differs from that of its environment.

ovarian cycle (25) The cycle in which a woman's hormones regulate the timing and development of egg production.

ovary (25) The female gonad. [Lat., *ovum*, egg]

oviduct (25) See **Fallopian tube.**

oviparity (25) A reproductive strategy in which the fertilized egg moves outside the body for embryonic development.

ovoviviparity (25) A reproductive strategy in which most embryonic development takes place in the female's body until the egg hatches (or is released just before hatching).

ovulate (25) To release a secondary oocyte from an ovarian follicle into a Fallopian tube from where it moves to the uterus.

ovum (*pl.* **ova**) (25) See **egg.**

P

pancreas (22) An organ that secretes digestive juice into the small intestine and hormones into the blood.

parthenogenesis (25) The asexual reproductive process in which a female's egg develops into a new organism without fertilization by a sperm cell.

pathogen (21) A disease-causing substance or organism.

penis (25) External male reproductive structure.

pepsin (22) A protein-dismantling enzyme produced by cells in the stomach lining.

peripheral nervous system (20) The part of an organism's nervous system that transmits information to and from the central nervous system; includes the sensory and motor neurons.

peristalsis (22) Waves of smooth muscle contractions that propel food along the digestive tract. [Gk., *peri*, around + *stellein*, to place]

pheromone (25) A chemical that affects the behavior of other individuals of the same species.

physiology (20) The study of the internal functions of organisms.

placenta (25) The structure that connects the developing embryo to the wall of the uterus, delivering nourishment and removing wastes.

plasma (21) The liquid part of blood, containing dissolved metabolites and wastes, salts and ions, and proteins that transport lipids, vitamins, and other chemicals to the tissues where they are required.

platelets (21) Cellular fragments, components of the blood, formed by the pinching off of fragments from large cells (megakaryocytes) in the bone marrow; they lack organelles but are filled with enzymes and chemicals important for blood clotting.

polar body (25) One of the two cells formed when a primary oocyte divides; it gets almost no cytoplasm and eventually disintegrates.

polygraph (21) The "lie detector" test; measures breathing rate, sweat gland activity, and heart rate to evaluate whether an individual is telling the truth.

positive feedback (20) A control mechanism in which a deviation from normal internal conditions causes an increase or acceleration of the change.

primary oocyte (25) In female gametogenesis, a cell produced by meiosis, which then completes meiosis; it can become an egg (ovum).

primary spermatocyte (25) In sperm production, one of the two cells resulting from division of the spermatogonium; it undergoes meiosis in the first step of sperm production.

progesterone (25) A hormone secreted by the corpus luteum of the ovary that causes thickening of the endometrium to prepare for gestation. [Lat., *pro*, for + *gestare*, to bear]

prostate gland (25) A gland in males that secretes enzymes and nutrients into the semen.

pulmonary circuit (21) Flow of blood from the heart to the lungs and back to the heart; the returning blood is oxygenated.

R

red blood cells (21) Hemoglobin-containing, oxygen-transporting blood cells, the most common type of blood cell. Also called *erythrocytes.*

regulator (20) An organism that, for a given physiological variable, maintains homeostasis for that variable, keeping it within a narrow range, even in the face of external changes in the environment.

ruminant (22) A herbivorous animal with a four-chambered stomach. Ruminants include cows, bison, deer, goats, and sheep.

S

scrotum (25) External sac that contains the testes.

secondary oocyte (25) One of the two cells formed by division of a primary oocyte; it completes meiosis after fertilization.

secondary spermatocyte (25) One of the two cells produced by the first meiotic division of a primary spermatocyte, which then complete the second meiotic division; each produces two spermatids.

semen (25) A fluid expelled at ejaculation that contains sperm along with enzymes and nutrients that foster survival of the sperm.

seminal vesicle (25) One of a pair of male reproductive glands that secrete sugar, enzymes, vitamin C, proteins, and immune suppressants into semen.

seminiferous tubules (25) Coiled tubes in the testes that are lined with the cells that divide to produce sperm.

set point (20) A target value or range; in homeostasis, the normal range of values for a variable (such as temperature, pH, solute concentration).

sexual reproduction (25) A type of reproduction in which offspring are produced by the fusion of gametes from two distinct sexes.

sexually transmitted disease (STD) (25) A disease passed from one person to another through sexual activity.

skeletal muscle (20) A type of muscle tissue, usually attached to bones, that is responsible for generating most of the movement in animals; accounts for about 40% of human body weight. Also called *voluntary muscle*.

small intestine (22) A long, thin tube of the digestive tract between the stomach and large intestine; the part of the digestive system where most digestion and absorption take place.

smooth muscle (20) A type of muscle tissue found in the walls surrounding blood vessels, the stomach and intestines, bladder, and many other organs and inner "tubes" within the body. It generates slow, rhythmic contractions that can gradually move blood, food, or other substances through the organ; not under conscious control

special connective tissue (20) A type of connective tissue, including bone, cartilage, and blood, in which the matrix differs from that of connective tissue proper in that it is rigid or liquid.

sperm (25) A male gamete.

spermatogenesis (25) The process of sperm production.

sphincter (22) A ring of muscle that opens or closes a passage between two chambers in the body, such as between the esophagus and the stomach.

stem cells (21) Cells that can develop into a diverse range of cell types.

stomach (22) A J-shaped digestive organ with thick, elastic walls; the part of the digestive system where food is mixed and partially digested.

systemic circuit (21) Flow of blood from the heart to the body (other than the lungs) and back to the heart; returning blood is low in oxygen and high in carbon dioxide.

systolic pressure (21) The first blood pressure reading; a measure of the pressure when the heart contracts, pumping blood into the arteries.

T

tendon (20) A connective tissue that joins muscle to bone.

testis (*pl.* **testes**) (25) The male gonad.

testosterone (25) The principal male sex hormone; influences development of an embryo as male and the production of male secondary sex characteristics.

thermoregulation (20) The maintenance of body temperature within its normal range in homeostasis.

tissue (20) A group of similar cells that act together to perform specific functions in the body.

trachea (22) A structure in the respiratory system that conducts air to the lungs. Also called *windpipe*.

trimester (25) In human development, one of the three three-month periods of pregnancy.

U

umbilical cord (25) A mass of tissue that connects the embryo to the placenta and through which nutrients and wastes are exchanged.

uterus (25) Reproductive organ in female mammals where an embryo develops. Also called *womb*.

V

vagina (25) Tube-like chamber connecting the female external genitals to the uterus, into which sperm are released during copulation.

vas deferens (25) A tube of smooth muscle tissue that passes from each testis into the body.

vein (21) A blood vessel that transports blood, at lower pressure than in arteries, from capillaries in the body to the heart.

ventricle (21) A chamber of the heart from which blood is pumped to the lungs, gills, or the rest of the body.

vitamin (22) An organic compound that is an essential nutrient required by the body in small amounts.

viviparity (25) A strategy in which the embryo develops inside the mother, and live offspring are born.

W

white blood cells (21) Blood cells that defend against pathogens; the primary components of the immune response system. Also called *leukocytes*.

Z

zona pellucida (25) The glycoprotein layer between the granulosa cells and the egg's membrane.

INDEX